GCSE

Combined Science

A wise woman once said, "There's no combustion without oxygen, and no Grade 9-1 GCSE Combined Science exam success without practice." Truly profound.

Well as luck would have it, this super CGP book is simply bursting with realistic exam-style questions for every topic. All the required practicals are covered too and there are plenty of targeted analysis questions to test those tricky AO3 skills.

We've also included sections of mixed questions for Biology, Chemistry and Physics, just like in the real exams. You'll find complete answers to every question at the back. Enjoy!

Exam Practice Workbook
Higher Level

Published by CGP

Editors:
Eleanor Crabtree, Mary Falkner, Katie Fernandez, Emily Garrett, Rob Hayman, Paul Jordin, Chris Lindle,
Duncan Lindsay, Sarah Pattison, Rachael Rogers, Camilla Sheridan, Sarah Williams and George Wright.

Contributors:
Sophie Anderson, Helen Brace, Ian Davis, Alison Dennis, John Duffy, Mark A. Edwards, Mark Ellingham, James Foster, Barbara Mascetti,
Brian Mills, Bethan Parry, Alison Popperwell, Jonathan Schofield and Chris Workman.

With thanks to Glenn Rogers for the proofreading.
With thanks to Lottie Edwards, Jan Greenway and Emily Smith for the copyright research.

Data in Figure 1 on page 31 source: Health Survey for England 2018. Licensed under the Open Government Licence v3.0
http://www.nationalarchives.gov.uk/doc/open-government-licence/version/3/

Data in Figure 2 on page 31 contains information from NHS Digital. Licensed under the Open Government Licence v3.0
http://www.nationalarchives.gov.uk/doc/open-government-licence/version/3/

Graph on page 180 based on data provided by NOAA ESRL Global Monitoring Division, Boulder, Colorado, USA (http://esrl.noaa.gov/gmd/).
By Dr. Pieter Tans, NOAA/ESRL (www.esrl.noaa.gov/gmd/ccgg/trends/) and Dr. Ralph Keeling, Scripps Institution of Oceanography
(scrippsco2.ucsd.edu/).

Data on the graph on page 180 showing the change in global temperature from GISTEMP Team, 2015: GISS Surface Temperature Analysis
(GISTEMP). NASA Goddard Institute for Space Studies. Dataset accessed 2016-04-11 at http://data.giss.nasa.gov/gistemp/.

Data for the level of carbon dioxide in the atmosphere in the table on page 180: Hansen, J., R. Ruedy, M. Sato, and K. Lo, 2010:
Global surface temperature change, Rev. Geophys., 48, RG4004, doi:10.1029/2010RG000345.

Data for the level of methane in the atmosphere in the table on page 180: IPCC, 2013: Climate Change 2013: The Physical Science Basis.
Contribution of Working Group I to the Fifth Assessment Report of the Intergovernmental Panel on Climate Change
[Stocker, T. F., D. Qin, G.-K. Plattner, M. Tignor, S. K. Allen, J. Boschung, A. Nauels, Y. Xia, V. Bex and P. M. Midgley (eds.)].
Cambridge University Press, Cambridge, United Kingdom and New York, NY, USA. (From Chapter 8.3.2)

Data for the level of CFC-12 in the atmosphere in the table on page 180. IPCC, 2013: Climate Change 2013: The Physical Science Basis.
Contribution of Working Group I to the Fifth Assessment Report of the Intergovernmental Panel on Climate Change
[Stocker, T. F., D. Qin, G.-K. Plattner, M. Tignor, S. K. Allen, J. Boschung, A. Nauels, Y. Xia, V. Bex and P. M. Midgley (eds.)].
Cambridge University Press, Cambridge, United Kingdom and New York, NY, USA. (From Table 8.A.1)

Data for the greenhouse gas lifetimes in the atmosphere and global warming potentials in the table on page 180: IPCC, 2013: Climate Change
2013: The Physical Science Basis. Contribution of Working Group I to the Fifth Assessment Report of the Intergovernmental Panel on Climate
Change [Stocker, T. F., D. Qin, G.-K. Plattner, M. Tignor, S. K. Allen, J. Boschung, A. Nauels, Y. Xia, V. Bex and P. M. Midgley (eds.)].
Cambridge University Press, Cambridge, United Kingdom and New York, NY, USA. (From Chapter 8, Table 8.A.1)

Data for the global temperature anomaly and CO_2 concentration in the table on page 181:
NOAA National Centers for Environmental information, Climate at a Glance: Global Time Series, published November 2020,
retrieved on November 18, 2020 from https://www.ncdc.noaa.gov/cag/

Table on page 267 contains public sector information licensed under the Open Government Licence v3.0.
http://www.nationalarchives.gov.uk/doc/open-government-licence/version/3/

Every effort has been made to locate copyright holders and obtain permission to reproduce sources. For those sources where it has been difficult
to trace the originator of the work, we would be grateful for information. If any copyright holder would like us to make an amendment to the
acknowledgements, please notify us and we will gladly update the book at the next reprint. Thank you.

Clipart from Corel®
Illustrations by: Sandy Gardner Artist, email sandy@sandygardner.co.uk
Printed by Elanders Ltd, Newcastle upon Tyne

Based on the classic CGP style created by Richard Parsons.

Contents

☑ Use the tick boxes to check off the topics you've completed.

You can find some useful information about What to Expect in the Exams
and other exam tips at cgpbooks.co.uk/GCSEScienceHigher/Exams

How to Use This Book

- Hold the book <u>upright</u>, approximately <u>50 cm</u> from your face, ensuring that the text looks like <u>this</u>, not s̅ı̅ɥ̅ʇ̅.
  Alternatively, place the book on a <u>horizontal</u> surface (e.g. a table or desk) and sit adjacent to the book,
  at a distance which doesn't make the text too small to read.
- Before attempting to use this book, familiarise yourself with the following <u>safety information</u>:

There are warm-up questions for the trickier sub-topics, to ease you in and get you thinking along the right lines.

20% of marks in the real exams test analytical skills that come under Assessment Objective 3 (AO3). AO3 skills include evaluating data, drawing conclusions and suggesting ways to improve procedures. The skills needed to earn these precious AO3 marks are easily overlooked, so sections targeting these skills are marked up like this.

In the real exams, some questions will be marked using a 'levels of response' mark scheme. In this book, these questions are marked with an asterisk (*). You'll be marked on the <u>overall quality</u> of your answer, so make sure you give a full, detailed answer that is logical and coherent.

Exam Tips give you hints to help with answering exam questions.

These grade stamps help to show how difficult the questions are. Remember, to get a top grade you need to be able to answer <u>all</u> the questions, not just the hardest ones.

You're told how many marks each question part is worth, and then the total for the whole question.

You'll have done some 'required practical activities' as part of your course, and you could be asked about any of them in your exams. Whenever one of the required practical activities crops up in this book, it's marked up like this.

Tick the box that matches how confident you feel with the questions in each sub-topic. This should help show you where you need to focus your revision.

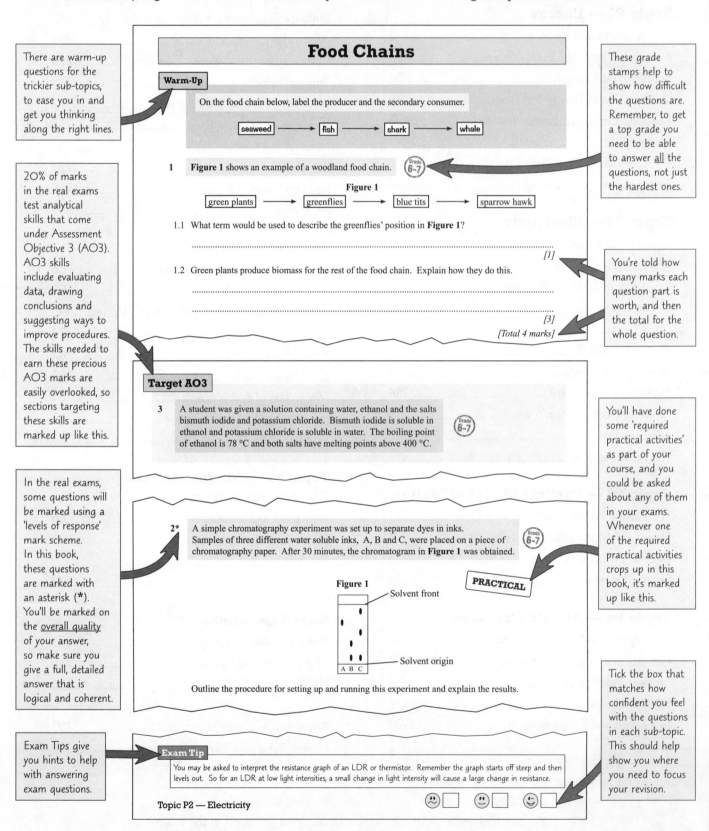

Food Chains

Warm-Up

On the food chain below, label the producer and the secondary consumer.

seaweed → fish → shark → whale

1   **Figure 1** shows an example of a woodland food chain.   *Grade 6-7*

Figure 1

green plants → greenflies → blue tits → sparrow hawk

1.1 What term would be used to describe the greenflies' position in **Figure 1**?

....

[1]

1.2 Green plants produce biomass for the rest of the food chain. Explain how they do this.

....

....

[3]

[Total 4 marks]

Target AO3

3   A student was given a solution containing water, ethanol and the salts bismuth iodide and potassium chloride. Bismuth iodide is soluble in ethanol and potassium chloride is soluble in water. The boiling point of ethanol is 78 °C and both salts have melting points above 400 °C.   *Grade 6-7*

2* A simple chromatography experiment was set up to separate dyes in inks.
    Samples of three different water soluble inks, A, B and C, were placed on a piece of chromatography paper. After 30 minutes, the chromatogram in **Figure 1** was obtained.   *Grade 6-7*

PRACTICAL

Figure 1
— Solvent front
— Solvent origin
A B C

Outline the procedure for setting up and running this experiment and explain the results.

Exam Tip

You may be asked to interpret the resistance graph of an LDR or thermistor. Remember the graph starts off steep and then levels out. So for an LDR at low light intensities, a small change in light intensity will cause a large change in resistance.

Topic P2 — Electricity   ☹ ☐   🙂 ☐   😊 ☐

- There's also a Physics Equations List at the back of this book — you'll probably be given these in your exam.
  You can look up equations on this list to help you answer some of the physics questions in this book.

How to Use This Book

Cells

Use the words on the right to correctly fill in the gaps in the passage.
You don't have to use every word, but each word can only be used once.

many
smaller   plant
bacterial
single   larger
animal
simpler

Most eukaryotic organisms are made up of .... cells.

They include .... and .... cells.

Prokaryotic organisms are .... cells. They are

.... and .... than eukaryotic cells.

1   **Figure 1** shows a diagram of an animal cell.

Figure 1

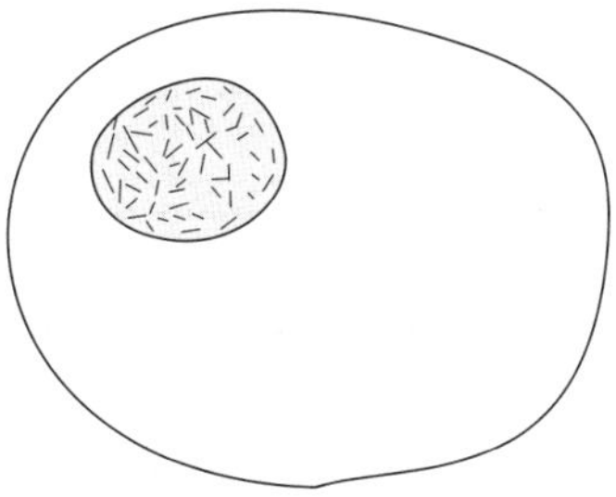

1.1   Label the cell membrane, cytoplasm and nucleus on **Figure 1**.

[3]

1.2   Give the function of each part of the cell on **Figure 1**.

Cell membrane ....

Cytoplasm ....

Nucleus ....

[3]

1.3   Name **two** other subcellular structures that can be found in an animal cell.
Describe the function of each structure.

....

....

....

[4]

1.4   Give **one** reason why the diagram in **Figure 1** does not represent a plant cell.

....

[1]

[Total 11 marks]

Exam Tip

If you get a question in the exam where you need to label a diagram, make sure you draw your label lines very carefully.
If it's not clear what part of the diagram the end of your line is touching, you might miss out on some valuable marks.

2   **Figure 2** shows a diagram of a prokaryotic cell.

Figure 2

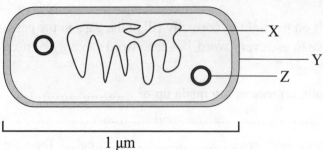

1 µm

2.1 Which of the following is a prokaryotic cell?
Tick **one** box.

☐ root hair cell   ☐ bacterium   ☐ sperm   ☐ nerve cell

[1]

2.2 Name structures X, Y and Z on **Figure 2**.

X ....

Y ....

Z ....

[3]

2.3 Which of the following is true for structure Z? Tick **one** box.

☐ It is where photosynthesis occurs.

☐ It is part of the cell membrane.

☐ It contains genetic material.

[1]

Look at the scale on **Figure 2**.

2.4 A eukaryotic cell measures 10 µm long.
How many times larger is it than the cell in **Figure 2**?

....

[1]

2.5 The head of a pin is approximately 1 mm in diameter.
How many prokaryotic cells would fit lengthways across it?

.... cells

[2]

2.6 Give **one** difference between prokaryotic and eukaryotic cells, other than their size.

....

....

[1]

[Total 9 marks]

☹ ☐   😐 ☐   😊 ☐

Microscopy

1 A student observed blood cells under a microscope.
A scale drawing of one of the cells is shown in **Figure 1**.

Figure 1

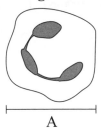

A

In **Figure 1**, A is the image width. The real width of the cell is 0.012 mm.
What is the magnification of the image? Use the formula:

$$\text{magnification} = \frac{\text{size of image}}{\text{size of real object}}$$

magnification = × ....
[Total 2 marks]

2 A plant cell is magnified 1000 times using a light microscope.

2.1 The length of the image of the plant cell is 10 mm.
Calculate the actual length of one plant cell in millimetres (mm).
Use the formula:

$$\text{magnification} = \frac{\text{size of image}}{\text{size of real object}}$$

.... mm
[2]

2.2 What is the length of one plant cell in micrometres (μm)?

.... μm
[1]

2.3 How do magnification and resolution compare between electron and light microscopes?

....

....
[2]

2.4 Explain how electron microscopy has increased understanding of subcellular structures.

....

....
[2]
[Total 7 marks]

Exam Tip

Keep a close eye on units in any calculation questions in the exam. If the question tells you to give your answer in a specific unit, make sure that's the one you use. And check what units they have used for values in the question too.

Topic B1 — Cell Biology

More on Microscopy

1 A student wants to use a light microscope to view a sample of onion cells. **Grade 4-6**

1.1 The student adds a drop of iodine stain to her sample. Which statement best describes when a stain might be used to view a sample of tissue? Tick **one** box.

☐ When the specimen is too thick for light to pass through.

☐ When the specimen is colourless.

☐ When there aren't many sub-cellular structures present in the cells.

☐ When a cover slip is not being used.

[1]

Figure 1 shows a diagram of the light microscope that the student plans to use.

1.2 The three different objective lenses are labelled in **Figure 1** with their magnification. Which lens should the student select first when viewing her cells?

Figure 1

....

[1]

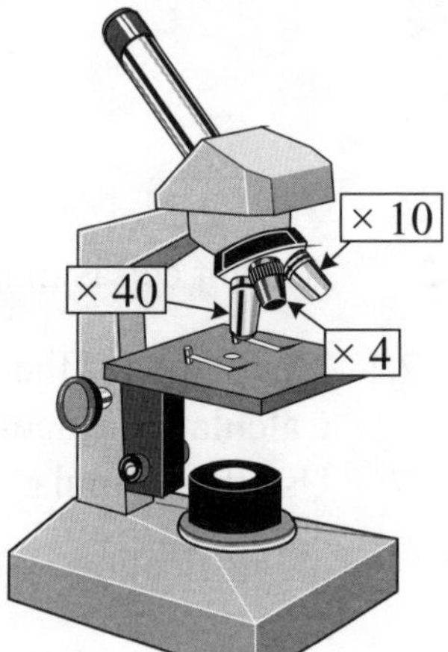

1.3 After she has selected the objective lens, she looks down the eyepiece and uses the adjustment knobs. Describe the purpose of the adjustment knobs.

....

....

....

[1]

1.4 The student wants to see the cells at a greater magnification. Describe the steps that she should take.

....

....

....

[2]

1.5 After she has viewed the cells, she wants to produce a scientific drawing of them. Her teacher has advised her to use clear, unbroken lines to draw the structures she can see. Give **two** other ways in which she can ensure she produces an accurate and useful drawing.

1. ....

2. ....

[2]

[Total 7 marks]

Exam Tip

Make sure you pay attention to the number of marks that a question is worth. For some questions, they're a bit like a secret tip from the examiners about how much they want you to write. For example, if a 'describe' question is worth two marks, you'll usually need to make two separate points to get full marks. So check you're happy with your answers.

Cell Differentiation and Specialisation

Different types of cell have different structures that help them carry out specific functions. Draw arrows below to match up each type of plant cell with its structure and function.

Plant cell

root hair cell

xylem

phloem

Structure and Function

Very few subcellular structures and holes in the end cell walls allow dissolved sugars to move from one cell to the next.

Lots of chloroplasts for absorption of sunlight.

Cells that are hollow in the centre and have no end cell walls form a continuous tube for transporting water from roots to leaves.

Long finger-like projection increases surface area for absorption of water.

---

1 As an organism develops, some of its cells develop different structures and change into different types of cells. This allows the cells to carry out specific functions. What is this process called? Tick **one** box.

Grade 4-6

☐ mitosis ☐ adaptation ☐ differentiation ☐ specialisation

[Total 1 mark]

2 Sperm cells are specialised to help them achieve their function. **Figure 1** shows the structure of a sperm cell.

Grade 6-7

Figure 1

lots of mitochondria — streamlined head

long tail — head contains enzymes

2.1 What is the function of a sperm cell?

....

[1]

2.2 Explain how the structure of a sperm cell helps it to achieve its function. Use **Figure 1** to help you.

....

....

....

....

[4]

[Total 5 marks]

Topic B1 — Cell Biology

Chromosomes and Mitosis

1   **Figure 1** shows different stages of the cell cycle.

Figure 1

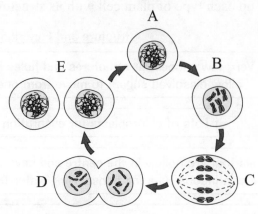

1.1 Label the chromosomes on cell B.

[1]

1.2 Name the chemical molecule that chromosomes are made of.

....

[1]

1.3 Cell A is preparing to divide. What is happening to the cell?
Tick **two** boxes.

☐ The nucleus
is dividing.   ☐ The number of subcellular
structures is increasing.   ☐ The chromosomes
are splitting.

☐ The cytoplasm
is dividing.   ☐ The chromosomes
are doubling.

[2]

1.4 Describe what is happening to cell D.

....

....

[2]

1.5 How do the two cells produced at stage E compare to parent cell A?
Tick **one** box.

☐ They are genetically different.

☐ They are genetically similar.

☐ They are genetically identical.

[1]

[Total 7 marks]

Exam Tip

In the exam, you might be asked to interpret what's going on in photos of real cells undergoing mitosis. Don't panic
if the cells themselves don't look familiar — the main thing you have to look at is what the chromosomes are doing.

Topic B1 — Cell Biology

Stem Cells

1 Stem cells can be found in the growing areas of plants. (Grade 4-6)

1.1 What are these growing areas of a plant called?
Tick **one** box.

☐ cloning zones ☐ meristems ☐ leaves ☐ mesophyll layers

[1]

1.2 You can produce cloned plants from plant stem cells.
Describe **three** benefits of producing cloned plants from stem cells.

....

....

....

[3]

[Total 4 marks]

2 Stem cells can be extracted from bone marrow and used to grow different types of cells. **Figure 1** illustrates this process. (Grade 6-7)

Figure 1

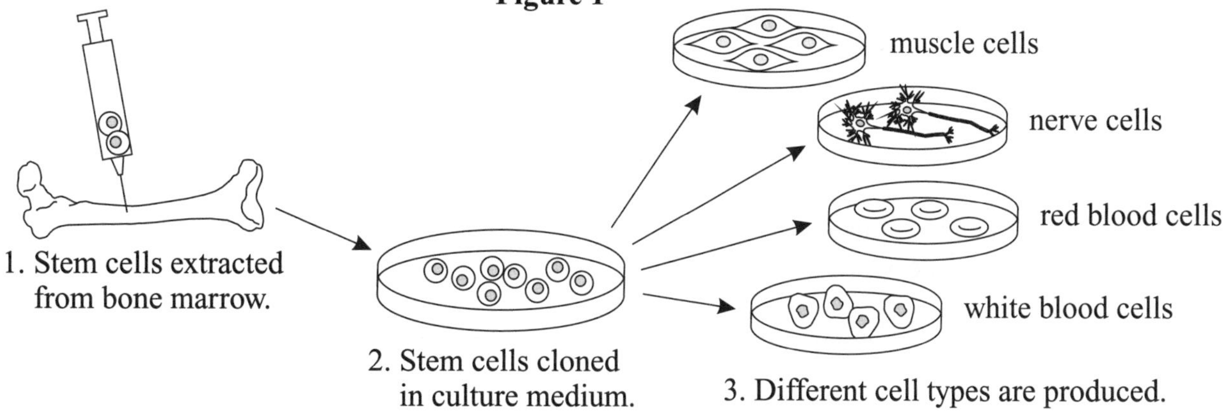

1. Stem cells extracted from bone marrow.

2. Stem cells cloned in culture medium.

3. Different cell types are produced.

muscle cells

nerve cells

red blood cells

white blood cells

2.1 Which of these statements about stem cells is correct? Tick **one** box.

☐ Stem cells are extracted from bone marrow because they are dangerous.

☐ Stems cells are differentiated cells.

☐ Stem cells can be found in every organ of the body.

☐ Stem cells can differentiate into many types of body cell.

[1]

2.2 Why are the stem cells cloned?

....

[1]

2.3 Why can't all body cells be used to grow different types of cell?

....

....

[1]

Topic B1 — Cell Biology

The technique shown in **Figure 1** could be used to produce cells for some medical treatments.

2.4 Besides bone marrow, where else can stem cells for medical treatments be obtained from?

....

[1]

2.5 Name **one** medical condition that may be helped by treatment using stem cells.

....

[1]

2.6 Give **one** potential risk of using stem cells in medical treatments.

....

[1]

[Total 6 marks]

3   **Figure 2** shows the process of therapeutic cloning.   Grade 7-9

Figure 2

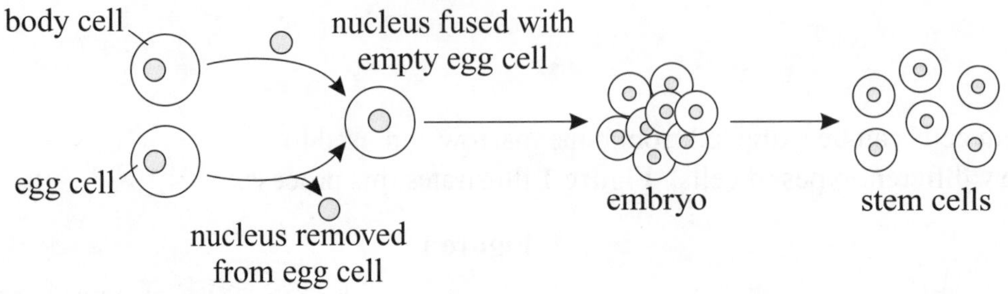

3.1 Describe what therapeutic cloning is.

....

[1]

3.2 Explain the benefit of using stem cells produced by therapeutic cloning for medical treatments compared to stem cells from a donor.

....

....

[2]

Therapeutic cloning involves creating an embryo, from which the stem cells for treatment are sourced. For this reason, some people are against using therapeutic cloning.

3.3* Discuss the ethical issues surrounding the use of embryonic stem cells in medicine and research.

....

....

....

....

....

[4]

[Total 7 marks]

Exam Tip

If you're asked to write about social or ethical issues on a topic in your exam, it's a good idea to write down different points of view, so that you give a well-balanced answer. You don't have to agree with the opinions you write about.

Topic B1 — Cell Biology

Diffusion

The diagram on the right shows three cells. The carbon dioxide concentration inside each cell is shown. Draw arrows between the cells to show in which directions the carbon dioxide will diffuse.

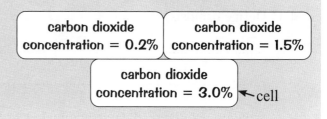

| carbon dioxide concentration = 0.2% | carbon dioxide concentration = 1.5% |

carbon dioxide concentration = 3.0% ← cell

1 Which of these molecules is not able to diffuse through a cell membrane? Tick **one** box.

☐ protein ☐ oxygen ☐ glucose ☐ water

[Total 1 mark]

2 A scientist investigated the diffusion of ammonia along a glass tube. **Figure 1** shows the apparatus she used.

Figure 1

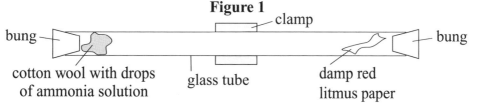

bung — clamp — bung

cotton wool with drops of ammonia solution   glass tube   damp red litmus paper

When the ammonia reaches the end of the tube, the litmus paper changes colour. The scientist timed how long this colour change took at five different concentrations of ammonia. **Table 1** shows her results.

Table 1

Concentration of ammonia (number of drops)	1	2	3	4	5
Time (s)	46	35	28	19	12

2.1 Define diffusion in terms of the particles of a gas.

....

....

[3]

2.2 What do the results in **Table 1** show about the effect of concentration on the rate of diffusion?

....

[1]

2.3 State **two** factors, other than concentration gradient, that affect the rate of diffusion into a cell.

....

....

[2]

2.4 Suggest how the scientist could increase the precision of her results.

....

[1]

[Total 7 marks]

Topic B1 — Cell Biology

Osmosis

1 Osmosis is a form of diffusion. (Grade 4-6)

1.1 Define osmosis.

....

....

....

[3]

1.2 In which of these is osmosis occurring? Tick **one** box.

☐ A plant is absorbing water from the soil.

☐ Sugar is being taken up into the blood from the gut.

☐ Water is evaporating from a leaf.

☐ Oxygen is entering the blood from the lungs.

[1]

[Total 4 marks]

PRACTICAL

2 A student did an experiment to see the effect of different salt solutions on pieces of potato. He cut five equal-sized rectangular chips from a raw potato and determined the mass of each chip. Each chip was placed in a beaker containing a different concentration of salt solution. The mass of each chip was measured again after 24 hours. The results are shown in **Table 1**. (Grade 6-7)

Table 1

Beaker	1	2	3	4	5
Concentration of salt solution (%)	0	1	2	5	10
Mass of potato chip at start of experiment (g)	5.70	5.73	5.71	5.75	5.77
Mass of potato chip after 24 hours (g)	6.71	6.58	6.27	5.46	4.63

2.1 Explain why it is important that all the potato pieces come from the same potato.

....

[1]

2.2 Calculate the percentage change in mass after 24 hours for the potato chip in beaker 2.

.... %

[2]

2.3 The student wanted to find a solution that would not cause the mass of the chip to change. Suggest what concentration of salt solution the student should try.

....

[1]

[Total 4 marks]

Exam Tip

When you get calculation questions in the exam, remember to check what quantity they're actually asking you to find out, show all the steps of your working clearly and double-check every number that you type into your calculator.

Target AO3

3   A student is investigating osmosis. She takes three beakers and puts a different concentration of sucrose solution into each one. Then she places a length of Visking tubing (a partially permeable membrane) containing 0.5 M sucrose solution into each beaker. She places a glass capillary tube in the Visking tubing so that the end dips into the sucrose solution. A diagram of her experiment is shown in **Figure 1**.

Figure 1

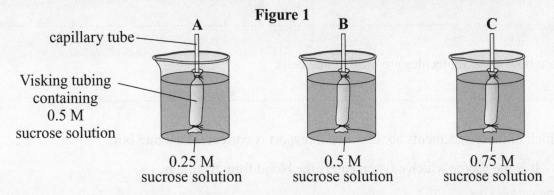

capillary tube

Visking tubing containing 0.5 M sucrose solution

A   B   C

0.25 M sucrose solution   0.5 M sucrose solution   0.75 M sucrose solution

The student records the level of the sucrose solution in each beaker and each capillary tube at the start of the experiment. She plans to record the level of the solution in each beaker every 30 minutes for 8 hours.

3.1 Give **two** variables that the student should keep constant in this experiment.

....

....

[2]

3.2 Predict what will happen to the level of the solution in Beaker B after 1 hour.
     Explain your answer.

....

....

....

[2]

3.3 Describe and explain what you would expect to happen to the level of solution in Beaker C over the course of 8 hours.

....

....

....

....

....

[4]

[Total 8 marks]

Exam Tip

If you get a question in the exam where you need to explain the effects of osmosis, make sure you word your answer really carefully. For example. remember to write about the movement of <u>water</u> molecules (not just molecules) and talk about <u>water</u> concentration (not just 'the concentration') — these details will show the examiners you really know your stuff.

            Topic B1 — Cell Biology

Active Transport

1 Sugar molecules can be absorbed from the gut into the blood by active transport. (Grade 4-6)

1.1 Define active transport.

....

....

[1]

1.2 State how sugar molecules are used inside cells.

....

[1]

1.3 Which of these statements about active transport is correct? Tick **one** box.

☐ It is the way in which oxygen enters the blood from the lungs.

☐ It can only occur down a concentration gradient.

☐ It needs energy from respiration.

[1]

[Total 3 marks]

2 Plants absorb mineral ions from the soil by active transport. (Grade 6-7)

2.1 Explain why plants need mineral ions.

....

[1]

2.2 Explain why plants are not able to rely on diffusion to absorb mineral ions from the soil.

....

....

[2]

2.3 State **two** ways in which active transport differs from diffusion.

....

....

[2]

2.4 Describe the function and structure of the root hair cells of a plant.
Include details of how the structure of the root hair cell helps it to carry out its function.

....

....

....

....

[3]

[Total 8 marks]

Topic B1 — Cell Biology

Exchange Surfaces

Place the following organisms in order according to their surface area to volume ratio. Number the boxes 1 to 4, with 1 being the smallest and 4 being the largest.

☐ Bacterium ☐ Tiger ☐ Domestic cat ☐ Blue whale

1 Give **four** features of an effective gas exchange surface in an animal. (Grade 4-6)

....

....

....

....

[Total 4 marks]

2 A student was investigating the effect of size on the uptake of substances by diffusion. He cut different sized cubes of agar containing universal indicator and placed them in beakers of acid. The student timed how long it took for the acid to diffuse through to the centre of each cube (and so completely change the colour of the agar). (Grade 7-9)

Table 1 shows the relationship between the surface area and volume of the agar cubes.

Table 1

Cube size (cm)	Surface area (cm²)	Volume (cm³)	Simple ratio
$2 \times 2 \times 2$	24	8	3:1
$3 \times 3 \times 3$	**X**	**Y**	2:1
$5 \times 5 \times 5$	150	125	**Z** : 1

2.1 Calculate the values of X and Y in **Table 1**.

X = ... cm²

Y = ... cm³

[2]

2.2 Calculate the value of Z.

Z = ...

[1]

2.3 Predict which cube took the longest to change colour. Give **one** reason for your answer.

Cube ....

Reason ....

[1]

[Total 4 marks]

Exchanging Substances

1 **Figure 1** shows an alveolus in the lungs. (Grade 4-6)

Figure 1

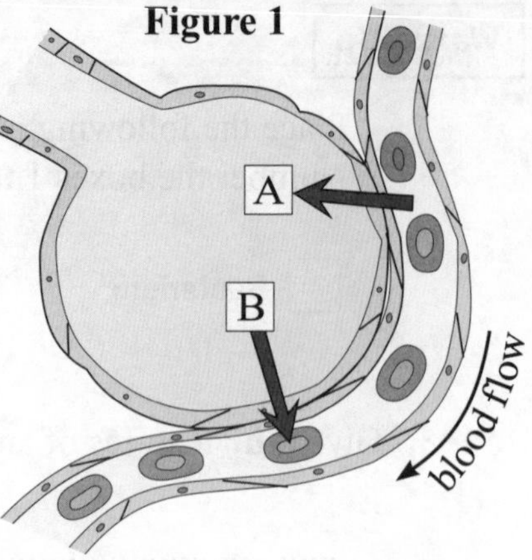

1.1 Name gases A and B.

A ....

B ....

[2]

1.2 By what process do these gases move across the membrane?

....

[1]

1.3 State which feature of the lungs gives them:

a short diffusion pathway ....

a large surface area ....

[2]

[Total 5 marks]

2 Emphysema is a disease that weakens and breaks down the walls of the alveoli. (Grade 6-7)

A person with emphysema may suffer from lower energy levels during physical exercise. Suggest and explain the cause of this symptom.

....

....

....

....

[Total 3 marks]

3 Describe and explain how the structure of the small intestine is adapted for absorbing the products of digestion. (Grade 6-7)

....

....

....

....

....

....

....

[Total 6 marks]

Exam Tip

It may seem obvious, but if you're asked to explain how the structure of something relates to its function, don't just dive straight in and rattle off what it looks like. First, focus on the function being asked about, then pick out the individual structures that help to do that function and for each structure, make sure you give a clear explanation of how it helps.

More on Exchanging Substances

1 Leaves are adapted for gas exchange. **Figure 1** shows the cross-section of a leaf. Grade 4-6

1.1 Name the channels labelled X.

....
[1]

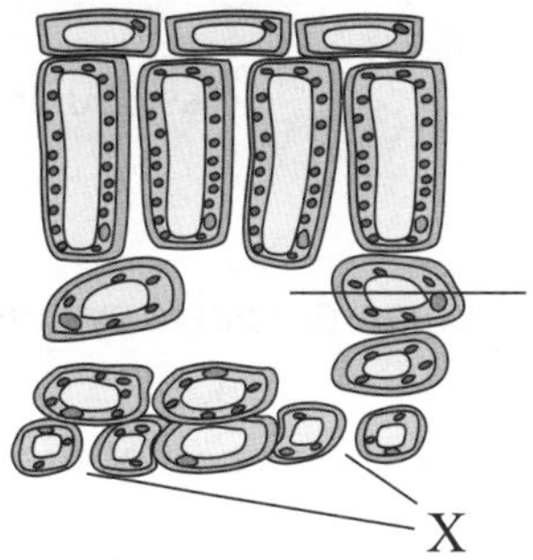

1.2 Describe the movement of gases into and out of the leaf.

....

....

....
[3]

Figure 1

air space

X

1.3 Suggest the purpose of the air spaces in the leaf.

....

....
[1]

[Total 5 marks]

2 **Figure 2** shows a diagram of a fish gill, which is a gas exchange surface. Grade 6-7

2.1 How do gill filaments increase the efficiency of the gas exchange surface?

....

....
[1]

Figure 2

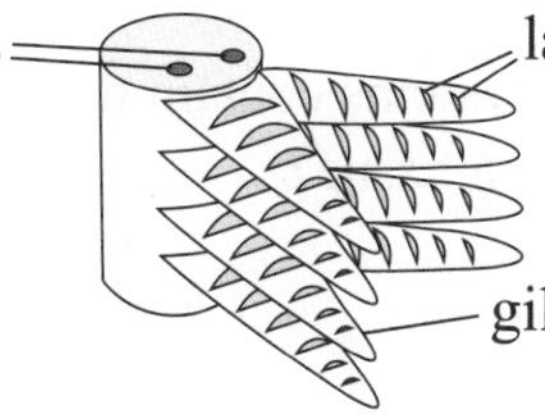

arteries

lamellae

gill filament

2.2 What is the purpose of the lamellae?

....
[1]

2.3 Describe one other feature of an efficient gas exchange surface that is present in **Figure 2**.

....
[1]

The number and length of gill filaments differ between types of fish.
2.4 Describe the differences in the gill filaments you would expect between a fast-moving fish and a slow-moving fish.

....
[1]

2.5 Explain why you would expect to see these differences.

....

....
[2]

[Total 6 marks]

Topic B1 — Cell Biology

Cell Organisation

Warm-Up

Number the boxes 1 to 4 to put the body components in order of size from smallest to largest, 1 being the smallest and 4 being the largest.

☐ Organ system ☐ Tissue ☐ Cell ☐ Organ

1 The human digestive system is an example of an organ system. Grade 4-6

1.1 **Figure 1** shows part of the digestive system.

Figure 1

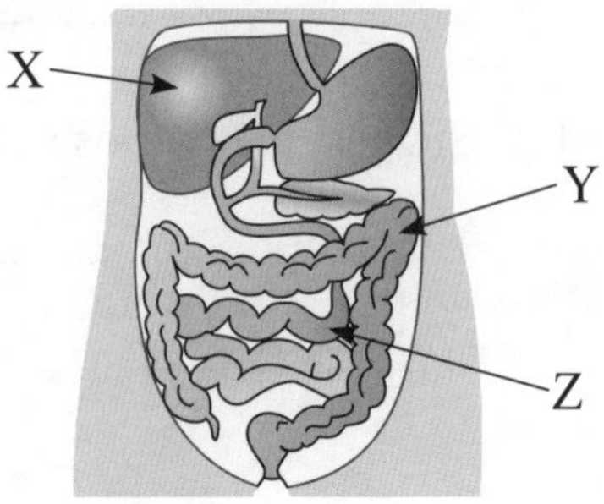

Name organs X, Y and Z.

X: ....

Y: ....

Z: ....

[3]

1.2 What is meant by the term 'organ system'?

....

....

[1]

1.3 Organ systems contain multiple types of tissue.
What is a tissue?

....

....

[1]

1.4 What is the role of the digestive system?

....

[1]

1.5 The stomach is an organ that is part of the digestive system.
What is an organ?

....

....

[1]

[Total 7 marks]

Exam Tip

The examiners like to give you questions where you need to name or label things in a diagram. If they give you letters for different parts of the diagram, make sure that you write the right name next to the right letter and don't get them mixed up. Otherwise the examiners won't be able to give you the marks even though you clearly know your stuff.

Enzymes

1 Enzymes are biological catalysts. They increase the rate of biological reactions. **Figure 1** shows a typical enzyme.

Grade 4-6

X → Figure 1

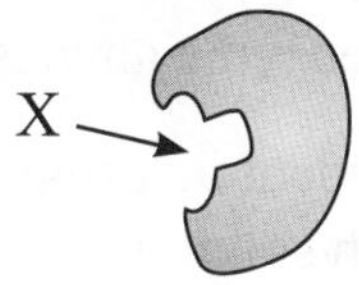

1.1 Name the part of the enzyme labelled X.

....

[1]

1.2 Explain the function of part X in the action of an enzyme in a chemical reaction.

....

[1]

[Total 2 marks]

2 **Figure 2** shows how temperature affects the rate of a reaction when catalysed by two different enzymes. Enzyme A is from a species of bacteria found in a hot thermal vent and Enzyme B is from a species of bacteria found in soil.

Grade 6-7

Figure 2

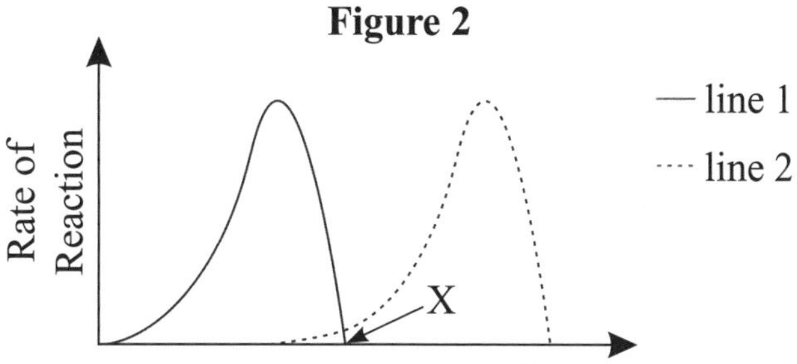

— line 1
···· line 2

Rate of Reaction

X

Temperature

2.1 Suggest which line represents Enzyme A.

....

[1]

2.2 Explain your answer to 2.1.

....

....

....

[3]

2.3 Describe and explain what is happening at point X on the graph.

....

....

....

[4]

[Total 8 marks]

Exam Tip

Whenever you see the word 'suggest' in an exam question, that's your cue to gather all your knowledge on that topic and then apply it to a situation that you haven't seen before. So don't panic if you see an unfamiliar experiment or example — if the word 'suggest' is there just take what you already know and use it to have the best educated guess you can.

Topic B2 — Organisation

Investigating Enzymatic Reactions

1 The enzyme amylase is involved in the breakdown of starch into simple sugars.

A student investigated the effect of pH on the activity of amylase in starch solution. Amylase and starch solution were added to test tubes X, Y and Z. A different buffer solution was added to each test tube. Each buffer solution had a different pH value, as shown in **Figure 1**. Spotting tiles were prepared with a drop of iodine solution in each well. Iodine solution is a browny-orange colour but it turns blue-black in the presence of starch.

Figure 1

Test tube	pH
X	4
Y	6
Z	11

Every 30 seconds a drop of the solution from each of the test tubes was added to a separate well on a spotting tile. The resulting colour of the solution in the well was recorded as shown in **Figure 2**.

Figure 2

Time (s)	30	60	90	120	150
Tube X	Blue-black	Blue-black	Blue-black	Browny-orange	Browny-orange
Tube Y	Blue-black	Browny-orange	Browny-orange	Browny-orange	Browny-orange
Tube Z	Blue-black	Blue-black	Blue-black	Blue-black	Blue-black

1.1 State the pH at which the rate of reaction was greatest. Explain your answer.

....

....

....

[2]

1.2 Suggest an explanation for the results in tube **Z**.

....

....

[1]

1.3 In any experiment, it is important to control the variables that are not being tested. State how the student could control the temperature in the test tubes.

....

[1]

1.4 Give **two** other variables that should be controlled in this experiment.

1. ....

2. ....

[2]

1.5 The student repeated her experiment at pH 7 and got the same results as she got for her experiment at pH 6. Describe how she could improve her experiment to find whether the reaction is greatest at pH 6 or 7.

....

....

[1]

[Total 7 marks]

Topic B2 — Organisation

Enzymes and Digestion

Warm-Up

The diagram on the right shows some of the organs in the digestive system. Lipases and proteases are examples of digestive enzymes.

Write an 'L' on the organs that produce lipases and write a 'P' on the organs that produce proteases.

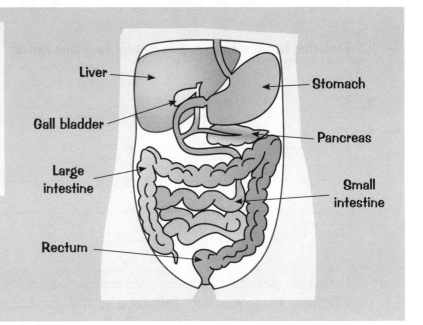

Liver

Stomach

Gall bladder

Pancreas

Large intestine

Small intestine

Rectum

1 Amylase is a digestive enzyme.

1.1 Which group of digestive enzymes does amylase belong to?
Tick **one** box.

☐ Carbohydrases ☐ Lipases ☐ Proteases

[1]

1.2 What is the product of the reaction catalysed by amylase?
Tick **one** box.

☐ Sugars ☐ Amino acids ☐ Glycerol ☐ Fatty acids

[1]

[Total 2 marks]

2 The process of digestion relies on the action of many different types of digestive enzyme.

2.1 Describe the role of digestive enzymes in the process of digestion.

....

....

....

[2]

2.2 Give **two** ways in which the products of digestion can be used by the body.

....

....

[2]

[Total 4 marks]

Topic B2 — Organisation

3 Bile plays an important role in the digestive system. **Grade 6-7**

3.1 Name the organ where bile is produced and the organ where it is stored.

Produced .... Stored ....

[2]

3.2 Describe **two** functions of bile and for each one explain why it is important.

....

....

....

....

....

[4]

[Total 6 marks]

4* Different types of food molecule are broken down by different digestive enzymes. Using your knowledge of digestive enzymes and where they are produced in the body, fully outline the processes involved in the digestion of a meal containing carbohydrates, proteins and lipids. **Grade 7-9**

....

....

....

....

....

....

....

....

....

....

....

....

....

....

[Total 6 marks]

Exam Tip

When you come to a long-answer question, before you start your answer it's ok to use spare space on your exam paper to jot down the key points you want to make. Just remember to cross your jottings out afterwards so they don't get marked.

Topic B2 — Organisation

Food Tests

Warm-Up

Draw lines to connect the tests on the left with the biological molecules that they identify.

Biuret test   Benedict's test   Lipids   Proteins

Sudan III test   Iodine test   Starch   Reducing sugars

1* A student is analysing the nutrient content of egg whites. **Grade 6-7**

Fully describe an investigation that the student could carry out to find out if protein is present in a sample of the egg whites.

....

....

....

....

....

....

....

....

[Total 6 marks]

2 A student was given test tubes containing the following glucose concentrations: 0 M, 0.02 M, 0.1 M, 1 M. The test tubes were not labelled and he was asked to perform tests to determine which test tube contained which glucose solution. **Grade 6-7**

2.1 Describe the test he could carry out to try and distinguish between the glucose solutions.

....

....

....

[3]

2.2 **Table 1** shows the substance observed in the test tubes following his tests. Complete the table to show which glucose solution (0 M, 0.02 M, 0.1 M, 1 M) each test tube contained.

Table 1	Tube 1	Tube 2	Tube 3	Tube 4
substance observed	yellow precipitate	blue solution	red precipitate	green precipitate
glucose concentration (M)	....	....	....	....

[1]

[Total 4 marks]

Topic B2 — Organisation

22

The Lungs

1   **Figure 1** shows the human respiratory system. Grade 4-6

Figure 1

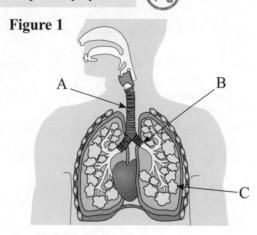

1.1   Name the parts labelled A, B and C in **Figure 1**.

A ....   B ....   C ....

[3]

Figure 2 shows a close-up of part C from **Figure 1**.

Figure 2

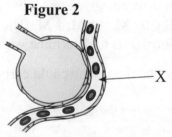

1.2   Name the structure labelled X in **Figure 2**.

....

[1]

1.3   Describe the role that structure X plays in gas exchange in the lungs.

....
....
....
....

[4]

[Total 8 marks]

Topic B2 — Organisation

Circulatory System — The Heart

1   Humans have a double circulatory system. The heart pumps blood around the body through a network of veins and arteries. **Figure 1** shows a diagram of the heart. *(Grade 4-6)*

1.1   Name the parts of the heart labelled X, Y and Z in **Figure 1**.

X ....

Y ....

Z ....

[3]

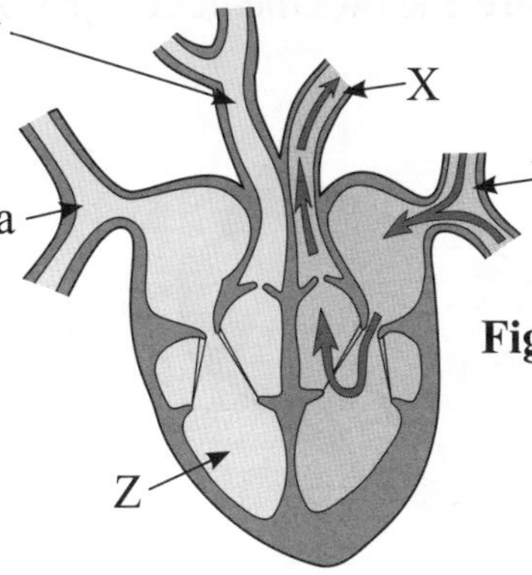

pulmonary artery

vena cava

X

Y

Z

Figure 1

1.2   Draw arrows on **Figure 1** to show the direction of blood flow through the right side of the heart.

[1]

1.3   Explain why the human circulatory system is described as a 'double circulatory system'.

....

....

....

....

....

[3]

[Total 7 marks]

2   The heart beats to circulate blood around the body. *(Grade 6-7)*

2.1   Describe how the heartbeat is controlled.

....

....

[2]

2.2   Atrial fibrillation is a condition where the heartbeat is irregular. It is caused by problems with the heart's ability to control its own beat. Suggest how atrial fibrillation could be treated.

....

....

....

[2]

[Total 4 marks]

Exam Tip

Keep an eye out for different styles of questions where you're not given lines to write your answers on (like Q1.2 above). These sorts of questions can be easy to miss when you're under pressure, meaning you could be throwing away marks.

Topic B2 — Organisation

Circulatory System — Blood Vessels

1   Blood is carried around the body in blood vessels.
Different types of blood vessel perform different functions.

Figure 1 shows the three types of blood vessel.

Figure 1

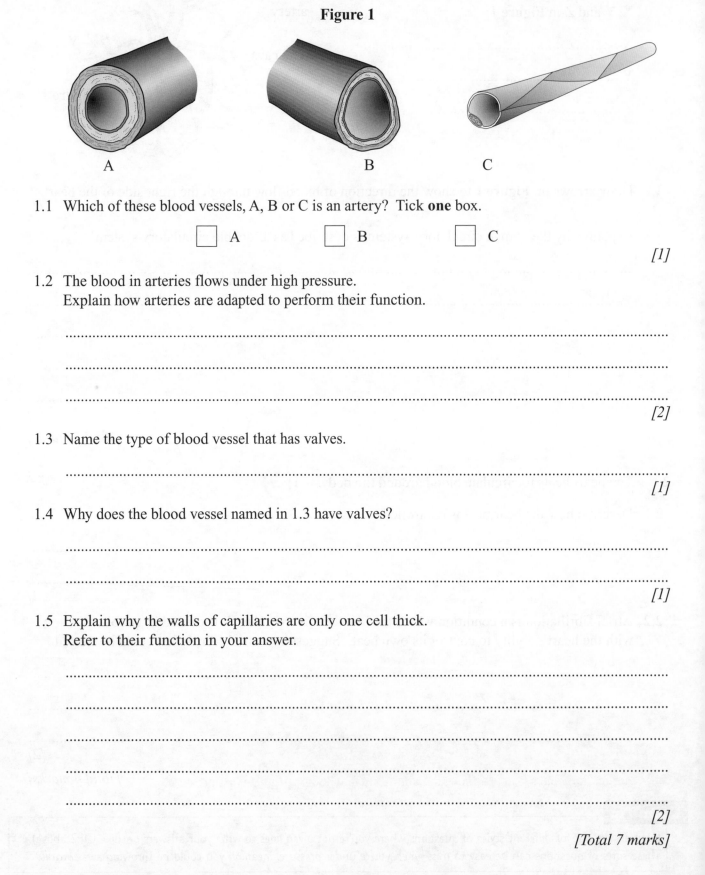

A   B   C

1.1   Which of these blood vessels, A, B or C is an artery? Tick **one** box.

☐ A   ☐ B   ☐ C

[1]

1.2   The blood in arteries flows under high pressure.
Explain how arteries are adapted to perform their function.

....

....

....
[2]

1.3   Name the type of blood vessel that has valves.

....
[1]

1.4   Why does the blood vessel named in 1.3 have valves?

....

....
[1]

1.5   Explain why the walls of capillaries are only one cell thick.
Refer to their function in your answer.

....

....

....

....

....
[2]

[Total 7 marks]

Target AO3

2 An investigation was carried out into the elasticity of arteries and veins.

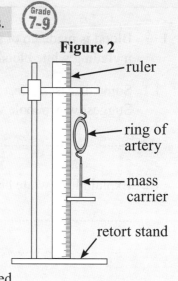

The experiment was set up as shown in **Figure 2**.
The method used was as follows:

1. Cut a ring of tissue from an artery and attach it to the hook.
2. Attach a mass carrier to the bottom of the ring.
3. Measure the length of the ring with the mass carrier attached.
4. Add a 10 g mass to the mass carrier.
5. Measure the length of the ring with the mass attached, and then again with the mass removed.
6. Repeat steps 4 and 5 with a 20 g mass, 30 g mass, etc.
7. Repeat the experiment using a ring of vein of the same width.

The percentage change between the original length of the ring with just the mass carrier attached and its length after each mass was removed was calculated for each mass. The results are plotted in **Figure 3**.

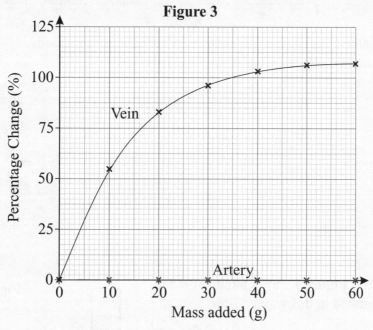

2.1 Describe what the graph shows for each type of blood vessel.

....

....

....

....

....

....

[4]

2.2 Suggest **one** safety precaution that should be carried out for this experiment.

....

[1]

[Total 5 marks]

Topic B2 — Organisation

Circulatory System — Blood

1 Blood is made up of several different components, including white blood cells, red blood cells and platelets.

Grade 7-9

1.1 Some diseases affect the body's ability to produce enough white blood cells.
Suggest why people with these diseases are more likely to experience frequent infections.

....

[1]

1.2 Explain how white blood cells are adapted to perform their function.

....

....

....

....

[3]

1.3 Red blood cells carry oxygen from the lungs to other tissues in the body.
Explain how red blood cells are adapted for their function.

....

....

....

....

....

[3]

The components of blood can be separated by spinning them at high speed. **Figure 1** shows a tube of blood that has been separated in this way.

Figure 1

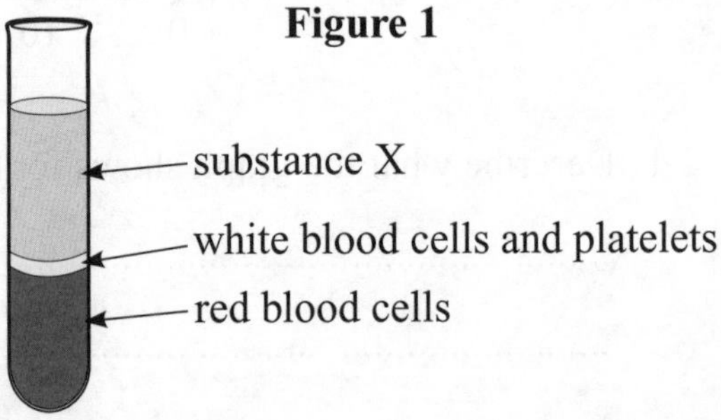

substance X

white blood cells and platelets

red blood cells

1.4 Identify the substance labelled X.

....

[1]

1.5 A scientist analysing the blood sample found that it had a lower than normal concentration of platelets. Describe the structure and function of platelets.

....

....

[2]

[Total 10 marks]

Exam Tip

Scientific terminology and key words are, well, key to use in science exams. You might find it easy to describe something in everyday language — but examiners often won't give you the marks unless you use the right scientific terminology.

Topic B2 — Organisation

Cardiovascular Disease

Warm-Up

Use the correct words to fill in the gaps in the passage. Not all of them will be used.

pulmonary vein   blood vessels   asthma   aorta   coronary heart disease
coronary arteries   fatty acids   toxins   fatty material   cystic fibrosis

Cardiovascular disease is a term used to describe diseases of the ....

and heart. .... is an example of a cardiovascular disease.

It is caused by narrowing of the .... due to the build-up of

.... on the inside wall.

---

1   The coronary arteries surround the heart.   **(Grade 6-7)**
A patient has a blockage of fatty material in a coronary artery.

1.1   Explain why a blockage in the coronary arteries could cause damage to the patient's heart muscle.

....

....

[2]

1.2   Suggest and describe a method of treatment that a doctor might recommend to the patient.

....

....

....

[2]

[Total 4 marks]

---

2   Patients with, or at risk of, developing coronary   **(Grade 6-7)**
heart disease are sometimes prescribed statins.

2.1   Explain how statins prevent or slow the progression of coronary heart disease.

....

....

....

[2]

2.2   A patient is offered statins. Suggest **one** reason why he may not wish to take them.

....

....

[1]

[Total 3 marks]

3 Doctors were assessing the heart of a patient recovering from a serious heart infection.

3.1 They found that one of the valves in the heart had become leaky.
Suggest the effects this might have on blood flow through the heart and around the body.

....

....

....
[2]

3.2 Describe **one** other way that a valve might be faulty.

....
[1]

Surgeons decided to replace the faulty valve with a replacement biological valve.

3.3 What is a biological valve?

....
[1]

3.4 A mechanical valve is sometimes used in transplants instead of a biological valve.
What is a mechanical valve?

....
[1]

A second patient at the same hospital needed a heart transplant.
Heart transplants can use donor hearts or artificial hearts.

3.5 Artificial hearts are rarely used as a permanent fix.
Suggest when they are most likely to be used instead of a natural donor heart.

....

....

....
[2]

3.6 Suggest **one** advantage and **one** disadvantage of using a natural donor heart rather than an artificial heart in heart transplant operations.

Advantage ....

....

Disadvantage ....

....
[2]

[Total 9 marks]

Exam Tip

There are quite a few different ways to treat cardiovascular disease that could come up in your exam. As well as knowing what they are and how they work, make sure you can discuss the advantages and disadvantages of them too.

Topic B2 — Organisation

Health and Disease

1 Ill health is often caused by communicable and non-communicable diseases.
Grade 4-6

1.1 What is meant by the term 'communicable disease'?

....

....

[1]

1.2 List **two** factors other than disease that can cause ill health.

....

....

[2]

[Total 3 marks]

2 **Figure 1** and **Table 1** show the number of employees in five different rooms in a large office building who have had at least one common cold in the last 12 months.
Grade 6-7

Figure 1

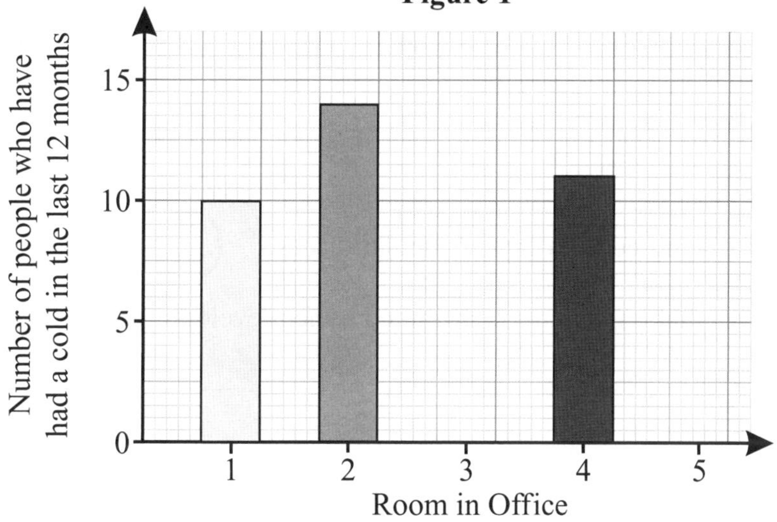

Table 1

	Room 1	Room 2	Room 3	Room 4	Room 5	**Total**
Number of people who have had a cold in the last 12 months	10		12	11		**60**

2.1 Complete **Figure 1** and **Table 1**.

[4]

2.2 Some people have a defective immune system. Explain what effect this could have on the likelihood of a person contracting a communicable disease like the common cold.

....

....

....

[2]

[Total 6 marks]

Topic B2 — Organisation

Risk Factors for Non-Communicable Diseases

1   Substances in a person's environment can be risk factors for certain diseases.   (Grade 4-6)

1.1   What is meant by a risk factor for a disease?

....

....

....

[1]

1.2   Other than substances in the environment, state **two** other types of risk factor.

....

....

[2]

1.3   Obesity is a risk factor for many different diseases.
Name **one** disease that obesity is a risk factor for.

....

[1]

[Total 4 marks]

2   A patient has been diagnosed with cardiovascular disease.   (Grade 4-6)

2.1   Give **two** risk factors that might have contributed to her developing cardiovascular disease.

....

....

[2]

2.2   Suggest **two** reasons why non-communicable diseases can be financially costly.

....

....

....

....

[2]

[Total 4 marks]

Exam Tip

Remember that risk factors are identified by scientists looking for correlations in data, and they don't always directly cause a disease. Sometimes, they are just related to another factor that does. It's rarely a single risk factor that leads to someone developing a disease — diseases are often caused when multiple risk factors interact with each other.

Target AO3

3 **Figures 1** and **2** show the prevalence of adult obesity in England and the number of people diagnosed with diabetes in England, respectively, between 2012 and 2018.

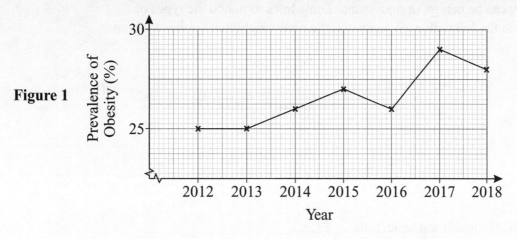

Figure 1

Figure 2

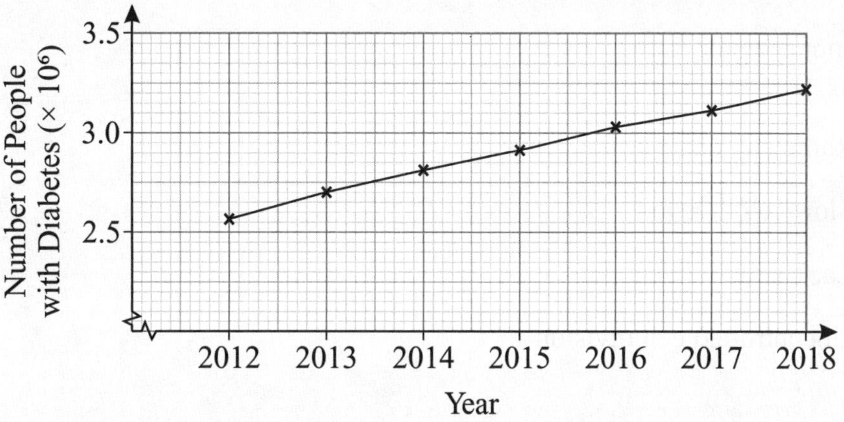

3.1 Describe the trend shown in **Figure 2**.

....

....

[1]

3.2* A student says: "the increasing rate of obesity has caused the rate of diabetes to increase".
Evaluate the student's statement using the data shown in **Figures 1** and **2**.

....

....

....

....

....

....

....

....

[4]

[Total 5 marks]

Cancer

Tumours can be benign or malignant. Draw lines to match the types of tumour on the left with each characteristic on the right that applies to them.

Are cancerous

Malignant Tumours

Are not cancerous

Benign Tumours

Can invade neighbouring tissues

1 Some types of tumour are cancerous. **Grade 4-6**

1.1 What do tumours result from?
Tick **one** box.

☐ Rapid cell death

☐ Slow cell division

☐ Lack of cell division

☐ Uncontrolled cell division

[1]

1.2 There are many known lifestyle-related risk factors for cancer. However, not all risk factors for cancer are related to lifestyle. Give **one** other type of risk factor for cancer.

....

[1]

[Total 2 marks]

2 Doctors found a tumour in the left lung of a patient.
They were concerned that the patient was at risk of developing secondary tumours. **Grade 6-7**

2.1 Was the tumour in the patient's lung malignant or benign?

....

[1]

2.2 Explain how a secondary tumour forms.

....

....

....

[2]

[Total 3 marks]

Topic B2 — Organisation

Plant Cell Organisation

1   The roots, stem and leaves are involved in the transport of substances around a plant. *(Grade 4-6)*

1.1 What do the roots, stem and leaves of a plant form? Tick **one** box.

☐ A tissue   ☐ An organ system   ☐ An organ   ☐ A tissue system

[1]

1.2 Name **two** substances that are transported around a plant in the xylem.

....

[2]

[Total 3 marks]

2   Plants have many types of tissue, including meristem tissue. *(Grade 4-6)*

2.1 Name **two** sites in a plant where you would find meristem tissue.

....

....

[2]

2.2 Give **one** reason why meristem tissue is important throughout the life of the plant.

....

[1]

[Total 3 marks]

3   **Figure 1** shows a transverse section of a leaf. *(Grade 6-7)*

Figure 1

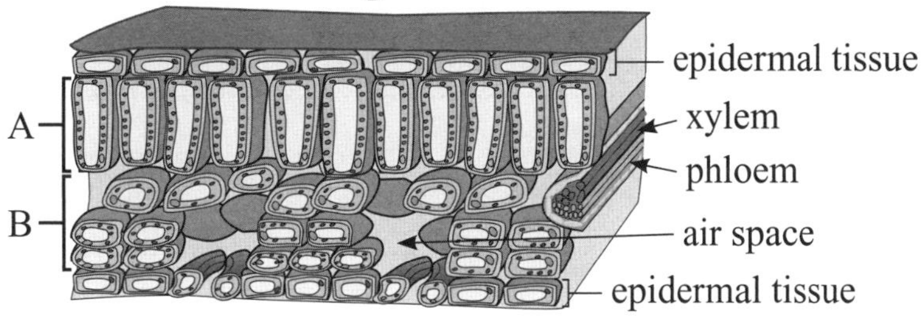

3.1 Name the tissues labelled A and B.

A ....   B ....

[2]

3.2 Explain how the tissue labelled A is adapted for the function of photosynthesis.

....

....

....

[2]

3.3 What is the function of the air spaces?

....

[1]

[Total 5 marks]

☹ ☐   😐 ☐   🙂 ☐   Topic B2 — Organisation

Transpiration and Translocation

Use the words below to correctly fill in the gaps in the passage.
You don't have to use every word, but each word can only be used once.

leaves   phloem   translocation   mineral ions   condensation   evaporation

roots   perspiration   xylem   transpiration   sugars   guard cells   stem

The process by which water is lost from a plant is called ....

It is caused by the .... and diffusion of water from a plant's surface,

most often from the .... Another process, called ....,

is the transport of .... from where they're made in the leaves to the rest

of the plant via the .... vessels.

1*   Describe how xylem tissue and phloem tissue work to:
   • supply water and mineral ions to all parts of a plant,
   • transport dissolved sugars around a plant.

Grade 7-9

Include details of the **structure** and **function** of the tissues involved.

....

....

....

....

....

....

....

....

....

....

....

....

[Total 6 marks]

Transpiration and Stomata

1 **Figure 1** is a drawing of a magnified image of part of the surface of a leaf

Figure 1

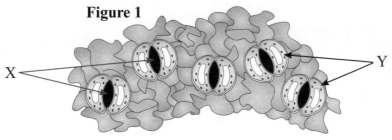

1.1 Name the structures labelled X and the cells labelled Y in **Figure 1**.

X .... Y ....

[2]

1.2 What is the function of the cells labelled Y?

....

....

....

[2]

[Total 4 marks]

2 **Table 1** shows the diameter of ten stomata from each of two leaves, A and B.

Table 1

Diameter of stomata (μm)	
Leaf A	Leaf B
25.2, 20.1, 18.7, 17.9, 19.1, 19.3, 22.0, 23.1, 21.8, 20.3	14.7, 12.8, 14.1, 13.2, 12.9, 11.9, 12.1, 13.4, 10.9, 11.7

2.1 Calculate the mean width of the stomata for each leaf.

Leaf A = ... μm   Leaf B = ... μm

[2]

2.2 Leaves A and B are from the same species. Which leaf do you think had its stomatal measurements taken in lower light intensity?

....

[1]

2.3 Explain your answer to 2.2.

....

....

....

[2]

[Total 5 marks]

Topic B2 — Organisation

3 An investigation was carried out to assess the rate of water uptake by a plant over a 16-hour period.

A potometer was set up and readings were taken every two hours between 00:00 and 16:00. The rate in cm³/hour was calculated for each two-hour period. The results are shown in **Table 2**.

Table 2

Time of day	00:00	02:00	04:00	06:00	08:00	10:00	12:00	14:00	16:00
Rate of water uptake (cm³/hour)	2.6	1.0	1.6	2.0	3.8	6.2	8.0	10.2	7.6

3.1 Complete **Figure 2** using the data displayed in **Table 2**.
   • Select a suitable scale and label for the y-axis
   • Plot the rate of water uptake in cm³/hour for all the times given in **Table 2**
   • Join the points with straight lines

Figure 2

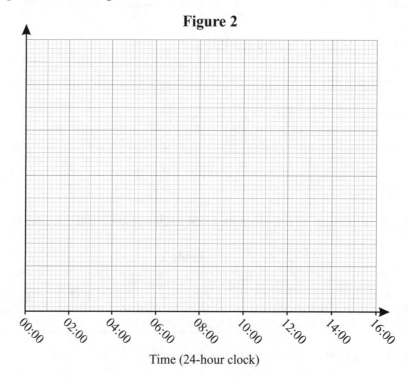

Time (24-hour clock)

[4]

3.2 Use the graph to estimate the rate of water uptake at 09:00.

....

[1]

3.3 How much did the rate of water uptake increase between 06:00 and 11:00?

....

[1]

3.4 Suggest **two** environmental changes that could have caused the change in water uptake between 06:00 and 14:00.

....

....

[2]

[Total 8 marks]

Exam Tip

Make sure you look at the scales on graphs very carefully. Read the numbers written next to the big squares and then carefully work out how much each small square is worth. For example, it's easy to assume they're worth 0.1 instead of 0.2.

Topic B2 — Organisation

Communicable Disease

1 Viruses and bacteria can both reproduce inside the human body. (Grade 4-6)

1.1 Which of the following sentences is correct? Tick **one** box.

☐ Both bacteria and viruses can reproduce quickly in the body.

☐ Bacteria reproduce quickly in the body, but viruses reproduce slowly.

☐ Viruses reproduce quickly in the body, but bacteria reproduce slowly.

☐ Both bacteria and viruses reproduce slowly in the body.

[1]

1.2 Viruses reproduce inside cells. Describe what problem this can cause for the cells.

....

[1]

[Total 2 marks]

2* **Figure 1** shows a housefly. Houseflies are vectors because they can transmit disease to humans. (Grade 7-9)

Figure 1

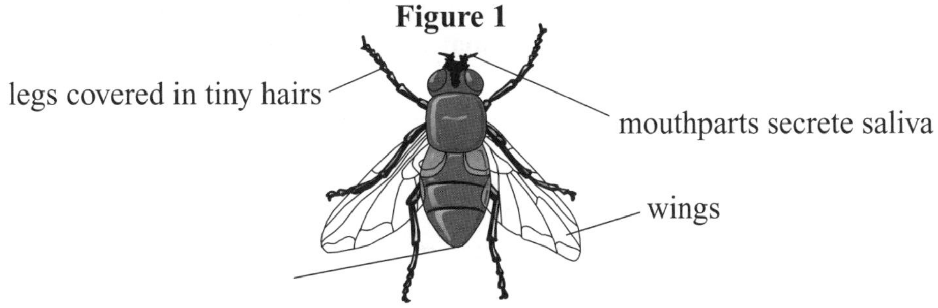

legs covered in tiny hairs

mouthparts secrete saliva

wings

Use information from **Figure 1** to explain how the housefly can transmit disease to humans. Include details of how the housefly can pick up pathogens and spread them to humans.

....

....

....

....

....

....

....

....

....

[Total 6 marks]

Exam Tip

It might not feel like it, but the examiners really aren't trying to confuse you. Every word in a question is there for a reason. So, for example, if the question tells you to 'include details' of something, you need to do that to get the marks.

 ☐   ☐   ☐

Topic B3 — Infection and Response

Viral, Fungal and Protist Diseases

Warm-Up

Fill in the gaps in the passage about malaria. Use the words on the left.
Not all of the words will be used.

protist   breeding

vectors

fever   fungi

virus   bacterium

Malaria is caused by a .... Mosquitoes are the

.... that carry the malaria pathogen to humans.

Malaria causes repeating episodes of .... The spread of

malaria can be reduced by stopping the mosquitoes from ....

---

1   Measles is a highly infectious disease.   **Grade 4-6**

1.1   What type of pathogen causes measles? Tick **one** box.

☐ bacterium   ☐ virus   ☐ protist   ☐ fungus

[1]

1.2   A person suffering from measles travels to work by train. Explain how, 10 days later, other people who were on the same train may also be suffering from measles.

....

....

....

[3]

1.3   Measles can be fatal if there are complications.
What can be done to prevent someone from developing measles?

....

[1]

[Total 5 marks]

2   A virus called HIV causes a disease known as AIDS.   **Grade 4-6**

2.1   What type of drug can be used to control HIV?

....

[1]

2.2   What system in the body does HIV attack?

....

[1]

2.3   State **two** ways in which HIV can be spread.

....

....

[2]

[Total 4 marks]

3   The tobacco mosaic virus (TMV) is a widespread plant pathogen affecting many species of plants.   *Grade 6-7*

3.1   Name **one** species of plant that is often attacked by the tobacco mosaic virus.

....
[1]

3.2   Describe the appearance of a plant with TMV.

....
[1]

3.3   Outline why a plant affected by TMV cannot grow properly.

....

....
[1]

3.4   **Table 1** shows the mean diameter and mass of fruits from 100 healthy plants and 100 plants infected with TMV.

Table 1

	Healthy plants	Plants with TMV
Mean diameter of fruit (mm)	50	35
Mean mass of fruit (g)	95	65

Describe the effect of TMV on the diameter and mass of fruit produced in the infected plants compared to the healthy plants.

....

....

....
[2]

[Total 5 marks]

4   Rose black spot is a disease that can affect rose plants.   *Grade 6-7*

4.1   Describe the appearance of leaves that are infected with rose black spot and state what happens to these leaves.

....

....
[3]

4.2   A gardener notices that one of her rose plants is infected with rose black spot.
She is worried about the rest of her rose plants becoming infected with the fungus.
Why are the other rose plants in her garden at risk from being infected with the disease?

....
[1]

4.3   Rose black spot can be treated by removing and destroying the infected leaves and treating the rest of the plant with a fungicide. Suggest why it is important to destroy the removed leaves.

....

....
[1]

[Total 5 marks]

Topic B3 — Infection and Response

Bacterial Diseases and Preventing Disease

1 *Salmonella* food poisoning in humans is caused by a bacterium. (Grade 4-6)

1.1 List **two** symptoms of *Salmonella* food poisoning.

....

....

[2]

1.2 What does the *Salmonella* bacterium produce that causes these symptoms?

....

[1]

1.3 In the UK, poultry are vaccinated against the bacterium that causes food poisoning.
Explain why it is necessary to vaccinate poultry.

....

....

....

[2]

1.4 Suggest **one** way that a person suffering from *Salmonella* food poisoning can prevent passing the disease on to someone else.

....

[1]

[Total 6 marks]

2 Gonorrhoea is a disease that can affect both men and women. (Grade 4-6)

2.1 How is gonorrhoea spread from person to person?

....

[1]

2.2 State **two** symptoms of the disease in women.

....

....

[2]

2.3 Name the antibiotic that was originally used to treat people infected with gonorrhoea.

....

[1]

2.4 Name **one** barrier method of contraception that prevents the spread of gonorrhoea.

....

[1]

[Total 5 marks]

Exam Tip

You'll often get questions that specify how many things you need to include in your answer. Double-check you've written the right number of things before you move on — there's no way you can get full marks if you don't write enough.

Topic B3 — Infection and Response

Fighting Disease

1 The body has many features that it can use to protect itself against pathogens.   Grade 4-6

1.1 Describe how the skin helps to defend the body against pathogens.

....

....

[2]

1.2 How do structures in the nose help to defend the body against the entry of pathogens?

....

....

[1]

[Total 3 marks]

2* Describe how the human body works to defend itself against pathogens that have entered the body. Include details of the body's defences and the role of the immune system.   Grade 6-7

....

....

....

....

....

....

....

....

....

....

....

....

[Total 6 marks]

Exam Tip

Think carefully about 6 mark questions like the one on this page. Don't just start scribbling everything you know about the topic. Stop and think first — work out what the question is wanting you to write about, and then make sure you write enough points to bag yourself as many marks as possible. Good job you've got some practice on this page.

Topic B3 — Infection and Response

Fighting Disease — Vaccination

1 Children are often vaccinated against measles. (Grade 4-6)

1.1 What is injected into the body during a vaccination?

....

[1]

1.2 Describe what happens when a vaccine is injected into the body. Tick **one** box.

☐ Red blood cells are stimulated to produce antibodies.

☐ White blood cells are stimulated to produce antibiotics.

☐ Red blood cells are stimulated to produce antibiotics.

☐ White blood cells are stimulated to produce antibodies.

[1]

[Total 2 marks]

2 People can be vaccinated against a large number of diseases. (Grade 6-7)

2.1 If the mumps pathogen enters the body of someone who has had the mumps vaccination, why would they be unlikely to become ill with mumps?

....

[1]

2.2 A large proportion of a population is vaccinated against a particular pathogen. Suggest why this can reduce the spread of the pathogen.

....

....

....

[2]

[Total 3 marks]

3 When visiting some other countries, it is recommended that travellers are vaccinated against some of the serious diseases found in those countries. (Grade 7-9)

3.1 If a traveller planned to visit a country where there had been a recent outbreak of the communicable disease cholera, they might get vaccinated against cholera before they travelled. Give **two** reasons why this could be beneficial.

....

....

[2]

3.2 Some countries insist that travellers have had particular vaccinations before they are allowed to enter the country. Suggest why.

....

[1]

[Total 3 marks]

Fighting Disease — Drugs

1 There are many different types of drugs with different functions. **Grade 6-7**

1.1 Explain why it is difficult to develop drugs to kill viruses.

....

....

[2]

1.2 Many people suffer from sore throats caused by bacteria. Other than an antibiotic, name a type of drug that could be used to ease the symptoms of the infection.

....

[1]

1.3 Explain why the type of drug named in 1.2 would not be able to cure the bacterial infection.

....

[1]

[Total 4 marks]

2 A hospital records the number of cases of infections that are caused by antibiotic-resistant bacteria each year. The figures for three years are shown in **Table 1**. **Grade 6-7**

Table 1

Year	2013	2014	2015
No. of infections	84	102	153

2.1 What is meant by antibiotic-resistant bacteria?

....

....

[1]

2.2 Describe the trend shown in **Table 1**.

....

....

[1]

2.3 Use **Table 1** to calculate the percentage change in antibiotic resistant infections between 2013 and 2015.

.... %

[2]

[Total 4 marks]

Exam Tip

When you're answering an exam question about drugs and disease, think very carefully about whether the drug kills the pathogens causing the disease (and so cures it), or whether it just helps to make the symptoms of the disease better.

Topic B3 — Infection and Response

Developing Drugs

1   New drugs have to be tested and trialled before they can be used.   (Grade 4-6)

1.1 List **three** things drugs must be tested for, to ensure they are safe and effective.

....

....

....

[3]

1.2 Which of the following is preclinical testing carried out on? Tick **one** box.

☐ healthy human volunteers   ☐ patients in a hospital

☐ cells, tissues and dead animals   ☐ cells, tissues and live animals

[1]

[Total 4 marks]

2   Clinical trials are always carried out on healthy volunteers before patients.   (Grade 7-9)

2.1 Suggest why very low doses of the drug are given at the start of clinical trials.

....

[1]

2.2 Clinical trials are often double-blind. Explain what would happen in a double-blind clinical trial.

....

....

....

[3]

2.3 Suggest why clinical trials are carried out using a double-blind method.

....

....

[1]

The final results of clinical trials cannot be published until they have been checked
by other scientists. Such checking is often referred to as peer review.

2.4 Suggest why peer review is important in these trials.

....

[1]

2.5 Suggest why it is important that the scientists who carry out the peer review have
no links to the people who carried out the original trials.

....

....

[2]

[Total 8 marks]

Topic B3 — Infection and Response

Photosynthesis and Limiting Factors

1 Photosynthesis is where energy is transferred to plants and used to make glucose. *(Grade 4-6)*

1.1 What is the source of energy for photosynthesis?

....

[1]

1.2 Complete the following word equation for photosynthesis.

.... + water → glucose + ...

[2]

Plants use the glucose they produce in lots of different ways, including to make a substance to strengthen cell walls.

1.3 Name the substance that plants use to strengthen cell walls.

....

[1]

1.4 Give **two** other ways that plants use the glucose produced during photosynthesis.

....

....

....

....

[2]

[Total 6 marks]

2 Photosynthesis is an endothermic reaction. Various factors affect its rate. *(Grade 6-7)*

2.1 Explain what is meant by an endothermic reaction.

....

[1]

2.2 Which of the following factors does not affect the rate of photosynthesis? Tick **one** box.

☐ carbon dioxide concentration   ☐ nitrate concentration   ☐ light intensity   ☐ temperature

[1]

2.3 A lack of magnesium can cause chloroplasts not to make enough chlorophyll. Explain what effect this would have on the rate of photosynthesis of a plant.

....

....

[2]

[Total 4 marks]

Exam Tip

With multiple choice questions, it's a good idea to read them over a couple of times before choosing your answer. Check that you've looked at all the options and that you've understood the question properly. For example, does the question ask for the thing or <u>not</u> the thing (like in Q2.2 above)? Don't make silly mistakes by rushing into your answer.

The Rate of Photosynthesis

Choose from the words below to complete the sentences explaining how temperature affects the rate of photosynthesis, as shown in the graph. Some words may not be used at all.

quickly   low   high   slowly   damaged   replaced

If the temperature is too

.... ,

enzymes needed for photosynthesis will work more

....

If the temperature is too

.... ,

enzymes needed for all reactions will be

....

1   **Figure 1** shows a greenhouse. Greenhouses are used to create the ideal conditions for photosynthesis.

Grade 6-7

Figure 1

1.1   Suggest **two** ways that a farmer could improve the conditions for photosynthesis in a greenhouse. For each of the ways, explain how it affects the rate of photosynthesis.

Improvement ....

Explanation ....

....

Improvement ....

Explanation ....

....

[4]

1.2   Creating the ideal conditions in a greenhouse costs money. Explain why it may still be beneficial for the farmer to do this.

....

....

[2]

[Total 6 marks]

Topic B4 — Bioenergetics

2   A student carried out an experiment to investigate the effect of changing
     the concentration of carbon dioxide on the rate of photosynthesis in a
     green plant. The results were plotted on the graph shown in **Figure 2**.

Figure 2

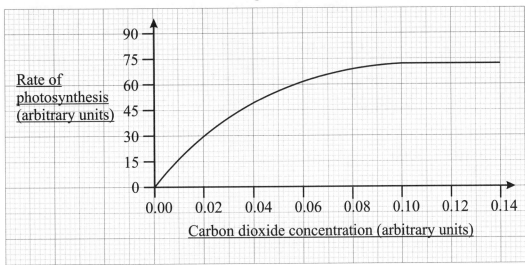

2.1 Describe the trend shown in the graph.

....

....

....

[2]

2.2 At a certain point, the CO_2 concentration is no longer limiting the rate of photosynthesis.
     Suggest **two** factors that could be limiting the rate at this point.

....

....

[2]

2.3 In the space below, sketch a graph to show how light intensity affects the rate of photosynthesis.

[2]

[Total 6 marks]

Exam Tip

If a question asks you to 'sketch' a graph, it doesn't mean it needs to be a work of art. It just means that you've got
to draw some axes (with labels, of course) and then draw approximately what the shape of the graph would look like.

Topic B4 — Bioenergetics

PRACTICAL

3 A student was investigating the effect of light intensity on the rate of photosynthesis in a water plant. She set up the experiment as shown in **Figure 3**.

Figure 3

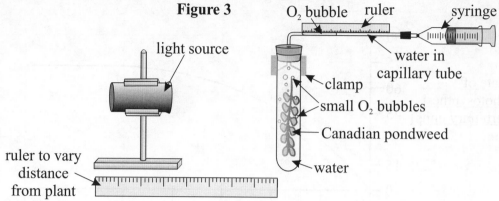

3.1 Predict what will happen to the volume of gas produced when the light is moved closer to the pondweed.

....

[1]

3.2 The formula 1/distance^2 can be used as a measure of light intensity. It's called the inverse square law. Use the inverse square law to calculate the light intensity when the lamp is 20 cm from the pondweed.

light intensity = ... arbitrary units

[2]

3.3* Suggest how the student could adapt the experiment shown in **Figure 3** to investigate the effect of temperature on the rate of photosynthesis. Include details of the variables that should be controlled.

....

....

....

....

....

....

....

....

[6]

[Total 9 marks]

Exam Tip

There's a lot to learn about limiting factors and the rate of photosynthesis. It's a good idea to practise drawing the graphs to show the effect of light intensity, carbon dioxide concentration and temperature on the rate of photosynthesis. You should also make sure you're able to interpret the graphs too, including those with more than one factor involved.

Topic B4 — Bioenergetics

Respiration and Metabolism

1 Respiration is a reaction carried out by all living organisms. It transfers energy from an organism's food to their cells.

Grade 6-7

1.1 Name the type of reaction where energy is transferred to the environment.

....

[1]

Figure 1 shows a gull.

Figure 1

1.2 Give **three** examples of how a gull uses the energy transferred by respiration.

....

....

....

[3]

[Total 4 marks]

2 Metabolism is the sum of all of the reactions that happen in a cell or the body. Metabolism includes reactions that make molecules.

Grade 6-7

2.1 Some metabolic reactions involve using glucose molecules to make other molecules. Name a molecule made from glucose in plants, and a molecule made from glucose in animals.

Plants ....

Animals ....

[2]

2.2 Describe the components of a lipid molecule.

....

....

[2]

2.3 Briefly describe how protein molecules are formed.

....

....

[2]

2.4 Metabolism also involves breaking down molecules. What is excess protein broken down to produce?

....

[1]

[Total 7 marks]

Topic B4 — Bioenergetics

Target AO3

3   A student is investigating respiration in germinating peas. She predicts that germinating peas will respire, and so will release energy as heat.

The student sets up her experiment as shown in **Figure 2**.

Figure 2

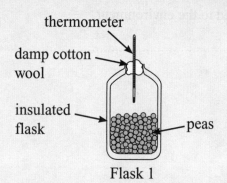

thermometer

damp cotton wool

insulated flask — peas

Flask 1

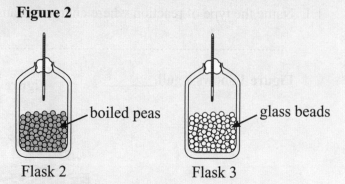

boiled peas

glass beads

Flask 2   Flask 3

The student records the temperature of each flask at the beginning of the experiment (day 0), then every day for three days.

Table 1 shows her results.

Table 1

Day	Temperature (°C)		
	Flask 1	Flask 2	Flask 3
Day 0	20	20	20
Day 1	23	20	20
Day 2	25	21	20
Day 3	28	22	20

3.1 Give **two** variables that the student needed to control to make the experiment a fair test.

....

....

[2]

3.2 The student's results could have been affected by random error.
Suggest **one** way that the student could reduce the effect of any random error on her results.

....

....

[1]

3.3 Flasks 2 and 3 are control experiments. Explain why the student included both of these controls.

....

....

....

[2]

3.4 The student hypothesises that the temperature of flask 2 increased slightly over the course of the experiment due to the presence of respiring microorganisms on the surface of the peas. Suggest how the student could modify her method in order to test this hypothesis.

....

....

[1]

[Total 6 marks]

Topic B4 — Bioenergetics

Aerobic and Anaerobic Respiration

Draw lines to match up each process on the left with its correct description on the right.

| Aerobic respiration |
| Anaerobic respiration |
| Fermentation |

| Respiration without oxygen. |
| Respiration using oxygen. |

1 An experiment was set up using two sealed beakers, each with a carbon dioxide monitor attached. The set up is shown in **Figure 1**.

Figure 1

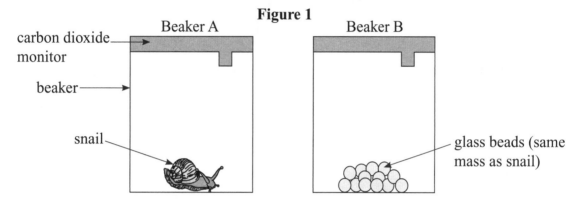

The percentage (%) of carbon dioxide in the air in both beakers was measured at the start of the experiment and again after 2 hours. The results are shown in **Table 1**.

Table 1

Time (hours)	% carbon dioxide in the air	
	Beaker A	Beaker B
0	0.04	0.04
2	0.10	0.04

1.1 Suggest **one** ethical consideration that must be taken into account during this experiment.

....

[1]

1.2 Describe and explain the results for Beaker A.

....

....

[1]

1.3 Describe and explain the results for Beaker B.

....

....

[1]

1.4 What would have happened to the level of oxygen in Beaker A after two hours?
Explain your answer.

....

....

[2]

1.5 In the experiment, Beaker B was set up in the same way as Beaker A but with glass beads instead of a snail. Suggest why Beaker B is used in the experiment.

....

....

[1]

[Total 6 marks]

2 *S. cerevisiae* is a type of yeast. It carries out fermentation.

2.1 Complete the following word equation for fermentation.

.... → ethanol + carbon dioxide

[1]

2.2 For each of the products of fermentation in yeast, outline **one** industrial use.

Product ....

Industrial use ....

Product ....

Industrial use ....

[2]

[Total 3 marks]

3 **Figure 2** shows a muscle cell.
Compare aerobic respiration and anaerobic respiration in muscle cells.

Figure 2

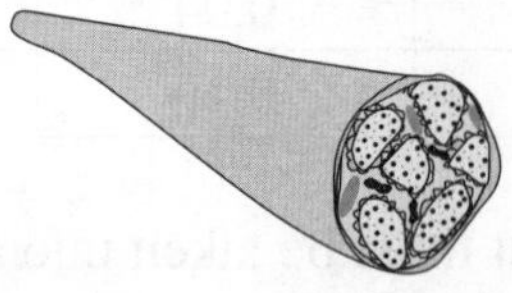

....

....

....

....

....

[Total 3 marks]

Exam Tip

To get the marks for 'compare' questions, you need to make sure each point you make mentions both the things you're comparing. For example, if you were asked to compare your brother and sister*, 'my brother is tall' wouldn't get any marks, but 'my brother is taller than my sister' might well just get a mark. (*Unlikely to be a real exam question, sorry.)

Exercise

Warm-Up

Choose from the words on the right to complete the sentences about exercise. Some words may not be used at all.

carbon dioxide   oxygen
aerobically   lactic acid   urea
oxygen debt   muscles

During exercise your .... may respire anaerobically resulting in an

.... This is the amount of extra .... your body

needs to react with the build up of .... and remove it from cells.

1   A student was investigating the effect of exercise on his own breathing rate.
He counted his number of breaths per minute before, during and after a period of exercise.
He repeated his experiment another two times. The results are shown in **Table 1** below.

Table 1

	Breathing rate (number of breaths per minute)			
	Before exercise	During exercise	One minute after exercise	Five minutes after exercise
	11	16	15	12
	12	15	14	11
	11	15	14	12
Mean	11	15	14	

1.1 Calculate the mean breathing rate five minutes after exercise.

Mean = ... breaths per minute

[1]

1.2 Describe and explain how the student's breathing rate changed during exercise compared to before exercise, as shown in **Table 1**.

....

....

....

[3]

1.3 Describe and explain how the student's breathing rate changed after exercise compared to during exercise, as shown in **Table 1**.

....

....

....

....

[5]

Topic B4 — Bioenergetics

1.4 Give **two** other variables that the student could have measured which would have shown the same trend as breathing rate during exercise.

....

[2]

[Total 11 marks]

2   **Figure 1** below shows the amount of lactic acid in an athlete's body before, during and after some vigorous exercise.

Grade 7-9

Figure 1

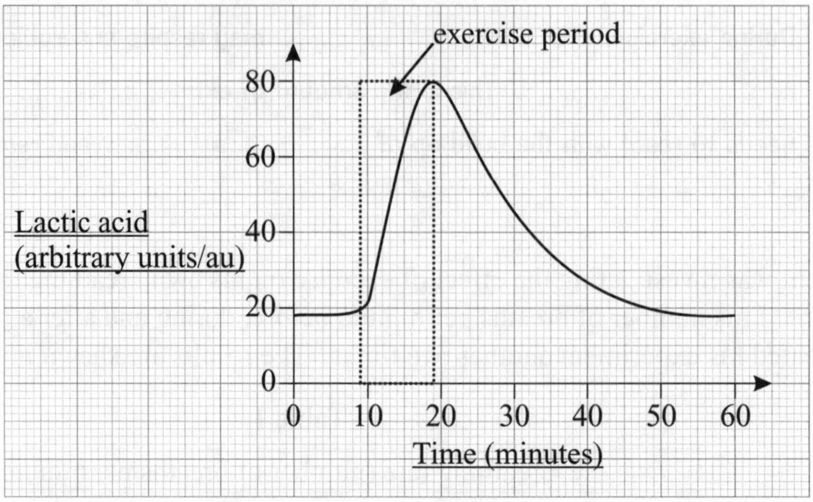

Lactic acid (arbitrary units/au)

2.1 The amount of lactic acid increases from 20 au to 80 au across the duration of the exercise period. Work out the percentage change in lactic acid during this time.

Percentage change = ...%

[2]

2.2 Explain why there was an increase in lactic acid during the exercise period.

....

....

....

[3]

2.3 What physical effects does a long period of vigorous exercise have on muscles?

....

....

[2]

2.4 The amount of lactic acid in the athlete's body decreases between 20 and 60 minutes. Explain how this lactic acid is cleared from the body.

....

....

[2]

[Total 9 marks]

Exam Tip

It's easy to make small mistakes in calculations when you're in that exam hall, so it's really important to show all your working. That way, even if you do make a mistake, at least you might still get some marks for how you worked it out.

Topic B4 — Bioenergetics

Homeostasis

1 Human blood pressure is maintained by a homeostatic control system.   Grade 6-7

1.1 What is homoeostasis?

....

....

....

[2]

1.2 Why are homeostatic control systems important in the body?

....

[1]

1.3 Blood pressure is monitored by sensors in the blood vessels.
Which component of a homeostatic control system senses blood pressure? Tick **one** box.

☐ coordination centre   ☐ receptor   ☐ stimulus   ☐ effector

[1]

1.4 Outline the stages in the negative feedback mechanism when blood pressure becomes too high.

....

....

....

[3]

[Total 7 marks]

2 A person's skin temperature was measured over a 50 minute period.   Grade 6-7

During that time, the person began exercising. They then returned to a resting state before the end of the investigation. **Figure 1** shows the change in the person's skin temperature over the 50 minutes.

Figure 1

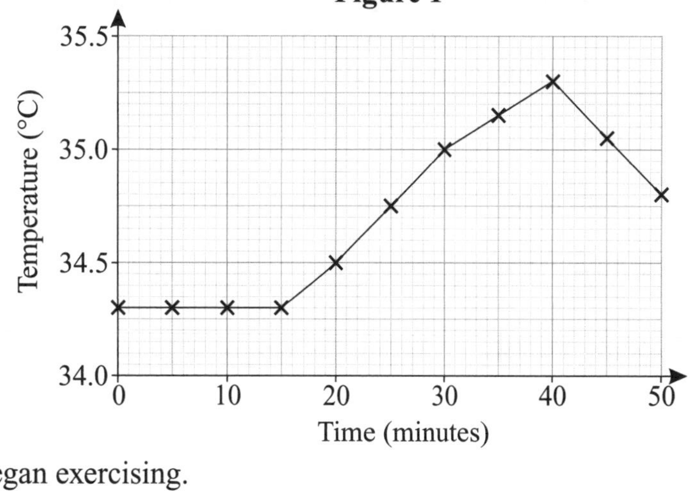

2.1 Suggest the time at which the person began exercising.

....

[1]

2.2 Calculate the rate at which the temperature increased between 20 and 30 minutes.

Rate = ...°C/min

[2]

[Total 3 marks]

The Nervous System

1   **Figure 1** shows part of the human nervous system. (Grade 4-6)

1.1   Name the structures labelled **X** and **Y** on **Figure 1**.   **Figure 1**

X ....

Y ....
                                                                        [2]

1.2   Which part of the nervous system do structures **X** and **Y** form?

....
                                                                        [1]

1.3   What is the role of the part of the nervous system formed by structures **X** and **Y**?

....

....
                                                                        [1]

[Total 4 marks]

2   Multicellular organisms such as humans have a nervous system. (Grade 6-7)

2.1   What is the function of the nervous system in humans?

....

....
                                                                        [2]

2.2   Receptor cells in the eye are sensitive to light.
For a nervous system response in the eye, state whether each of the following features is a stimulus, a coordinator or a response.

Spinal cord ....

Bright light ....

Blinking ....
                                                                        [3]

2.3   Name the **two** main types of neurones found in humans outside the central nervous system.

....

....
                                                                        [2]

2.4   Name **two** types of effector and state how they respond to nervous impulses.

....

....
                                                                        [2]

[Total 9 marks]

Topic B5 — Homeostasis and Response

Target AO3

3　Two students are investigating the sensitivity of the skin on different areas of the body using the method below.

> 1. Blindfold the person to be tested.
> 2. Tape two toothpicks onto a ruler so that they are 50 mm apart.
> 3. Lightly press the two toothpicks onto the person's arm.
> 4. Ask whether the person can feel one or two toothpicks.
> 5. If they can feel two toothpicks, move the toothpicks 5 mm closer together and repeat steps 3 and 4. Keep doing this until they can only feel one toothpick.

The students repeated the experiment for different areas of the body, and repeated it three times per area. Each time, they recorded the distance between the toothpicks at which the person could only feel one toothpick. Their results are shown in **Table 1**.

Table 1

Area of the body	Forearm			Palm			Back of hand		
Repeat	1	2	3	1	2	3	1	2	3
Distance between toothpicks (mm)	30	30	45	5	5	5	25	20	15

3.1　The students calculated the mean distance between toothpicks for each area of the body. Explain why the students repeated their readings and calculated a mean for each area.

....

....

[1]

3.2　Calculate the uncertainty in the students' results for the back of the hand.

.... mm

[2]

3.3　Suggest how the accuracy of this experiment could be improved.

....

....

[1]

3.4　The students think that the third repeat reading for the forearm is an anomalous result. Suggest how the students could confirm that the result is anomalous.

....

....

[1]

3.5　The students conclude from their results that the palm is the most sensitive part of the body. Explain why this is **not** a valid conclusion.

....

....

[2]

[Total 7 marks]

Topic B5 — Homeostasis and Response

Synapses and Reflexes

Warm-Up

Circle the examples that are reflex reactions.

Pedalling a bike.   The pupil widening in dim light.

Dropping a hot plate.   Running to catch a bus.   Writing a letter.

1 Which of the following sentences is correct? Tick **one** box.   [Grade 4-6]

☐ Reflex reactions are slow and under conscious control.

☐ Reflex reactions are slow and automatic.

☐ Reflex reactions are rapid and automatic.

☐ Reflex reactions are rapid and under conscious control.

[Total 1 mark]

2 **Figure 1** shows a reflex arc.   [Grade 4-6]

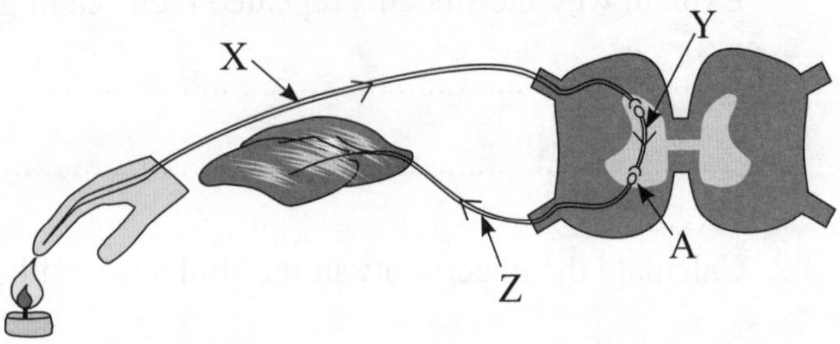

2.1 Name structures **X**, **Y** and **Z**.

Figure 1

X ....

Y ....

Z ....

[3]

2.2 In the reflex arc shown in **Figure 1**, name:

the stimulus ....

the coordinator ....

the effector ....

[3]

2.3 Structure **A** is the junction between two neurones. Name structure **A**.

....

[1]

2.4 How is a nerve signal transmitted across this junction?

....

[1]

[Total 8 marks]

Exam Tip

If an exam question asks you to 'name' something like a structure or process, don't start writing an essay. In fact, you can stay clear of explaining or describing anything at all. A little word or phrase is all the examiners are looking for.

Topic B5 — Homeostasis and Response

Investigating Reaction Time

1 Stimulants, such as caffeine, increase the rate at which nerve impulses travel. An investigation was carried out to assess the impact of different caffeinated drinks on reaction time.

The investigation involved measuring reaction time using a ruler drop test. In this test, a ruler is held above a student's outstretched hand by another person. The ruler is then dropped without warning and the student catches the ruler as quickly as possible. The distance down the ruler where the student caught it is used to calculate their reaction time in seconds (s).

Three different students (Students **1** to **3**) consumed a different caffeinated drink — each one contained a different amount of caffeine. Each student then undertook three ruler drop tests. The results are shown in the table below.

1.1 Calculate the mean reaction time for Student **2** and Student **3**.

	Reaction time (s)		
	Student 1	Student 2	Student 3
Test 1	0.09	0.16	0.20
Test 2	0.10	0.13	0.22
Test 3	0.43	0.15	0.19
Mean	0.21		

Student **2** = ... s

Student **3** = ... s

[2]

1.2 Identify the anomalous result in the table.

....

[1]

1.3 The students' reaction time without any caffeine was **not** measured. Explain why it should have been included in the investigation to assess the effect of each caffeinated drink.

....

....

....

[2]

1.4 Explain why the results of this investigation can't be used to **compare** the effect of the three different caffeinated drinks on reaction time.

....

....

[2]

1.5 An alternative version of the investigation was carried out. This time, the effect of a set quantity of caffeine on the reaction times of different individuals was investigated. Reaction times of three different students were measured, both before and after the consumption of caffeine. Give **three** variables that should have been controlled in this investigation.

....

....

....

[3]

[Total 10 marks]

Topic B5 — Homeostasis and Response

The Endocrine System

1 The endocrine system is a collection of glands in the body that secrete hormones. Grade 4-6

1.1 Which of the following statements about glands is correct? Tick **one** box.

☐ Glands secrete hormones directly into cells.

☐ Glands secrete hormones directly into tissues.

☐ Glands secrete hormones directly into the blood.

☐ Glands secrete hormones directly into organs.

[1]

1.2 Which of the following statements best describes hormones?
Tick **one** box.

☐ Hormones are tissues.   ☐ Hormones are chemical molecules.

☐ Hormones are cells.   ☐ Hormones are enzymes.

[1]

1.3 State **two** ways in which the effects of the endocrine system differ from the nervous system.

....

....

[2]

[Total 4 marks]

2 **Figure 1** shows the positions of some glands in the human body. Grade 4-6

2.1 Name glands A to E in **Figure 1**.

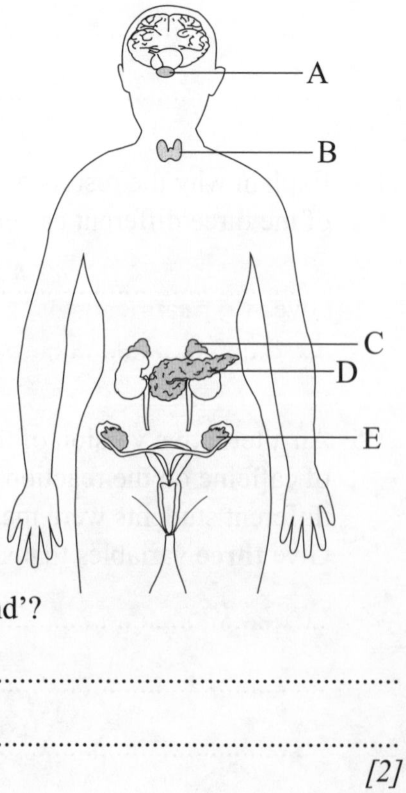

A ....

B ....

C ....

D ....

E ....

[5]

Figure 1

The 'master gland' secretes several hormones
into the blood in response to body conditions.

2.2 What is the name of the 'master gland'?

....

[1]

2.3 What is the function of the hormones released by the 'master gland'?

....

....

[2]

[Total 8 marks]

Topic B5 — Homeostasis and Response

Controlling Blood Glucose

1   The concentration of glucose in the blood is controlled by hormones.   *Grade 4-6*

1.1   Which gland in the human body monitors and controls blood glucose concentration? Tick **one** box.

☐ pancreas   ☐ pituitary gland   ☐ thyroid   ☐ testis

[1]

1.2   Which hormone is produced when blood glucose concentration becomes too high?

....

[1]

1.3   Describe what happens to excess glucose in the blood.

....

....

[2]

[Total 4 marks]

2   Diabetes exists in two different forms, Type 1 and Type 2.   *Grade 6-7*

2.1   What causes Type 1 diabetes?

....

[1]

2.2   What is the defining characteristic of Type 1 diabetes?

....

[1]

2.3   Type 1 diabetes is treated with insulin injections.
        Suggest **one** factor that might affect the amount of insulin injected by a patient.

....

[1]

2.4   What causes Type 2 diabetes?

....

[1]

2.5   Give **two** treatments that a doctor would recommend for Type 2 diabetes.

....

....

[2]

2.6   Give a risk factor for Type 2 diabetes.

....

[1]

[Total 7 marks]

Exam Tip

If a multiple choice question tells you to 'tick one box' then you know that only one of the options is right. If you don't know the answer, it might be helpful to cross out any options that you know are definitely <u>not</u> right so you have fewer to think about. And if you're really stumped, don't leave the tick boxes blank — you might as well have your best guess.

Topic B5 — Homeostasis and Response

62

3 In an experiment, the blood glucose concentration of a person without diabetes was recorded at regular intervals in a 90 minute time period. Fifteen minutes into the experiment, a glucose drink was given. **Figure 1** shows the results of the experiment.

Figure 1

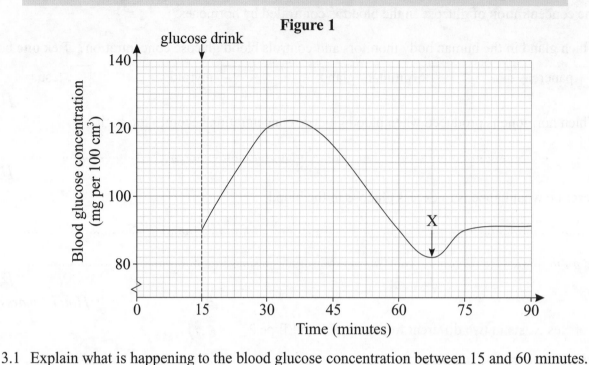

3.1 Explain what is happening to the blood glucose concentration between 15 and 60 minutes.

....

....

....

[3]

3.2 Name the hormone being released by the pancreas at point **X** on the graph.

....

[1]

3.3 Describe the effect that hormone **X** has on the blood glucose concentration.

....

[1]

3.4 Explain how hormone **X** causes this effect.

....

....

[1]

3.5 Suggest how the shape of the graph would differ if the person had Type 1 diabetes.

....

....

[1]

[Total 7 marks]

Exam Tip

There are a few similar-sounding names when it comes to the control of blood glucose, so make sure you've got your head around which is which (and how to spell them). You won't get the mark if, for example, you write about 'glucogen'...

Topic B5 — Homeostasis and Response

Puberty and the Menstrual Cycle

1 The release of sex hormones begins at puberty. *(Grade 4-6)*

1.1 What is the name of the main female hormone produced in the ovary? Tick **one** box.

☐ progesterone   ☐ oestrogen   ☐ luteinising hormone   ☐ follicle stimulating hormone

[1]

1.2 What is the name of the process by which eggs are released from the ovary?

....

[1]

1.3 How often is an egg released from an ovary? Tick **one** box.

☐ Every 7 days.   ☐ Every 14 days.   ☐ Every 21 days.   ☐ Every 28 days.

[1]

1.4 Name the hormone that stimulates the release of an egg.

....

[1]

1.5 Name the hormone that stimulates sperm production in men.

....

[1]

1.6 Where in the male body is this hormone produced?

....

[1]

[Total 6 marks]

2 Four main hormones interact with each other in the control of the menstrual cycle. *(Grade 6-7)*

2.1 Which two hormones are involved in maintaining the uterus lining?

....

....

[2]

2.2 What is the name of the gland that secretes follicle stimulating hormone (FSH)?

....

[1]

2.3 State **two** effects of FSH during the menstrual cycle of a woman.

....

....

[2]

2.4 Which hormone stimulates the release of luteinising hormone (LH)?

....

[1]

[Total 6 marks]

 ☐   ☐   ☐

Topic B5 — Homeostasis and Response

Controlling Fertility

Sort the methods of contraception into the correct places in the table.

abstinence

contraceptive injection

condom

diaphragm

plastic intrauterine device

sterilisation

contraceptive patch

Hormonal	Non-hormonal

---

1 Some methods of contraception use hormones to control the fertility of a woman. (Grade 4-6)

1.1 How is an oral contraceptive taken into the body? Tick **one** box.

☐ As an injection.

☐ As a tablet taken by mouth.

☐ Through the skin from a patch.

[1]

1.2 How do oral contraceptives containing multiple hormones prevent pregnancy? Tick **one** box.

☐ The hormones inhibit oestrogen production.

☐ The hormones inhibit FSH production.

☐ The hormones inhibit LH production.

[1]

1.3 The contraceptive implant is inserted under the skin of the arm.
Which hormone does it release?

....

[1]

1.4 How does the hormone released by the contraceptive implant prevent pregnancy?

....

[1]

[Total 4 marks]

2   Fertility can be controlled by non-hormonal methods of contraception.   (Grade 4-6)

2.1 Name a barrier method of contraception that can be used by men.

....
[1]

2.2 Name a barrier method of contraception that can be used by women.

....
[1]

2.3 How do barrier methods of contraception prevent a woman becoming pregnant?

....
[1]

2.4 What is the name given to chemicals that kill or disable sperm?

....
[1]

2.5 A couple not wishing to have children do not want to use any form of contraception.
Suggest how they could avoid pregnancy.

....
[1]

2.6 Name a surgical method of controlling fertility that can be carried out in both men and women.

....
[1]

2.7 Name a barrier method of contraception that protects against sexually transmitted infections.

....
[1]

[Total 7 marks]

3   A woman is considering which contraceptive to use.   (Grade 7-9)

3.1 Suggest **one** advantage of choosing the contraceptive injection over the contraceptive pill.

....
[1]

3.2 Suggest **one** disadvantage of choosing the contraceptive injection over the contraceptive pill.

....
[1]

3.3 Suggest **one** advantage of choosing a barrier method of contraception over a hormonal
contraceptive.

....
[1]

[Total 3 marks]

Exam Tip

Knowing how the hormones that control the menstrual cycle interact with each other can be handy when it comes to
understanding how these hormones are used to control fertility. So make sure you've got it all sorted out in your head.

Topic B5 — Homeostasis and Response

More on Controlling Fertility

1 A couple want to have children but the woman has not yet become pregnant. Blood tests have shown that she has a low level of follicle stimulating hormone (FSH). She is treated with a fertility drug.

Grade 6-7

1.1 Explain why a low level of FSH may be preventing the woman from becoming pregnant.

....

[1]

1.2 In addition to FSH, which other hormone will the fertility drug contain to help the woman become pregnant? Give a reason for your answer.

....

....

[2]

1.3 Suggest **one** advantage and **one** disadvantage of this method of fertility treatment.

Advantage: ....

Disadvantage: ....

[2]

[Total 5 marks]

2 *In vitro* fertilisation is a reproductive treatment that can help people with fertility problems have children.

Grade 7-9

2.1 Describe the stages involved in a course of *in vitro* fertilisation treatment.

....

....

....

....

....

....

....

[5]

2.2 Give **two** disadvantages of *in vitro* fertilisation treatment.

....

....

....

[2]

[Total 7 marks]

Topic B5 — Homeostasis and Response

Adrenaline and Thyroxine

Warm-Up

The graph below shows the change in the level of a hormone controlled by a negative feedback response over time.
Use the words on the right to fill in the labels on the graph.

normal   low   stimulated

inhibited   high

.... level of hormone detected

release of hormone ....

Blood hormone level

.... level of hormone

Time

.... level of hormone detected

release of hormone ....

---

1   Thyroxine is a hormone.   (Grade 4-6)

1.1   Which statement best describes the role of thyroxine in the body? Tick **one** box.

☐ Thyroxine inhibits development.

☐ Thyroxine regulates basal metabolic rate.

☐ Thyroxine decreases heart rate.

[1]

1.2   Which gland produces thyroxine?

....

[1]

[Total 2 marks]

2   The hormone adrenaline is produced in times of fear or stress.   (Grade 6-7)

2.1   Where is adrenaline released from?

....

[1]

2.2   Describe the effect that adrenaline has on the body.

....

....

....

[3]

2.3   Name the response that adrenaline prepares the body for.

....

[1]

[Total 5 marks]

 ☐   ☐   ☐

Topic B5 — Homeostasis and Response

DNA

1   DNA makes up the genetic material in animal and plant cells.   (Grade 4-6)

   1.1   Which of the following statements about DNA is correct? Tick **one** box.

     ☐   DNA is located in the cytoplasm of animal and plant cells.

     ☐   DNA is located in the ribosomes in animal and plant cells.

     ☐   DNA is located in the nucleus of animal and plant cells.

     ☐   DNA is located in vacuoles in animal and plant cells.

[1]

   1.2   What are chromosomes? Tick **one** box.

     ☐   Proteins coded for by DNA.

     ☐   The structures that contain DNA.

     ☐   The site of protein synthesis.

     ☐   The bases that make up DNA.

[1]

[Total 2 marks]

2   An organism's DNA contains lots of sections called genes.   (Grade 6-7)

   2.1   Outline the function of genes.

     ....

     ....

[2]

   2.2   What is meant by the term 'genome'?

     ....

     ....

[1]

   2.3   Give **one** reason why it is important for scientists to have an understanding of the human genome. Explain your answer.

     ....

     ....

     ....

     ....

     ....

[2]

[Total 5 marks]

Exam Tip

To properly understand this topic, you need to know how DNA, genes, genomes, chromosomes, proteins and amino acids all relate to each other. Once you've got that sussed, it'll make answering the questions a whole lot easier.

Reproduction

1 Reproduction can be sexual or asexual. **Grade 4-6**

In sexual reproduction, gametes from a male and female fuse together.

1.1 Name the male gamete in animals.

....

[1]

1.2 Name the female gamete in plants.

....

[1]

1.3 Which type of cell division is involved in the production of gametes?

....

[1]

Asexual reproduction does not involve gametes.

1.4 What name can be given to the cells resulting from asexual reproduction?

☐ gametes   ☐ clones   ☐ eggs   ☐ chromosomes

[1]

1.5 Name the type of cell division used in asexual reproduction.

....

[1]

[Total 5 marks]

2 Sexual reproduction involves the fusion of gametes to form a fertilised egg cell. **Grade 6-7**

2.1 Explain how a fertilised egg cell has the correct number of chromosomes.

....

....

....

[2]

2.2 Asexual and sexual reproduction are very different methods.
Give **four** ways in which asexual reproduction is different to sexual reproduction.

....

....

....

....

....

....

[4]

[Total 6 marks]

Topic B6 — Inheritance, Variation and Evolution

Meiosis

1 Sexual reproduction in humans involves meiosis. **Grade 4-6**

1.1 Where in the body does meiosis take place?

....

[1]

1.2 What happens to the DNA at the very start of meiosis, before the cell starts to divide?

....

[1]

1.3 How many cell divisions are there during the process of meiosis?

....

[1]

1.4 Briefly describe the results of meiosis.

....

....

....

....

[3]

[Total 6 marks]

2 During fertilisation, two gametes formed by meiosis join together. **Grade 4-6**

2.1 How many copies of each chromosome does the resulting cell have?

....

[1]

After the two gametes join to produce a fertilised egg, the cells divide repeatedly.

2.2 What type of cell division do these cells undergo?

....

[1]

2.3 The dividing cells form an embryo.
What happens to the cells in the embryo as it develops in order to form the whole organism?

....

....

[1]

[Total 3 marks]

Exam Tip

It's outrageously easy to get mixed up between meiosis and mitosis when the pressure is on in an exam. Remember, meiosis is the one that makes — eggs and sperm. Mitosis makes twin (identical) cells. Even if you know the difference, it's still really easy to accidentally write one when you mean the other 'cos the words are so similar, so always check twice.

Topic B6 — Inheritance, Variation and Evolution

X and Y Chromosomes

1   In humans, the biological sex of offspring is determined by a pair of sex chromosomes — X and Y.

Grade 6-7

1.1   Including the sex chromosomes, how many chromosomes are there in a normal body cell?
Tick **one** box.

☐ 22 single chromosomes   ☐ 22 pairs of chromosomes

☐ 23 pairs of chromosomes   ☐ 23 single chromosomes

[1]

Figure 1 shows how the biological sex of offspring is determined.

Figure 1

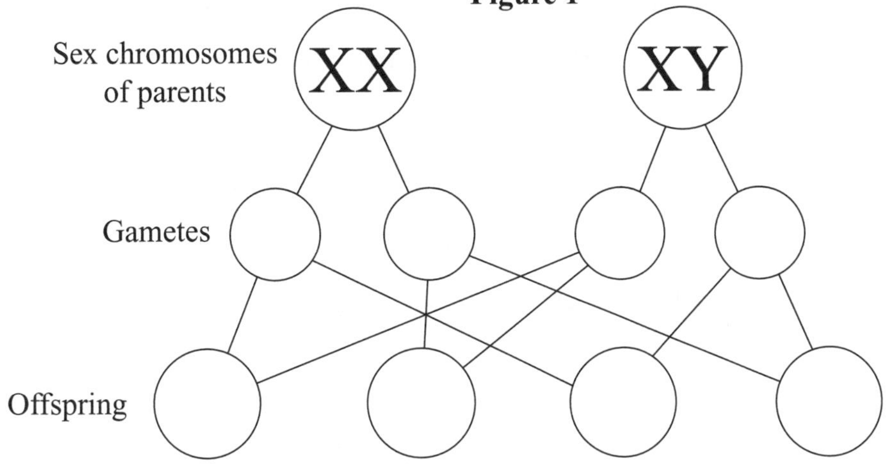

Sex chromosomes of parents   XX   XY

Gametes

Offspring

1.2   Circle the male parent in **Figure 1**.

[1]

1.3   Fill in the sex chromosomes of the gametes produced by each parent in **Figure 1**.

[1]

1.4   Complete **Figure 1** to show the combination of sex chromosomes in the offspring.

[1]

1.5   What is the ratio of male to female offspring?

....

[1]

1.6   Sex determination can also be shown in a Punnett square.
Produce a Punnett square to show how the biological sex of offspring is determined.

[2]

[Total 7 marks]

Exam Tip

If you're asked to draw a Punnett square in the exam, make sure you end up with four single letters outside the square, and four pairs of letters inside the square. Getting just one letter wrong could lose you a mark, so be careful.

 ☐   ☐   ☐   Topic B6 — Inheritance, Variation and Evolution

Genetic Diagrams

Warm-Up

Use the words and phrases to complete the passage below. You don't have to use every one.

homozygous	dominant	multiple genes	genotypes	homologous

| | alleles | recessive | heterozygous | a single gene |

Genes exist in different versions called .... These can be dominant or .... If an individual has two copies of the same version of a gene, they are said to be ...., but if they have two different versions, they are said to be .... Some characteristics are controlled by ...., but most are controlled by ....

1 **Figure 1** shows a family tree for the inheritance of a genetic disease.

Figure 1

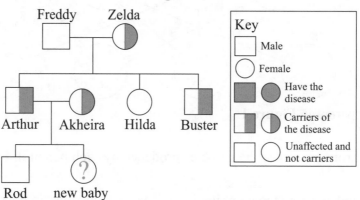

1.1 How can you tell that the allele for the disease is not dominant?

....

....

[1]

1.2 The alleles for the disease are D and d. Both Arthur and Akheira are carriers of the disease. Complete the Punnett square in **Figure 2** to determine the probability of their new baby being unaffected and not a carrier of the disease.

Figure 2

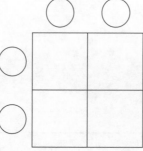

probability = ... %

[4]

[Total 5 marks]

Topic B6 — Inheritance, Variation and Evolution

2 Hair length in dogs is controlled by two alleles. Long hair is caused by the allele 'H' and short hair is caused by the allele 'h'. **Figure 3** shows a genetic diagram of a cross between two dogs with the genotype Hh.

Figure 3

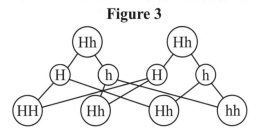

2.1 What is the expected ratio of long-haired puppies to short-haired puppies in this cross?

....

[1]

2.2 A dog with the genotype HH was crossed with a dog with the genotype hh.
They had 8 puppies. How many of those puppies would you expect to have long fur?

Complete **Figure 4** below to explain your answer.

Figure 4

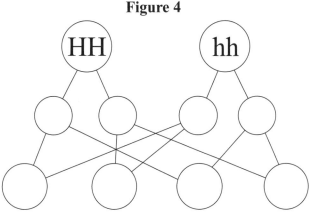

number of long-haired puppies = ...

[3]

2.3 A male dog heterozygous for long hair was then crossed with a female dog homozygous for short hair. What would you expect the ratio of long-haired to short-haired puppies to be in the offspring of this cross?

Construct a Punnett square to explain your answer.

ratio = ...

[3]

[Total 7 marks]

Exam Tip

It's really important that you draw your diagrams as neatly as possible. You could know exactly what it should look like, but if the person marking your paper can't understand what you've drawn they won't be able to give you the marks. So draw it with a pencil and use all the space that you're given. A tiny squiggle in the corner would be tricky to read.

Topic B6 — Inheritance, Variation and Evolution

Inherited Disorders

1 Polydactyly and cystic fibrosis are examples of inherited disorders. *Grade 6-7*

1.1 What are the symptoms of polydactyly?

....

[1]

1.2 A person only has to have one allele for polydactyly to have symptoms.
What does this tell you about the allele that causes polydactyly?

....

[1]

1.3 Even if both parents each carry one copy of the allele that causes cystic fibrosis, there is only
a relatively small chance that their offspring will have the disorder. Explain why this is the case.

....

....

....

[3]

[Total 5 marks]

2 Embryos can be screened for genetic disorders like cystic fibrosis.
The results of screening sometimes results in the embryo being destroyed.
There are lots of arguments for and against embryo screening. *Grade 7-9*

2.1 Suggest **three** arguments against embryo screening.

....

....

....

....

....

....

[3]

2.2 Suggest **three** arguments for embryo screening.

....

....

....

....

....

....

[3]

[Total 6 marks]

Topic B6 — Inheritance, Variation and Evolution

Variation

1 Variation occurs in many different organisms.

1.1 Dalmatians and pugs are both members of the same species. However, they look very different. For example, dalmatians have spots but pugs do not.
What type of variation is causing this difference?

....

[1]

Figure 1 and **Figure 2** show two plants of the same species growing in opposite corners of a garden. The plant in **Figure 1** was grown in a sunny corner, whereas the plant in **Figure 2** was grown in a shady corner.

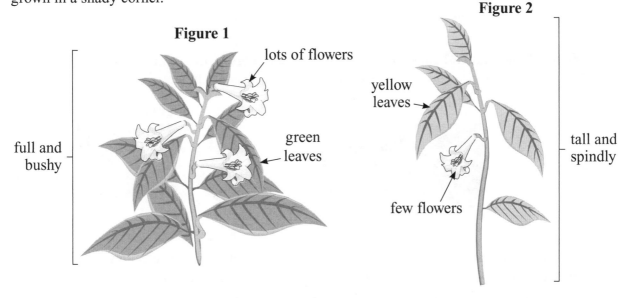

1.2 What type of variation is causing the differences between the two plants?

....

[1]

[Total 2 marks]

2 Mutations can occasionally lead to a rapid change in a species.
Explain how a mutation could lead to a rapid change in a species.

....

....

....

....

[Total 3 marks]

Exam Tip

Remember that while variation can be caused by either genetic or environmental factors, it's usually caused by a mixture of both interacting with each other. In the exam, you might get an example of variation that you've never heard of before. Don't worry if you do, all the information you need to answer the question will be there. Just apply your knowledge.

Topic B6 — Inheritance, Variation and Evolution

Evolution

1   Extinction is when a species completely dies out because they're not able to evolve quickly enough to adapt to a change in their environment. Give **five** factors that can cause a species to become extinct.

(Grade 6-7)

....

....

....

....

....

[Total 5 marks]

2   **Figure 1** and **Figure 2** show two hares. The hare in **Figure 1** lives in a very cold climate. The hare in **Figure 2** lives in a warmer climate.

(Grade 7-9)

Figure 1   **Figure 2**

The hare in **Figure 2** uses its large ears as a cooling mechanism. They allow lots of heat to leave the hare's body. The hare in **Figure 1** has smaller ears.

Suggest how the species of hare in **Figure 1** evolved to have smaller ears than hares that live in warmer climates.

....

....

....

....

....

....

....

....

....

[Total 5 marks]

Exam Tip

In the exam, be careful you don't just rewrite information that you were given in the question — it won't earn you any extra marks, so it's really just wasting valuable time. For example, in your answer to Q2 above, you don't need to bother explaining how having big ears will help the hare in Figure 2 cool down, as you were told that in the question.

Topic B6 — Inheritance, Variation and Evolution

Selective Breeding

1 Selective breeding is used in several different industries. **Grade 4-6**

1.1 Which of these is another name for the process of selective breeding?
Tick **one** box.

☐ Evolution ☐ Natural selection ☐ Inheritance ☐ Artificial selection

[1]

1.2 What is selective breeding?

....

....

[1]

1.3 Suggest why dairy farmers might use selective breeding.

....

[1]

[Total 3 marks]

2 A dog breeder used selective breeding to produce a litter of puppies that all had a good, gentle temperament. **Grade 6-7**

2.1* Describe how the breeder could have achieved this, starting from a mixed population of dogs.

....

....

....

....

....

....

[4]

2.2 Suggest why the puppies may be more susceptible to genetic defects.

....

....

....

[2]

2.3 Suggest why a new disease might be an issue for the puppies produced using selective breeding.

....

....

....

[3]

[Total 9 marks]

Topic B6 — Inheritance, Variation and Evolution

Genetic Engineering

Draw circles to show whether the statements below are **true** or **false**.

Genetic engineering can only be carried out on plants.	True / False
Genetic engineering has been proven to be 100% risk free.	True / False
Crops that have been genetically engineered are already being grown.	True / False
Vectors in genetic engineering can be bacterial plasmids.	True / False

1 Genetic engineering is being investigated for use in a wide variety of applications. **Grade 6-7**

1.1 What is genetic engineering?

....

....

[2]

The process of genetic engineering has several steps.

1.2 The useful gene is first isolated from an organism's DNA. Explain how this is done.

....

....

[1]

1.3 The gene is then inserted into the target organism's genome.
Explain how this is achieved so that the organism develops with the desired characteristics.

....

....

....

....

[3]

1.4 Scientists are currently investigating the applications of genetic engineering in medicine.
Give **two** examples of how genetic engineering has been used to treat human diseases,
or how it could potentially be used.

....

....

....

....

[2]

[Total 8 marks]

Exam Tip

The issues around genetic engineering are far from simple — not everyone agrees it's a good idea. Whatever your opinion is, before your exam make sure you know the steps involved and be aware of its potential benefits and risks.

2 Genetic engineering can be used to alter the genes and characteristics of food crops. The resulting crops are known as GM crops.

(Grade 6-7)

2.1 What does 'GM' stand for when referring to crops that have been genetically engineered?
Tick **one** box.

☐ genetically manufactured ☐ genetically mutated ☐ genetically modelled ☐ genetically modified

[1]

2.2 GM crops are often altered to increase their yield. One way in which this can be achieved in some crops is by modifying their genes to make them produce larger fruit.
Suggest **two** other ways in which a crop plant's genes can be altered to increase its yield.

....

....

[2]

A scientist was researching the effect of a genetic modification on fruit size in a species of plant.
He first grew a normal individual of the species in controlled conditions (Plant 1).
He then measured the circumferences of the 10 largest fruits after a set amount of time.
He repeated these steps with a genetically modified individual from the same species (Plant 2).
Table 1 shows the results.

Table 1

	Fruit Circumference (cm)									
Plant 1	16.4	16.8	15.9	16.2	15.7	16.4	16.3	16.0	15.9	16.0
Plant 2	20.2	20.4	19.8	19.6	20.4	20.6	20.2	19.9	20.1	20.0

2.3 Use the data in **Table 1** to calculate the mean fruit circumference for each plant.

Plant 1 = ... cm   Plant 2 = ... cm

[2]

2.4 Calculate the percentage change in mean fruit circumference between Plant 1 and Plant 2.

..............%

[2]

2.5 Not everyone thinks that GM crops are a good idea.
Give **one** concern that people may have about GM crops.

....

....

[1]

[Total 8 marks]

Topic B6 — Inheritance, Variation and Evolution

Fossils

Draw circles to show whether the statements below are **true** or **false**.

Fossils are all between 100 and 1000 years old.	True / False
Fossils are the remains of organisms.	True / False
Fossils are often found in rocks.	True / False

1   The fossil record provides an account of how much different organisms have changed over time. Fossils can be formed in three ways.

1.1 **Figure 1** shows a fossilised insect preserved in amber. Amber is fossilised tree sap. The insect became trapped in the sap as it fed from the tree.

Figure 1

Explain how insects trapped in amber become fossilised rather than decaying.

....

....

[2]

1.2 Describe **two** other ways that fossils are formed.

....

....

....

....

[2]

1.3 Scientists are unable to use the fossil record as conclusive evidence to support or disprove theories on how life on Earth first began. Explain why this is the case.

....

....

....

....

....

....

[3]

[Total 7 marks]

Topic B6 — Inheritance, Variation and Evolution

Antibiotic-Resistant Bacteria

1 Antibiotic resistance in bacteria is becoming an increasing problem in medicine. This is partly due to the overuse of antibiotics.

Grade 4-6

1.1 The overuse of antibiotics is sometimes caused by them being prescribed inappropriately. Give **two** examples of antibiotics being prescribed inappropriately.

....

....

[2]

1.2 Explain why patients prescribed a course of antibiotics should always complete the full course.

....

....

....

[3]

[Total 5 marks]

2 Antibiotic-resistant strains of bacteria are harder to treat because the conventional antibiotics used to kill them are now ineffective. New antibiotics are being developed, but it's unlikely that we'll be able to keep up with the emergence of new resistant strains.

Grade 6-7

2.1 Explain why the development of antibiotics is unlikely to keep up with the emergence of new antibiotic-resistant bacteria.

....

....

[2]

2.2 Explain how antibiotic-resistant strains of bacteria develop and spread.

....

....

....

....

....

....

....

....

....

[5]

[Total 7 marks]

Topic B6 — Inheritance, Variation and Evolution

Target AO3

3 A scientist has samples of two strains of the same species of bacterium, strain A and strain B. This species of bacterium is usually killed by the antibiotic ampicillin, but the scientist believes that strain B may have become resistant to ampicillin.

Grade 6-7

3.1* The scientist has the following materials and equipment:

> • ampicillin solution
> • samples of bacterial strain A and strain B, growing in nutrient broth solution
> • sterile small glass bottles, with lids
> • sterile nutrient broth solution (culture medium)
> • sterile pipettes of different sizes

The sterile nutrient broth is clear, but turns cloudy when bacteria grow in it.

Write a method that the scientist could use to test his hypothesis using this equipment.

....

....

....

....

....

....

....

....

....

....

....

....

[6]

3.2 Give **one** reason why it is important that the scientist makes sure that all of the material from the experiment is disposed of safely when it is over.

....

....

[1]

[Total 7 marks]

Exam Tip

You could be asked to write a method for an experiment in your exams. If you are, don't worry. Just think carefully through what you'd need to do if you were actually doing the experiment, and write it all down in a sensible order. Remember to include details of what you would do to make it a fair test — otherwise your results wouldn't be valid.

Classification

1 Evolutionary trees show how scientists think that organisms are related to each other. **Figure 1** shows the evolutionary tree for species A – K.

Figure 1

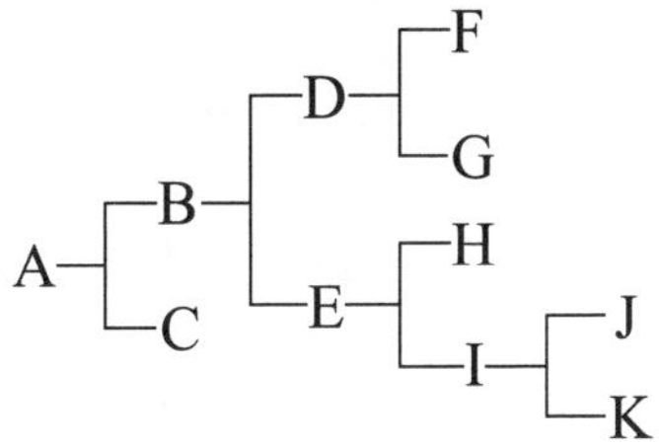

1.1 Give **two** pieces of information that scientists use to prepare evolutionary trees for living and extinct organisms.

....

[2]

1.2 Which species is the most recent common ancestor of species G and species J?

....

[1]

1.3 Which pair of species, G and H or J and K are more distantly related?

....

[1]

[Total 4 marks]

2 Organisms used to be classified into groups using the Linnaean system.

2.1 What is the correct order for the groups of the Linnaean system, from largest to smallest?
Tick **one** box.

☐   kingdom, phylum, class, order, family, genus, species

☐   species, genus, class, phylum, order, family, kingdom

☐   kingdom, family, phylum, order, class, genus, species

☐   species, class, genus, family, order, phylum, kingdom

[1]

A new classification system, known as the three-domain system, was proposed in the 1990s. In this system, organisms are first divided into domains.

2.2 What is the name of the scientist who proposed the three-domain system?

....

[1]

2.3 Other than fungi, state **three** types of organisms found in the domain Eukaryota.

....

[3]

[Total 5 marks]

Exam Tip

Evolutionary trees are very handy for figuring out how species are related to each other. If you get given an evolutionary tree in the exam, you could well be asked to interpret it. But don't worry — just keep practising with questions like these.

 ☐   ☐   ☐   **Topic B6 — Inheritance, Variation and Evolution**

Competition

1 The plants in a community are often in competition with each other for water and mineral ions.

Grade 4-6

1.1 Where do plants obtain water and mineral ions from?

....

[1]

1.2 Name **two** other factors that plants often compete with each other for.

....

....

[2]

1.3 The animals in a community also compete with each other.
State **three** factors animals compete with each other for.

....

....

....

[3]

[Total 6 marks]

2 Within a community, each species depends on other species for things such as food, shelter, pollination and seed dispersal.

Grade 6-7

2.1 What is this type of relationship called?

....

[1]

Blue tits are relatively common birds that live in woodland communities.
Blue tits feed on caterpillars. Caterpillars live and feed on plants.

2.2 If the caterpillars were removed from the community, suggest what might happen to the numbers of blue tits and plants. Explain your answers.

....

....

....

....

[4]

2.3 Some communities are not stable.
Explain fully what is meant by the term 'stable community'.

....

....

[2]

[Total 7 marks]

Abiotic and Biotic Factors

1 In an ecosystem, there will be both biotic and abiotic factors. *(Grade 4-6)*

1.1 Which of the following statements is correct? Tick **one** box.

☐ Light intensity, temperature and carbon dioxide level are all examples of biotic factors.

☐ Availability of food, carbon dioxide level and pathogens are all examples of abiotic factors.

☐ Light intensity, temperature and carbon dioxide level are all examples of abiotic factors.

☐ Availability of food, light intensity and pathogens are all examples of biotic factors.

[1]

1.2 Suggest **one** abiotic factor that could affect the distribution of animals living in aquatic areas.

....

[1]

1.3 Suggest **two** abiotic factors that could affect the distribution of plants growing in soil.

....

....

[2]

[Total 4 marks]

2 Red squirrels are native to southern Britain. When grey squirrels were introduced into the same area, the number of red squirrels declined. *(Grade 6-7)*

Suggest why the number of red squirrels declined.

....

....

....

[Total 3 marks]

3 Grasses make their own food by photosynthesis. In grassland communities, the grass leaves provide insects with shelter, a place to breed and a source of food. Visiting birds feed on insects. *(Grade 6-7)*

The birds that visit the grassland to feed become infected with a new pathogen that eventually kills them. What would you expect to happen to the number of grass plants? Explain your answer.

....

....

....

....

[Total 3 marks]

Topic B7 — Ecology

Target AO3

4   Herons are carnivorous birds that eat fish such as perch. The sizes of a population of herons and a population of perch in a lake ecosystem were monitored over ten years. The pH of the lake was also monitored over the same time period. The results are shown in **Figures 1** and **2**.

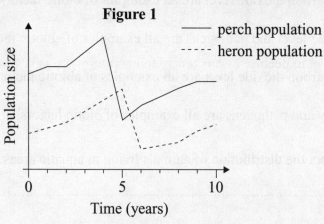

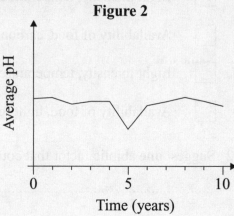

4.1   Describe the trends shown by the two populations in **Figure 1**.

....

....

....

[2]

4.2   Use the data to suggest a reason for the decrease in the perch population between years **4** and **5**. Explain why the data provided cannot be used to confirm what the reason is.

....

....

....

....

[3]

4.3   A new disease has emerged that is predicted to wipe out most of the perch population in the lake. A scientist thinks that the heron population will decrease as a result, because they will lose a source of food. Suggest why the scientist might not be correct.

....

....

....

....

[3]

[Total 8 marks]

Exam Tip

If a question in the exam asks you to use the data, make sure you actually do use the data you're given. It's sitting there in a nice little figure or table, just to help you out, so make the most of it. If you don't use it, you won't get all the marks.

Topic B7 — Ecology

Adaptations

1 Some organisms live in environments that are very extreme, such as environments with a high salt concentration.

Grade 4-6

1.1 What name is given to organisms that live in extreme environments?

....

[1]

1.2 Name **one** group of organisms that can live in deep sea vents where temperatures are very high.

....

[1]

1.3 Describe **one** extreme condition, other than a high salt concentration or a high temperature, that some organisms can tolerate.

....

[1]

[Total 3 marks]

2 Organisms are adapted to the conditions in which they live. **Figure 1** shows a camel and **Figure 2** shows a cactus. Both camels and cacti live in hot, dry desert conditions.

Grade 6-7

Figure 1

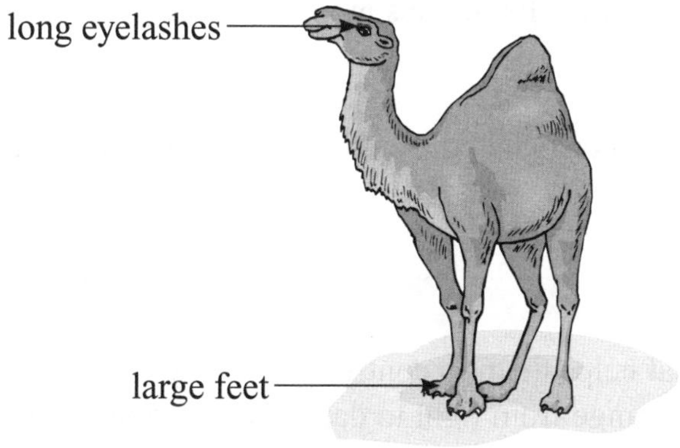

long eyelashes

large feet

Figure 2

spines

swollen stem

2.1 Suggest how each of the features in **Figure 1** allow the camel to live in desert conditions.

Long eyelashes ....

....

Large feet...

....

[2]

2.2 Suggest how having spines instead of leaves allows cacti to live in desert conditions.

....

[1]

2.3 Suggest how having a swollen storage stem allows cacti to live in desert conditions.

....

[1]

Cacti can have two types of roots — shallow, wide-spreading roots or long, deep roots.

2.4 For each of these types of root, suggest how the cacti are better adapted to live in desert conditions.

....

....

[2]

[Total 6 marks]

3 Lizards gain most of their heat from the environment. This means that their body temperatures change with the temperature of the environment. **Figure 3** shows a lizard.

(Grade 6-7)

Figure 3

Lizards control their body temperatures by adapting their behaviour to changes in the environment. For example, in the early morning they lie in the sun to gain heat and only then can they become active.

3.1 Suggest what behavioural adaptation lizards might show when the environmental temperature becomes too hot.

....

[1]

Some lizards also have a structural adaptation that helps them to control their body temperature. They can change the colour of their skin within a range from light to dark. Darker colours absorb more heat than lighter colours.

3.2 Would you expect a lizard in cold conditions to have a dark or light coloured skin?

....

[1]

3.3 There are different types of adaptation, including behavioural and structural. Name **one** other type of adaptation that organisms can have.

....

[1]

[Total 3 marks]

Exam Tip

All of the organisms on these pages are different and have different adaptations to their environment. You could be given information on any organism in the exam but, remember, each feature that the organism has gives it an advantage for living in its environment. You just need to have a think about what that advantage could be. Simple.

Topic B7 — Ecology

Food Chains

Warm-Up

On the food chain below, label the producer and the secondary consumer.

seaweed → fish → shark → whale

1 **Figure 1** shows an example of a woodland food chain. *Grade 6-7*

Figure 1

green plants → greenflies → blue tits → sparrow hawk

1.1 What term would be used to describe the greenflies' position in **Figure 1**?

....

[1]

1.2 Green plants produce biomass for the rest of the food chain. Explain how they do this.

....

....

[3]

[Total 4 marks]

2 In a stable community, the numbers of predators and prey rise and fall in cycles as shown in **Figure 2**. In this cycle the predator is a lynx and the prey is a snowshoe hare. *Grade 7-9*

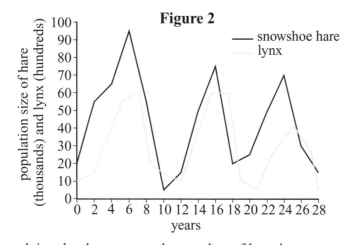

Figure 2

2.1 Describe and explain what happens to the number of lynx between years 4 and 6.

....

....

[2]

2.2 What causes the number of snowshoe hares to fall between years 6 and 10?

....

[1]

[Total 3 marks]

Using Quadrats

1   A group of students used a quadrat with an area of 0.5 m² to investigate the
    number of buttercups growing in a field. They counted the number of buttercups
    in the quadrat in ten randomly selected places. **Table 1** shows their results.

Table 1

Quadrat Number	Number of buttercups
1	15
2	13
3	16
4	23
5	26
6	23
7	13
8	12
9	16
10	13

1.1 Why is it important that the quadrats were placed randomly in the field?

....

[1]

1.2 What is the modal number of buttercups in **Table 1**?

.... buttercups
[1]

1.3 What is the median number of buttercups in **Table 1**?

.... buttercups
[1]

1.4 Calculate the mean number of buttercups per 0.5 m² quadrat.

.... buttercups per 0.5 m²
[1]

1.5 The total area of the field was 1750 m².
     Estimate the number of buttercups in the whole of the field.

.... buttercups
[3]

[Total 7 marks]

Exam Tip

The mode, median and mean are all different types of average. They all tell you useful, but slightly different, information about the data. Make sure you can remember how to find them all in case one comes up in your exam.

Using Transects

1   A transect was carried out from the edge of a small pond, across a grassy field and into a woodland. The distributions of four species of plant were recorded along the transect, along with the soil moisture and light levels. **Figure 1** shows the results.

Figure 1

Key   dandelion
       daisy   short grass   long grass

pond   zone A   zone B   zone C   woodland

soil moisture level: high ⟶ low
light level: high ⟶ low

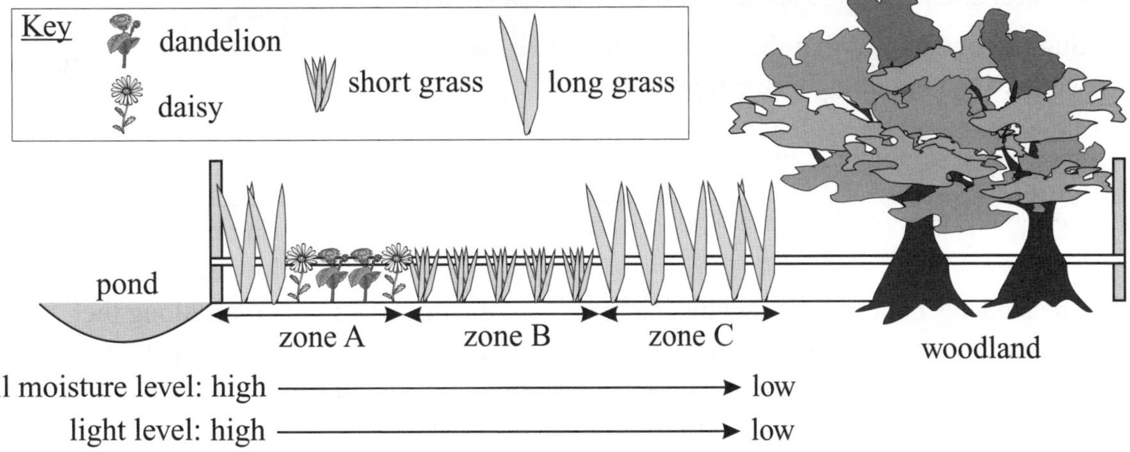

The grassy field is split up into three zones — A, B and C.

1.1 In **Figure 1**, which zones contained only one species of plant?

....
[1]

1.2 Which of the four species of plant can grow in soils with both a high and low moisture level, and at both low and high light intensities?

....
[1]

1.3 Suggest **two** reasons why long grass, daisies and dandelions all grow in zone A.

....

....
[2]

Children often play football on one zone of the grassy field.
The trampling that occurs here makes it difficult for plants to become established.

1.4 Suggest which zone might be used to play football. Explain your answer.

....

....
[2]

1.5 Suggest why there are no daisies or dandelions growing in the woodland.

....
[1]

A transect can also be used to determine the abundance of species in an ecosystem.

1.6 Explain how this transect could be used to determine the abundance of the four plant species.

....
[1]

[Total 8 marks]

Topic B7 — Ecology

Target AO3

2   A group of students are using a transect to investigate the distribution of organisms across a rocky shore.

Grade 6-7

PRACTICAL

Figure 2 shows a diagram of the shoreline as seen from above. The students plan to place a quadrat at set intervals along the transect and record the species in the quadrat at each point.

Figure 2

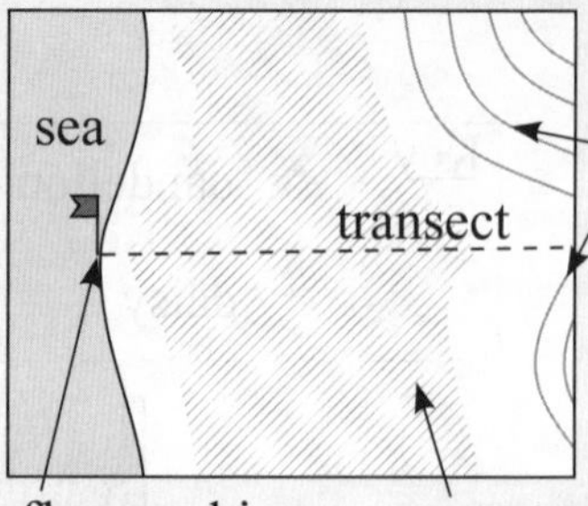

sea

transect

sand dunes

flag marking low tide point

area covered by rock pools

2.1 Suggest one hazard that the students should be aware of while carrying out their investigation.

....

.... *[1]*

2.2 The students collect their data by placing a 1 m² quadrat at 2 m intervals along the transect and estimating the percentage cover of each organism within the quadrat. Suggest **one** advantage and **one** disadvantage of placing the quadrat at 2 m intervals rather than every metre, with no gap between the intervals.

....

....

....

.... *[2]*

Table 1 shows the data that the students collected about a seaweed called bladderwrack.

Table 1

Distance from low tide point (m)	2	4	6	8	10	12	14	16	18	20
Percentage cover of bladderwrack in quadrat (%)	0	0	2	10	15	25	40	65	80	75

2.3 Describe the trend in the percentage cover of bladderwrack shown by the data in **Table 1**.

....

....

.... *[2]*

2.4 The students think that the salt concentration of the water in the rock pools around the bladderwrack affects its growth. Suggest how they could change their method to test this hypothesis.

....

[1]

[Total 6 marks]

Exam Tip

If you have time at the end of the exam, have a quick peep back at your answers to make sure that everything you've written is clear and that you've fully answered each question. For example, if you were asked to give advantages and disadvantages for a particular topic, make sure you've written an answer that actually covers both of them.

The Water Cycle

Choose from the words below to complete the sentences about the water cycle. Some words may not be used at all.

precipitation   evaporate   warms   cools   water vapour   carbon dioxide   condense

Energy from the Sun makes water .... from the land and sea,

turning it into .... This is carried upwards. When it gets higher

up it .... and condenses to form clouds. Water falls from the

clouds as .... onto land. It then drains into the sea, before the

whole process starts again.

1   **Figure 1** represents the stages in the water cycle.

Figure 1

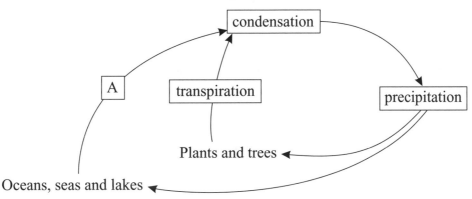

1.1   Name the process represented by **A** in the diagram.

....

[1]

1.2   Outline what is meant by the term 'precipitation'.

....

[1]

1.3   Explain why precipitation is an important stage in the water cycle.

....

....

[1]

[3 marks]

Topic B7 — Ecology

The Carbon Cycle

1   **Figure 1** shows an unfinished diagram of the carbon cycle.

Figure 1

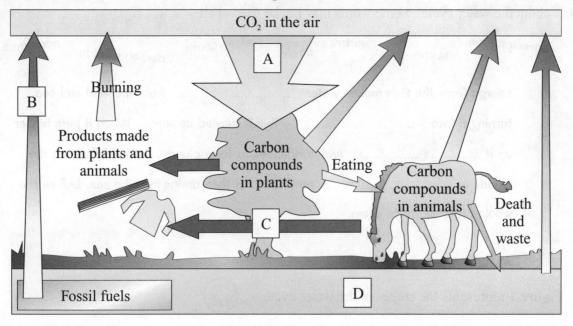

1.1   Name the process represented by **A** in **Figure 1**.

....
[1]

1.2   Which group of organisms remove carbon dioxide from the air?

....
[1]

1.3   Name the process represented by **B** in **Figure 1**.

....
[1]

1.4   Box **C** is the process of changing animal components into products. These can be recycled
to return carbon dioxide to the air. Suggest **one** animal product that can be recycled in this way.

....
[1]

1.5   Process **D** in **Figure 1** is decay. Describe the importance of decay in the carbon cycle.

....

....
[2]

[Total 6 marks]

Exam Tip

In the exam you could be tested on any part of the carbon cycle, so make sure you know the whole of it and not just bits
of it. Try sketching the whole cycle out and make sure you can link each bit together. Don't have your arrows going the
wrong way round, and make sure you understand why the carbon is moving around, e.g. because of respiration. Sorted.

Topic B7 — Ecology

Biodiversity and Waste Management

1 Many human activities have an impact on biodiversity. (Grade 4-6)

1.1 Define biodiversity.

....

....
[1]

1.2 Suggest **one** human activity that reduces biodiversity.

....
[1]
[Total 2 marks]

2 The global population is using an increasing amount of resources. (Grade 4-6)

2.1 State **two** reasons why humans are using more resources.

....

....
[2]

If waste is not handled correctly, pollution levels in water and in the air will increase.

2.2 State **two** ways that water can become polluted.

....

....
[2]

2.3 State **two** substances that pollute the air when they are released into the atmosphere.

....
[2]
[Total 6 marks]

3 Herbicides are used by farmers to control the growth of weeds on land where crops are grown. (Grade 6-7)

3.1 Give **two** reasons why using a herbicide can reduce biodiversity.

....

....
[2]

3.2 Explain why a high biodiversity creates a stable ecosystem.

....

....

....
[2]
[Total 4 marks]

Target AO3

4   The presence of indicator species in an area can provide evidence for the
      level of pollution in the ecosystem. A student is surveying the numbers of
      three indicator species in two small rivers as a measure of water pollution.

This is the method that the student used:

1. Place a long-handled net with a fine mesh on the bottom of the river.
   It should be positioned so that water is flowing into the net.
2. Stand upstream of the net and gently disturb the bottom
   of the river by moving your feet for 30 seconds.
3. Empty the contents of the net into a large tray filled with a 3 cm depth of water.
4. Identify and count the individuals of the indicator species in your sample.
5. Empty the contents of the tray back into the river.

Table 1 shows the results. **Table 2** gives details of the indicator species.

Table 1

Individuals counted in survey	River 1	River 2
freshwater shrimp	29	0
water louse	60	10
rat-tailed maggot	4	88

Table 2

Indicator species	Presence of species indicates:
freshwater shrimp	low level of pollution
water louse	medium level of pollution
rat-tailed maggot	high level of pollution

4.1 Use the results to compare the level of water pollution in the two rivers. Explain your answer.

....

....

....

....

[3]

4.2 A factory discharges waste water into River 2 at a site upstream of the sampling site
    used in the student's survey. A local newspaper claims that the factory discharges
    are causing an increase in pollution in the river.

Explain how the student's survey would need to change to investigate the newspaper's claim.

....

....

....

....

[3]

[Total 6 marks]

Exam Tip

In your exams, you could be given the method for an experiment and asked how you would need to adapt it to test a different hypothesis. You'll need to have a think about what the original method was testing. Then have a good old read of the new hypothesis you've been given, and work out what things you'd need to change in order to test that.

Topic B7 — Ecology

Global Warming

Warm-Up

Fill in the gaps in the passage below using the words on the right.
Not all words need to be used, but each word can only be used once.

insulating

the Sun

reflect

increases

the moon   space

gases   decreases

volcanoes

The temperature of the Earth is a balance between the energy

it gets from .... and the energy it radiates

back into .... The .... in the

atmosphere act like an insulating layer. They radiate some of

the energy back towards the Earth. This ....

the temperature of the planet.

---

1   Global warming is caused by the increasing
     levels of 'greenhouse gases' in the atmosphere.

Grade 6-7

1.1 Which of the following pairs of gases are the main contributors to global warming?
     Tick **one** box.

     ☐ carbon dioxide and sulfur dioxide

     ☐ carbon dioxide and methane

     ☐ sulfur dioxide and nitrogen dioxide

     ☐ nitrogen dioxide and methane

     [1]

There are a number of consequences of global warming,
including land becoming flooded.

1.2 Suggest why global warming might cause land to become flooded.

     ....

     ....

     [2]

1.3 Suggest **two** other consequences of global warming.

     ....

     ....

     [2]

     [Total 5 marks]

Exam Tip

Greenhouse gases cause the 'greenhouse effect', but don't go getting this muddled up with global warming. Without these
gases trapping energy in Earth's atmosphere, it'd be too cold for us to survive. But the increasing amounts of these gases
are increasing the amount of energy being trapped, and that's why we're getting all, ahem, hot and bothered about them.

 ☐   ☐   ☐

Deforestation and Land Use

1 State **two** ways in which humans reduce the amount of land available for other animals and plants.

Grade 4-6

....

....

[Total 2 marks]

2 Peat bogs are sometimes destroyed so that the peat can be burnt as fuel.

Grade 6-7

2.1 Give **one** other reason why peat bogs are destroyed by humans.

....

[1]

2.2 Explain what problem burning peat can cause.

....

....

[2]

2.3 Explain the effect that the destruction of peat bogs has on biodiversity.

....

....

[2]

[Total 5 marks]

3 Biofuel production has caused large-scale deforestation.

Grade 6-7

3.1 Explain why large-scale deforestation has been required to produce biofuels.

....

[1]

3.2 State **two** other reasons for large-scale deforestation.

....

....

[2]

[Total 3 marks]

4 Suggest and explain **two** harmful effects on the environment caused by the destruction of large areas of trees.

Grade 7-9

....

....

....

....

[Total 4 marks]

Maintaining Ecosystems and Biodiversity

1 In some areas, programmes have been put in place to reduce the negative effects of human activity on ecosystems and biodiversity.   *Grade 4-6*

1.1 Which of the following would reduce carbon dioxide emissions into the atmosphere? Tick **one** box.

☐ Setting up more breeding programmes for endangered species.

☐ Cutting down large areas of trees for housing development.

☐ Increasing the number of power stations.

☐ Burning fewer fossil fuels.

[1]

1.2 The government encourages people to recycle as much of their waste as possible.
Suggest how this could help to protect ecosystems.

....

....

[2]

[Total 3 marks]

2 Monoculture is a form of agriculture in which only one type of crop is grown in a field.   *Grade 6-7*

2.1 Suggest what effect monoculture has on biodiversity. Explain your answer.

....

....

[2]

2.2 Explain why farmers who grow crops using monoculture may be advised
to leave strips of grassland and plant hedgerows around the edges of their crops.

....

[1]

[Total 3 marks]

3 Suggest why some people might be opposed to programmes that maintain biodiversity.   *Grade 7-9*

....

....

....

....

....

....

....

....

[Total 4 marks]

Topic B7 — Ecology

Atoms

Warm-Up

Choose from the labels below to fill in the blanks in the passage.

protons

1×10^{-14}

0.1

1/10 000

charge   electrons

The radius of an atom is approximately .... nanometres.

The radius of the nucleus is around .... metres.

That's about .... of the radius of an atom.

An atom doesn't have an overall .... as it has equal

numbers of .... and ....

1   **Figure 1** shows the structure of a helium atom.   (Grade 4-6)

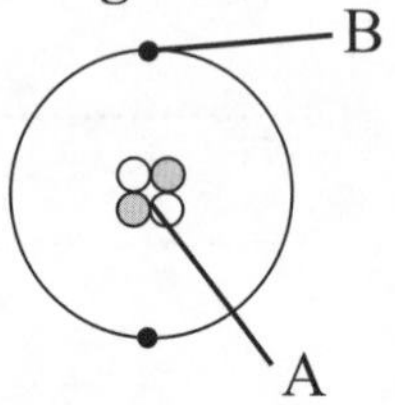

1.1   Name the region where most of the mass of the atom is concentrated.

....
[1]

Figure 1

1.2   What is the relative charge of particle **B**?

....
[1]

1.3   Name the particles in region **A** and give their relative charges.

....

....
[2]

[Total 4 marks]

2   A potassium atom can be represented by the nuclear symbol $^{39}_{19}K$.   (Grade 4-6)

2.1   What is the mass number of $^{39}_{19}K$?

....
[1]

2.2   What is the atomic number of $^{39}_{19}K$?

....
[1]

2.3   How many protons, neutrons and electrons does an atom of $^{39}_{19}K$ have?

protons: ....   neutrons: ....   electrons: ....
[3]

[Total 5 marks]

Exam Tip

The charges on atoms and particles are crucial to understanding chemistry, so make sure that you learn all about them before the exam. **P**rotons have a **p**ositive charge and **neut**rons are always **neut**ral. Unfortunately there isn't a handy way of remembering that electrons have a negative charge, but I'm sure you can figure it out.

Elements

1 $^{35}_{17}Cl$ and $^{37}_{17}Cl$ are the naturally occurring isotopes of the element chlorine. **Grade 4-6**

1.1 Which of the following statements about elements is true? Tick **one** box.

Atoms of an element can contain different numbers of protons. ☐

Chlorine is one of 200 different elements. ☐

Elements contain more than one type of atom. ☐

Atoms are the smallest part of an element that can exist. ☐

[1]

1.2 Explain why $^{35}_{17}Cl$ and $^{37}_{17}Cl$ are isotopes of the element chlorine.

....

....

....

[2]

[Total 3 marks]

2 This question is about isotopes. **Grade 6-7**

2.1 A neutral atom of sulfur, ^{32}S, has 16 electrons.
Sulfur has three other naturally occurring isotopes, with mass numbers 33, 34 and 36.
Complete the table below giving the number of protons, neutrons and electrons for each isotope.

isotope	number of protons	number of neutrons	number of electrons	% abundance
^{32}S	....	....	16	94.99
^{33}S	....	....	....	0.75
^{34}S	....	....	....	4.25
^{36}S	....	....	....	0.01

[3]

2.2 Using the information in the table above, calculate the relative atomic mass of sulfur.
Give your answer to one decimal place.

Relative atomic mass: ....

[2]

2.3 Atom **X** has a mass number of 51 and an atomic number of 23.
Atom **Y** has a mass number of 51 and an atomic number of 22.
Atom **Z** has a mass number of 52 and an atomic number of 23.

Identify which of the atoms are isotopes and explain why.

....

....

[3]

[Total 8 marks]

☹ ☐ 🙂 ☐ 😊 ☐

Topic C1 — Atomic Structure and the Periodic Table

Compounds

1 Ammonia is a compound with the formula NH_3. **(Grade 4-6)**

1.1 Why is ammonia classified as a compound? Tick **one** box.

It contains only one type of atom. ☐

It contains two elements chemically combined. ☐

It cannot be broken down into elements using chemical methods. ☐

It contains more than one atom. ☐

[1]

1.2 How many atoms are there in a single molecule of ammonia?

....

[1]

[Total 2 marks]

2 The following list contains a variety of substances identified by their chemical formula. **(Grade 6-7)**

A. O_2 **B.** NaCl   **C.** C_2H_4 **D.** P_4 **E.** H_2O **F.** H_2

2.1 Name substance **B**.

....

[1]

2.2 Identify **one** substance from the list that is a compound. Explain your choice.

....

....

[2]

2.3 How many atoms are there in a molecule of substance **C**?

....

[1]

2.4 **C** and **F** were reacted to form C_2H_6. Using the formulas of the substances, state if a new compound has been made and explain your answer.

....

....

....

[1]

[Total 5 marks]

Exam Tip

Make sure you know the difference between atoms, elements and compounds. Here's a quick summary... Everything is made of atoms (which contain protons, neutrons and electrons). Elements only contain one type of atom (all the atoms have the same number of protons). A compound consists of different atoms joined together by chemical bonds. Got it?

Topic C1 — Atomic Structure and the Periodic Table

Chemical Equations

The chemical word equation for a reaction is shown below:

magnesium + hydrochloric acid → magnesium chloride + hydrogen

For each of the following statements circle whether the statement is **true** or **false**.

1)	Hydrogen is a product in the reaction	True	Or	False
2)	The equation shows the reaction between chlorine and hydrogen	True	Or	False
3)	Hydrochloric acid is a reactant	True	Or	False
4)	The equation shows the reaction between magnesium and hydrochloric acid	True	Or	False

1 Sodium (Na) reacts vigorously with chlorine gas (Cl_2) to form sodium chloride (NaCl) only.   Grade 4-6

1.1 Write a word equation for this reaction.

....

[1]

1.2 Which of the following equations correctly represents this reaction?

$Na + Cl \rightarrow NaCl$ ☐

$Na_2 + 2Cl \rightarrow 2NaCl$ ☐

$Na_2 + Cl_2 \rightarrow 2NaCl$ ☐

$2Na + Cl_2 \rightarrow 2NaCl$ ☐

[1]

[Total 2 marks]

2 Nitric acid can be made using ammonia.   Grade 7-9

2.1 The first stage in the manufacture of nitric acid is to oxidise ammonia, NH_3, to nitrogen(II) oxide, NO. Balance the equation for the reaction.

.... NH_3 + ... O_2 → .... NO + ... H_2O

[1]

2.2 The reaction below shows the final stage in the manufacture of nitric acid. The equation is not balanced correctly. Explain how you can tell.

$$2NO_2 + O_2 + H_2O \rightarrow 2HNO_3$$

....

....

[1]

[Total 2 marks]

Topic C1 — Atomic Structure and the Periodic Table

Mixtures and Chromatography

1 Air contains many gases. It mainly consists of nitrogen, N_2, and oxygen, O_2 with a small amount of carbon dioxide, CO_2. There are also trace amounts of noble gases such as argon, Ar.

Grade 4-6

1.1 Is air an element, compound or mixture? Explain your answer.

....

....

....

[3]

1.2 Argon can be separated out from air. Will the chemical properties of argon as a separate gas be different from the properties of argon in air? Explain your answer.

....

....

[2]

[Total 5 marks]

2* A simple chromatography experiment was set up to separate dyes in inks. Samples of three different water soluble inks, A, B and C, were placed on a piece of chromatography paper. After 30 minutes, the chromatogram in **Figure 1** was obtained.

Grade 6-7

Outline the procedure for setting up and running this experiment and explain the results.

Figure 1

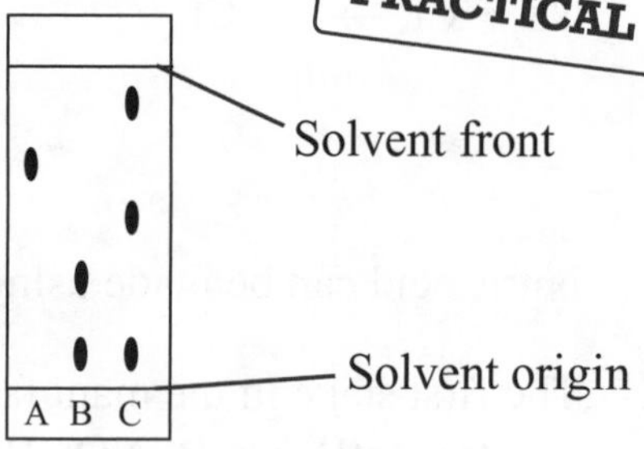

PRACTICAL

Solvent front

Solvent origin

A B C

....

....

....

....

....

....

....

....

....

[Total 6 marks]

Exam Tip

It's easy to get confused about whether a given substance is a compound or a mixture. The key difference is that you don't need to react things together to form a mixture. You don't even have to use chromatography to separate them...

Topic C1 — Atomic Structure and the Periodic Table

More Separation Techniques

1   A student was given a mixture of insoluble chalk powder and solid potassium chloride. Potassium chloride is water soluble. **Grade 6-7**

1.1 Outline a method for separating the chalk from potassium chloride.

....

....

....

[3]

1.2 Outline the process the student could use to obtain pure crystals of potassium chloride from a potassium chloride solution.

....

....

....

[1]

[Total 4 marks]

2   Powdered iron and powdered sulfur were mixed together. Information on the solubility of iron and sulfur is given in **Table 1**. **Grade 7-9**

Table 1

	Iron	Sulfur
Solubility in water	Insoluble	Insoluble
Solubility in methylbenzene	Insoluble	Soluble

2.1 Using the information in **Table 1**, explain how the iron and sulfur could be separated out again to form pure iron and crystals of sulfur.

....

....

....

....

....

[3]

2.2 Some of the mixture was heated in a fume cupboard. Iron(II) sulfide formed. A student stated the iron and sulfur could be separated back out using physical processes. Is the student correct? Explain your answer.

....

....

....

[3]

[Total 6 marks]

Topic C1 — Atomic Structure and the Periodic Table

Distillation

1 Sucrose is a sugar with the formula $C_{12}H_{22}O_{11}$. It is soluble in water. *(Grade 4-6)*

Which of the following techniques would be best for obtaining
pure water from a sugar solution? Tick **one** box.

☐ Evaporation ☐ Condensation ☐ Simple distillation ☐ Fractional distillation

[Total 1 mark]

2 A solution containing octane, which has a boiling point of 125 °C, was prepared.
The solution contained an impurity with a boiling point of 187 °C. The distillation
apparatus shown in **Figure 1** was set up to separate the octane from the impurity. *(Grade 6-7)*

Figure 1

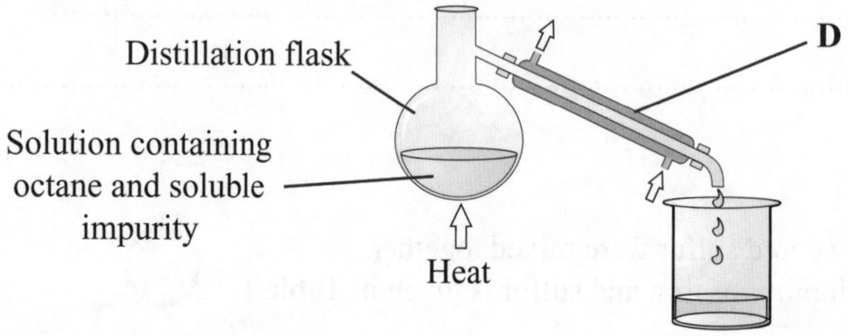

2.1 The apparatus is not correctly set up.
Explain how you would modify the apparatus to make it function correctly.

....

....

[1]

2.2 Explain how octane is separated from the impurity when the distillation apparatus
is set up correctly. Include the function of D in your answer.

....

....

....

....

[3]

2.3 If the distillation flask was placed in a boiling water bath and not directly heated,
the octane would not distil. Explain why.

....

....

[2]

[Total 6 marks]

Topic C1 — Atomic Structure and the Periodic Table

Target AO3

3 A student was given a solution containing water, ethanol and the salts bismuth iodide and potassium chloride. Bismuth iodide is soluble in ethanol and potassium chloride is soluble in water. The boiling point of ethanol is 78 °C and both salts have melting points above 400 °C.

Here is the method the student uses to produce pure samples of the two salts:

1. Using distillation apparatus, heat the mixture to 120 °C to separate the ethanol from the solution.
2. Pour the remaining mixture through a filter to remove the solid bismuth iodide.
3. Pour the filtrate into an evaporating dish.
4. Gently heat the filtrate until dry potassium chloride crystals are left.

3.1 The student's method will not produce separate samples of each salt, but a mixture of both. Identify which step in the method causes the two salts to remain as a mixture. Explain your answer.

....

....

....

[2]

3.2 Explain how the method should be changed to produce separate samples of each salt.

....

....

[1]

3.3 The student suggests using a Bunsen burner to heat the filtrate in step 4. Suggest a risk of carrying out step 4 if the filtrate still contains a large amount of ethanol.

....

[1]

3.4 Potassium hydrogencarbonate is another water-soluble salt. The student planned to produce potassium hydrogencarbonate crystals by heating a sample of potassium hydrogencarbonate solution in an evaporating dish until no more liquid remains. However, potassium hydrogencarbonate decomposes on heating. Describe how the student could adapt their method to ensure they make pure, dry crystals.

....

....

....

[2]

[Total 6 marks]

Exam Tip

You might be given a method in the exam with lots of different steps — the examiner could use any of them to introduce errors for you to spot. Read and think about each part of the method carefully to spot any potential problems.

Topic C1 — Atomic Structure and the Periodic Table

The History of The Atom

For the following statements, circle whether they are **true** or **false**.

New experimental evidence can disprove models	True Or False
Scientific models can be based on existing theories and new experimental evidence	True Or False
Older scientific theories must be ignored when new ones are adopted	True Or False

1 Models of the atom have changed over time. (Grade 4-6)

1.1 Which of the following statements is the best description of what scientists thought an atom was like before the electron was discovered?
Tick **one** box.

☐ Tiny solid spheres that can't be divided.   ☐ Formless 'clouds' of matter.   ☐ Flat geometric shapes.   ☐ Discrete packets of energy.

[1]

1.2 Draw one line from each atomic model to the correct description of that model.

Atomic Model   **Description**

Plum pudding model

A positively charged 'ball' with negatively charged electrons in it.

A small positively charged nucleus surrounded by a 'cloud' of negative electrons.

Bohr's model

Electrons in fixed orbits surrounding a small positively charged nucleus.

Rutherford's nuclear model

Solid spheres with a different sphere for each element.

[3]

1.3 In 1932, James Chadwick discovered a neutral sub-atomic particle found in the nucleus. Give the name of this particle.

....

[1]

[Total 5 marks]

2 In 1911, Ernest Rutherford fired alpha particles at gold foil. Most of the alpha particles passed straight through the gold foil without being deflected. Only a few of the particles bounced back at 180°.

Grade 6-7

2.1 Explain why most of the alpha particles passed through the foil.

....

....

[1]

2.2 Name the scientist that adapted Rutherford's nuclear model by suggesting that electrons orbit the nucleus at specific distances.

....

[1]

[Total 2 marks]

3 In 1897, J. J. Thomson discovered the electron. This discovery led Thomson to propose the 'plum pudding' model of the atom.

Grade 7-9

3.1 Thomson realised that there must be positive charge in an atom as well as the negative charge of the electrons. Suggest how Thomson could have worked this out using his knowledge of the atom and its charge.

....

....

[2]

3.2* Describe similarities and differences between the plum pudding model and the modern nuclear model of the atom.

....

....

....

....

....

....

....

....

....

[6]

[Total 8 marks]

Exam Tip

When looking at the history of the atom, it's not only important that you know the different theories of atomic structure — you also need to understand why, and describe how, scientific theories develop over time. So make sure you go through your notes on Working Scientifically before the exam. And then why not relax with some plum pudding...

Topic C1 — Atomic Structure and the Periodic Table

Electronic Structure

1 Calcium is a reactive metal with an atomic number of 20. **(Grade 4-6)**

1.1 What is the electron configuration of a neutral calcium atom? Tick **one** box.

☐ 2, 18   ☐ 2, 16, 2   ☐ 2, 8, 8, 2   ☐ 2, 2, 8, 8

[1]

1.2 Calcium has two electrons in its innermost shell. Explain why.

....

....

[2]

[Total 3 marks]

2 Electronic structures can be represented in different ways. **(Grade 6-7)**

Figure 1

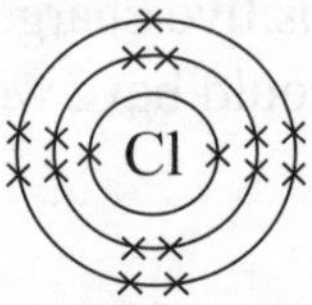

2.1 **Figure 1** shows the electronic structure of an atom of chlorine.
Give the electronic structure of chlorine in number form.

Chlorine: ....

[1]

2.2 Draw the electronic structure of sulfur.

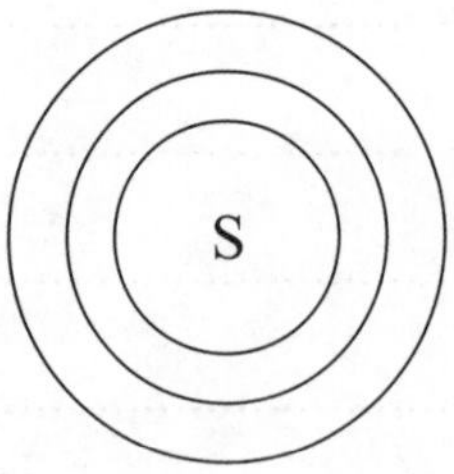

[2]

2.3 **Figure 2** shows the electronic structure of an atom of an element, **X**. Identify element **X**.

Figure 2

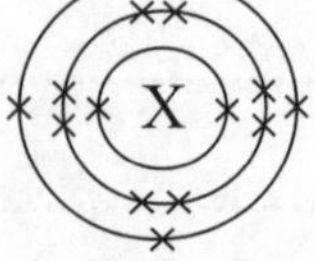

Element **X**: ....

[1]

[Total 4 marks]

Exam Tip

Electronic structures are the key to understanding lots of chemistry, so it's really important that you know how to work them out. Definitely make sure you know, or can work out, the electronic structures for the first 20 elements in the periodic table before going into your exam. It'll help you in all manner of questions, believe me.

Topic C1 — Atomic Structure and the Periodic Table

Development of The Periodic Table

1 Mendeleev, guided by atomic masses, grouped elements with similar properties to form an early version of the periodic table. He used his table to predict properties of undiscovered elements such as eka-silicon, now called germanium. **Table 1** shows some predictions.

Table 1

	Silicon (Si)	**Eka-silicon (Ek)**	**Tin (Sn)**
Atomic Mass	28	72	119
Density in g/cm³	2.3	**D**	7.3
Appearance	grey/silver non-metal	grey metal	grey metal
Formula of oxide	SiO_2	**E**	SnO_2
Formula of chloride	$SiCl_4$	**F**	$SnCl_4$
Reaction with acid	None	**G**	Slow

1.1 Mendeleev left gaps in his periodic table. Suggest why.

....

....

[1]

1.2 Predict properties **D** to **G**.

D ....   E ....

F ....   G ....

[4]

[Total 5 marks]

2 Before the development of the modern periodic table, scientists classified elements according to their atomic weights.

2.1 Why did early scientists use atomic weight and not atomic number?

....

....

[1]

2.2 Use the periodic table to identify two elements that would be in the wrong positions if the elements were ordered by atomic weight rather than atomic number.

....

[1]

2.3 How did the discovery of isotopes explain why atomic weights do not always give the correct order of elements?

....

....

[2]

[Total 4 marks]

Topic C1 — Atomic Structure and the Periodic Table

The Modern Periodic Table

1 Chemical elements are arranged in the periodic table. **(Grade 4-6)**

1.1 How are the elements ordered in the periodic table?

....

[1]

1.2 Why is the table called the periodic table?

....

[1]

1.3 Why do elements in groups have similar chemical properties? Tick **one** box.

They have the same number of shells of electrons. ☐

They have the same number of outer shell electrons. ☐

They all have at least one full inner shell of electrons. ☐

The atoms of the elements are similar in size. ☐

[1]

[Total 3 marks]

2 **Figure 1** below shows the electronic configuration for a neutral atom of element **X**. **(Grade 6-7)**

Figure 1

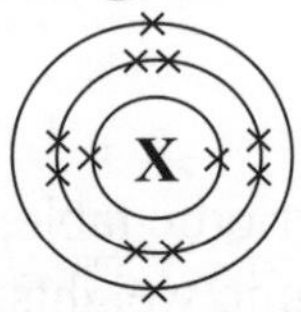

2.1 What group in the periodic table is element **X** in? Justify your answer.

....

....

[2]

2.2 Which period is element **X** in? Explain your answer.

....

....

[2]

2.3 Identify element **X**.

....

[1]

2.4 Name one element that will have similar chemical properties to element **X**.

....

[1]

[Total 6 marks]

Topic C1 — Atomic Structure and the Periodic Table

Metals and Non-Metals

1 Elements can be classified as metals or non-metals. Some metals will react with particular non-metals to form compounds made up of ions. *(Grade 4-6)*

1.1 Two elements, with the chemical symbols A and X, react together to form a compound made up of A^{2+} ions and X^{2-} ions. One of the elements is a metal and one is a non-metal. State which element is the metal and which is the non-metal.

A^{2+} .... X^{2-} ....

[1]

1.2 Element Z is a non-metal. State three physical properties that element Z is likely to have.

....

....

....

[3]

[Total 4 marks]

2 Metals make up about 80% of all the elements in the periodic table. Aluminium and magnesium are both metals. *(Grade 4-6)*

2.1 Describe where metals and non-metals can be found in the periodic table.

Metals: ....

Non-metals: ....

[1]

2.2 Which of the statements below is true? Tick **one** box.

Elements that react to form negative ions are metals. ☐

Elements that react to form positive ions are metals. ☐

Elements that react to form positive ions are non-metals. ☐

Elements that do not form ions are metals. ☐

[1]

2.3 Suggest one physical property that magnesium and aluminium have in common.

....

[1]

2.4 Explain why magnesium and aluminium react in a similar way.

....

....

[2]

[Total 5 marks]

Exam Tip

Something you can do to help you remember the different properties of metals and non-metals is to think of examples of these materials in everyday life and then consider how their properties help them to do their job.

Topic C1 — Atomic Structure and the Periodic Table

Group 1 Elements

1 Data for two alkali metals, **X** and **Y**, is shown in the table below.

	Melting Point / °C	Density / kg per m³
X	39	1532
Y	98	968

1.1 Given that melting point decreases as you go down Group 1, which metal has the lowest atomic number, **X** or **Y**? Justify your answer.

....

....

[2]

1.2 Construct a balanced equation for the reaction between **X** and water to form the hydroxide, **XOH**, and a gas.

....

[2]

1.3 **XOH** is soluble in water. State the pH of the solution formed: ....

[1]

[Total 6 marks]

2 The element caesium is in Group 1 of the periodic table. *(Grade 7-9)*

2.1 Complete **Table 1** by predicting the radius and boiling point of caesium. Use the data in the table to help you.

Table 1

	Boiling Point / °C	Radius of atom / pm
K	758.8	227
Rb	687.8	248
Cs	....	....

[2]

2.2 Predict how the reactivity of caesium will compare to rubidium. Justify your answer using your knowledge of caesium's electron arrangement.

....

....

....

[3]

2.3 Alkali metals react with phosphorus, P_4, to form ionic phosphides. Lithium reacts with phosphorus to form lithium phosphide Li_3P. Predict the formula of caesium phosphide and write a balanced equation for the reaction of phosphorus and caesium.

Formula: ....

Equation: ....

[3]

[Total 8 marks]

Topic C1 — Atomic Structure and the Periodic Table

Group 7 Elements

Warm-Up

Write the following Group 7 elements in order of increasing boiling point.

Iodine

Bromine

Chlorine

Fluorine

....

....

....

....

1 The elements in Group 7 of the periodic table are known as the halogens. *(Grade 4-6)*

1.1 Which of the following statements about the halogens is true? Tick **one** box.

They are non-metals that exist as single atoms. ☐

They are metals that exist as single atoms. ☐

They are non-metals that exist as molecules of two atoms. ☐

They are metals that exist as molecules of two atoms. ☐

[1]

1.2 Compare the chemical reactivity of chlorine and bromine. Explain your answer.

....

....

....

[3]

1.3 Halogens can react with other elements to form molecular compounds. Of the following elements, suggest which one might form a molecular compound with chlorine. Tick **one** box.

Ca ☐   Cr ☐   Na ☐   P ☐

[1]

[Total 5 marks]

2 Halogens react with many metals to form metal halides. *(Grade 6-7)*
For instance, iron reacts with bromine to form iron bromide.

2.1 Complete and balance the following symbol equation for this reaction.

.............Fe + ... → ....$FeBr_3$

[2]

2.2 Iron bromide is ionic. What is the charge on the bromide ion?

....

[1]

[Total 3 marks]

Topic C1 — Atomic Structure and the Periodic Table

3 Chlorine water was added to potassium bromide solution in a test tube and the contents shaken. **Grade 6-7**

3.1 Complete the word equation below.

Chlorine + Potassium bromide → .... + ...

[1]

3.2 What would you observe when the two reactants are mixed?

....

[1]

3.3 Give the name for this type of reaction.

....

[1]

3.4 Will chlorine water react with potassium fluoride solution? Explain your answer.

....

....

[2]

[Total 5 marks]

4 This question is about the halogens. **Grade 7-9**

4.1 Describe the electronic structure of the halogens and how it changes down Group 7.

....

....

....

[2]

4.2 Hydrogen gas reacts explosively with fluorine, even at low temperatures, to form hydrogen fluoride, HF. Predict and explain how astatine might react with hydrogen. Include a balanced equation in your answer.

....

....

....

....

....

....

....

[5]

[Total 7 marks]

Exam Tip

One of the most important things to learn about Group 7 elements is the trends you find as you go down or up the group. And you need to be able to explain these trends using the electronic structure of the halogens. Smashing.

Topic C1 — Atomic Structure and the Periodic Table

Group 0 Elements

1 The noble gases can be found in Group 0 of the periodic table. Grade 6-7

1.1 Using the information in Table 1, complete the table by predicting values for the boiling point of radon, the density of xenon and the atomic radius of argon.

Table 1

Element	Boiling Point / °C	Density / g/cm³	Atomic radius / pm
Ar	−186	0.0018	....
Kr	−152	0.0037	109
Xe	−108	....	130
Rn	....	0.0097	136

[3]

1.2 Explain the chemical reactivity of krypton in terms of electron configuration.

....

....

[2]

1.3 What is the difference between the electron configuration of helium and the rest of the noble gases?

....

....

[1]

[Total 6 marks]

2 Until 1962, no noble gas compounds existed. Since then, several noble gas compounds have been made. For instance, xenon difluoride exists as white crystals which are stable at room temperature in a dry atmosphere. Grade 7-9

2.1 Why were chemists surprised that a noble gas compound could be made?

....

[1]

2.2 Why is it unlikely that iodine would form a compound with xenon?

....

[1]

2.3 A liquid containing a mixture of neon and xenon was cooled down. One gas solidified at −249 °C and the other at −112 °C. Identify which noble gas solidified at −249 °C and which at −112 °C. Justify your answer.

....

....

....

[3]

[Total 5 marks]

Topic C1 — Atomic Structure and the Periodic Table

Formation of Ions

1   This question is about atoms forming ions by losing or gaining electrons.   Grade 4-6

1.1   Which of the following statements about the atoms of metallic elements is correct?
Tick **one** box.

☐ Metal atoms usually lose electrons to become negative ions.

☐ Metal atoms usually gain electrons to become negative ions.

☐ Metal atoms usually gain electrons to become positive ions.

☐ Metal atoms usually lose electrons to become positive ions.

[1]

1.2   The diagram below shows the ions of four elements and four descriptions about where the elements can be found in the periodic table.
Draw lines to match each of the four ions to their description.

A^+		A non-metal from Group 6
D^-		A metal from Group 2
X^{2+}		A metal from Group 1
Z^{2-}		A non-metal from Group 7

[2]

[Total 3 marks]

2   This question is about sulfur atoms and sulfur ions.   Grade 6-7

2.1   Sulfur is in Group 6 of the periodic table. What is the charge on a sulfur ion?

....

[1]

2.2   Sulfur atoms have the electronic structure 2,8,6. Write out the electronic structure for a sulfur ion. Explain your answer.

....

....

....

[3]

2.3   Name the element that has atoms with the same electronic structure as a sulfur ion.

....

[1]

[Total 5 marks]

Exam Tip

You can work out what sort of ions an element will form based on where it sits in the periodic table. For example, elements in Group 1 will always form positive ions, as they can form a full outer shell by losing one electron.

Ionic Bonding

Warm-Up

Choose from the formulas on the left to complete the table showing the dot and cross diagrams and formulas of various ionic compounds. You won't need to use all the formulas.

NaCl   MgCl₂   MgCl

Na₂O   NaO   NaCl₂

Dot and cross diagram	Ionic formula
$[Na]^+$ $[Cl]^-$	
$[Na]^+$ $[O]^{2-}$ $[Na]^+$	
$[Cl]^-$ $[Mg]^{2+}$ $[Cl]^-$	

---

1   Ionic bonding is one of the three types of chemical bonds found in compounds.

1.1   In which of the following compounds are the particles held together by ionic bonds?
Put a tick in the boxes next to the **two** compounds that you think are ionic.

☐ calcium chloride   ☐ carbon dioxide   ☐ phosphorus trichloride

☐ potassium oxide   ☐ nitrogen monoxide

[2]

1.2   The dot and cross diagram below shows the formation of lithium fluoride from its elements.
The diagram is incomplete. Complete the diagram by adding an arrow to show the transfer of electron(s), the charges of the ions and completing the outer shell electronic structure of the fluoride ion.

 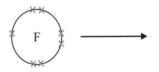

[3]

1.3   Name the force that holds the ions together in an ionic bond.

....

[1]

1.4   State how you can tell from a dot and cross diagram that the particles
in a compound are held together by ionic bonds.

....

[1]

[Total 7 marks]

Topic C2 — Bonding, Structure and Properties of Matter

2   **Figure 1** shows the outer electronic structure of magnesium and oxygen. **Grade 6-7**

2.1 Draw a similar diagram to show the electronic structures
and charges of the ions that form when magnesium reacts with oxygen.
You only need to show the outer shells of electrons.

Figure 1

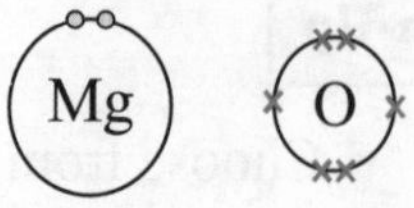

[4]

2.2 Explain how an ionic bond forms when magnesium atoms react with oxygen atoms.

....

....

....

....

[4]

[Total 8 marks]

3   **Figure 2** is a representation of the structure of a compound formed
from two unknown elements given the symbols X and Z.   **Grade 7-9**

Figure 2

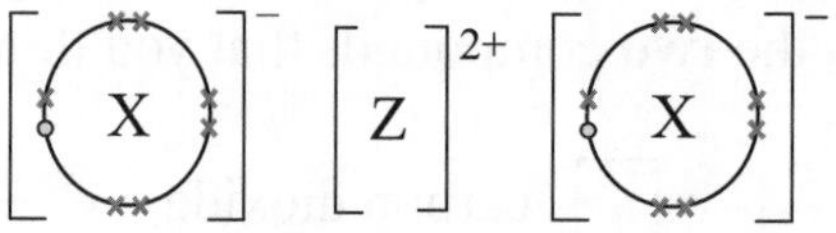

3.1 Suggest which group in the periodic table each element is from and give a reason for your choice.

Element X: Group: ....

        Reason: ....

Element Z: Group: ....

        Reason: ....

[4]

3.2* Discuss the uses and limitations of dot and cross diagrams.

....

....

....

....

....

....

[6]

[Total 10 marks]

Exam Tip

You'll be able to work out if a compound contains ionic bonds by looking at the elements it contains. An ionic compound will always contain at least one metal atom, such as lithium, and at least one non-metal atom, such as fluorine.

Topic C2 — Bonding, Structure and Properties of Matter

Ionic Compounds

Circle the correct words or phrases below so that the statement is correct.

In an ionic compound, the particles are held together by <u>weak</u>/<u>strong</u> forces of attraction. These forces act <u>in all directions</u>/<u>in one particular direction</u> which results in the particles bonding together to form <u>giant lattices</u>/<u>small molecules</u>.

1   This question is about the structure and properties of ionic compounds.   (Grade 4-6)

1.1   Which of the following properties is not typical for an ionic compound?
Tick one box.

☐ high melting points   ☐ high boiling points

☐ conduct electricity in the liquid state   ☐ conduct electricity in the solid state

[1]

1.2   Name the type of structure that ionic compounds have.

....

[1]

[Total 2 marks]

2   Sodium chloride is an ionic compound.   (Grade 6-7)

2.1   Describe the structure of a crystal of sodium chloride. You should state:
• What particles are present in the crystal.
• How these particles are arranged.
• What holds the particles together.

....

....

....

....

[4]

2.2   Explain why sodium chloride has a high melting point.

....

....

[2]

[Total 6 marks]

3 Potassium bromide has a lattice structure that is similar to sodium chloride.

3.1 Complete the diagram below to show the position and charge of the ions in potassium bromide. Write a symbol in each blank circle to show whether it is a potassium ion or a bromide ion.

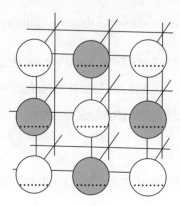

[3]

3.2 Give one advantage and one disadvantage of using the type of diagram above to represent the structure of an ionic compound.

Advantage: ....

Disadvantage: ....
[2]

3.3 What is the empirical formula of potassium bromide?

....
[1]

3.4 **Table 1** shows some data about potassium bromide. For each of the three properties shown in **Table 1**, explain how the structure of potassium bromide causes the particular property.

Table 1

Boiling point / °C	Electrical conductivity of solid	Electrical conductivity of solution
1435	Low	High

Boiling point ....

....

Electrical conductivity of solid ....

....

Electrical conductivity of solution ....

....
[6]

[Total 12 marks]

Exam Tip

Don't panic if you're asked about an ionic compound that you've not met before. Think about what you do know about ionic compounds, and read the question carefully to make sure you've picked up any extra information you've been given.

Topic C2 — Bonding, Structure and Properties of Matter

Covalent Bonding

1 Some elements and compounds consist of molecules that are held together by covalent bonds.

1.1 Describe how two atoms come together to form a single covalent bond.

....

[1]

1.2 What type of elements are able to form covalent bonds?

....

[1]

1.3 Borane is a compound that contains covalent bonds.
Use the diagram below to find the molecular formula of borane.

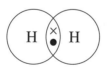

Diagram:

Formula: ....

[1]

[Total 3 marks]

2 The diagrams below show dot and cross diagrams of some simple covalent molecules. Draw out the displayed formulas of these molecules using straight lines to represent covalent bonds. One molecule (H_2) has been done as an example.

Dot and cross diagram	**Displayed formula**

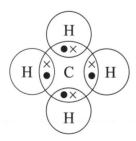

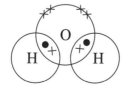

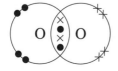

[Total 3 marks]

3 Methane, CH_4, is a covalent molecule. The structure of methane can be shown in a number of different ways. Two such diagrams are shown in **Figures 1** and **2**.

Figure 1

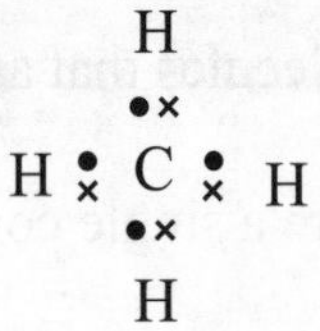

H
•×
H ⦂ C ⦂ H
•×
H

Figure 2

H
|
H—C—H
|
H

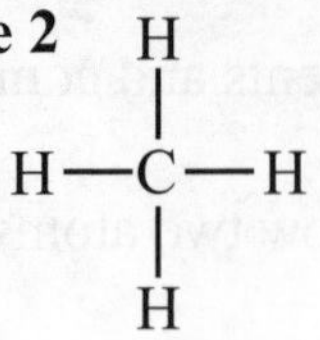

3.1 Suggest **two** different ways of telling, either from **Figures 1** and **2**, or from the molecular formula, that methane is a covalent molecule.

....

....
[2]

3.2 State **two** ways in which **Figures 1** and **2** do **not** represent a methane molecule accurately.

....

....
[2]

3.3 Briefly describe how the hydrogen atoms in a methane molecule are bonded to the carbon atom.

....

....

....
[3]

[Total 7 marks]

4 The structure of a covalent compound can be represented in many different ways.

4.1 Give one advantage and one disadvantage of using each of the representations of covalent molecules described below.

Displayed formula: ....

....

Dot and cross: ....

....

3D Model: ....

....
[6]

4.2 Suggest, with reasoning, which of the representations in 4.1 would be most suitable for drawing the structure of a large polymer in order to show what each atom is connected to.

....

....

....
[2]

[Total 8 marks]

Topic C2 — Bonding, Structure and Properties of Matter

Simple Molecular Substances

1 This question is about the forces in simple molecular substances. `(Grade 4-6)`

1.1 Compare the strength of the bonds that hold the atoms in a molecule together with the forces that exist between different molecules.

....

....

[2]

1.2 When a simple molecular substance melts, is it the bonds between atoms or the forces between molecules that are broken?

....

[1]

[Total 3 marks]

2 HCl and N_2 are both simple molecular substances. `(Grade 6-7)`

2.1 Draw a dot and cross diagram to show the bonding in a molecule of HCl. Show all of the outer shell electrons and use different symbols for electrons from different atoms. There is no need to show inner shell electrons.

[2]

2.2 Draw a dot and cross diagram to show the bonding in a molecule of N_2. Show all of the outer shell electrons and use different symbols for electrons from different atoms. There is no need to show inner shell electrons.

[2]

2.3 State **one** difference between the bonding in HCl compared to N_2.

....

....

[1]

[Total 5 marks]

3 Iodine, I_2, is a simple molecular substance. **(Grade 6-7)**

3.1 At room temperature, iodine is a solid. Explain, with reference to the forces between molecules, why this is unusual for a simple molecular substance.

....

....

[2]

3.2 Predict, with reasoning, whether iodine can conduct electricity in any state.

....

....

[2]

[Total 4 marks]

4 Both methane (CH_4) and butane (C_4H_{10}) are simple covalent compounds that are gases at room temperature. Methane has a lower boiling point than butane. **(Grade 7-9)**

4.1 Explain, in terms of particles, what happens when methane boils and why the boiling point of methane is lower than that of butane.

....

....

....

....

....

....

[5]

4.2 Explain why a carbon atom can form up to four covalent bonds, whilst a hydrogen atom only ever forms one covalent bond.

....

....

....

[2]

4.3 Suggest how many covalent bonds an atom of silicon would form. Explain your answer.

....

....

[2]

[Total 9 marks]

Exam Tip

Each atom in a molecule should have made enough covalent bonds to get a full outer shell. So to check that you've drawn your dot and cross diagrams correctly, count up how many electrons there are in the outer shell. Unless it's hydrogen, there should be eight electrons in the outer shell. Hydrogen should end up with two electrons in its outer shell.

Topic C2 — Bonding, Structure and Properties of Matter

Polymers and Giant Covalent Substances

Circle the diagram below that represents a compound with a giant covalent structure.

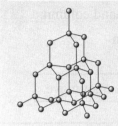 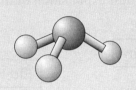 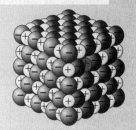

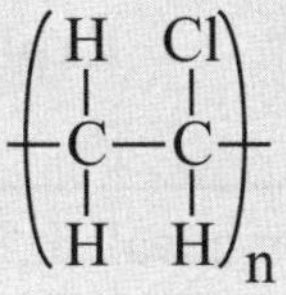

1   Graphite and diamond are compounds with very high melting points.   **Grade 4-6**

1.1 Which of the following compounds is not an example of a giant covalent structure?
Tick **one** box.

☐ Ammonia   ☐ Diamond   ☐ Graphite   ☐ Silicon dioxide

[1]

1.2 To melt a giant covalent compound, the covalent bonds between atoms must be broken.
Explain why this causes giant covalent compounds to have very high melting points.

....

....

[2]

[Total 3 marks]

2   **Figure 1** below represents a large molecule known as a polymer.   **Grade 6-7**

Figure 1

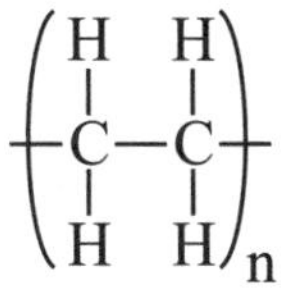

$$\left(\begin{array}{cc} H & H \\ | & | \\ -C & -C- \\ | & | \\ H & H \end{array}\right)_n$$

2.1 What is the molecular formula of this polymer?

....

[1]

2.2 Is this molecule likely to be a solid, liquid or gas at room temperature? Explain your answer.

....

....

....

[3]

2.3 State what type of bonds hold the atoms in the polymer together.

....

[1]

[Total 5 marks]

Topic C2 — Bonding, Structure and Properties of Matter

Allotropes of Carbon

1 Carbon forms a number of different allotropes. *Grade 4-6*

1.1 One allotrope of carbon is diamond. Draw lines to connect each of the properties of diamond in the left hand column to the best explanation of that property in the right hand column.

Property

Does not conduct electricity

High melting point

Hard (doesn't scratch easily)

Explanation

Electrons in covalent bonds cannot move.

Each carbon atom makes four strong covalent bonds.

[2]

1.2 Name each of the allotropes of carbon, A-C, shown in **Figure 1**.

Figure 1

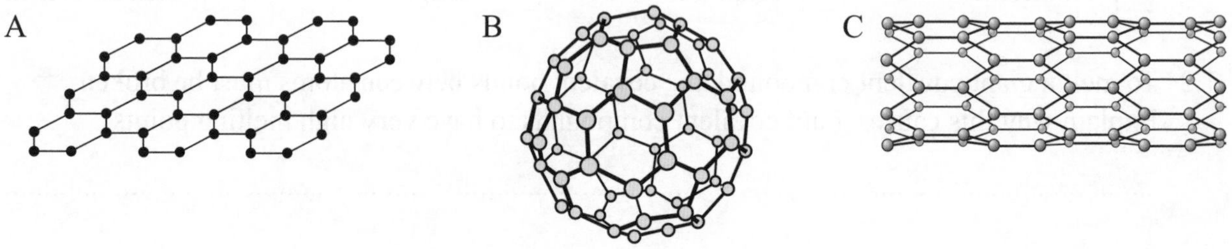

A ....   B ....   C ....

[3]

1.3 Suggest a use for allotrope C.

....

[1]

[Total 6 marks]

2 This question is about the carbon allotrope graphite. *Grade 6-7*

2.1 Describe the structure and bonding in graphite.

....

....

....

....

[4]

2.2 Graphite can be used to make components in electrical circuits.
Explain how the bonding and structure of graphite makes it suitable for this use.

....

....

[2]

[Total 6 marks]

Topic C2 — Bonding, Structure and Properties of Matter

Metallic Bonding

1   This question is about how the structure and bonding of metals affects their properties.

1.1   Draw a labelled diagram to show how the metal particles and the electrons that take part in bonding are arranged in a metal.

[3]

1.2   Explain how the atoms are held together in this arrangement.

....

....

[2]

1.3   Explain whether this arrangement causes metals to generally have high or low boiling points.

....

....

[2]

1.4   Explain whether this arrangement causes metals to be good or poor conductors of electricity.

....

....

[2]

[Total 9 marks]

2   Metals are able to be bent and shaped.

2.1   Explain how the structure and bonding in metals means they are able to be bent and shaped.

....

....

[2]

2.2   Alloys are mixtures of metals and a different element.
Explain why it is usually easier to change the shape of a pure metal than an alloy.

....

....

....

[3]

[Total 5 marks]

Exam Tip

The unique properties of metals are quite different to those of other materials. If you're asked to explain a specific property (I'm looking at you, Q2.1), have a think about the metal structure — that should set you on the right path.

  Topic C2 — Bonding, Structure and Properties of Matter

States of Matter

1 All substances can exist in three states of matter. **Grade 4-6**

1.1 Name the three states of matter.

....

[1]

1.2 Write the state of each substance next to each of the formulas below.

$NaCl_{(s)}$ ....

$O_{2(g)}$ ....

$Hg_{(l)}$ ....

[3]

[Total 4 marks]

2 Particle theory is a model used to explain how particles behave in the three states of matter. **Grade 6-7**

2.1 Describe how the particles in a substance are represented in particle theory.

....

[1]

2.2 Name the state of matter shown in **Figure 1**.

Figure 1

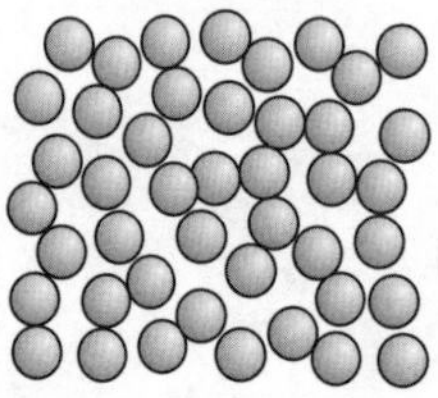

State: ....

[1]

2.3 Name two physical processes that particle theory can be used to explain.

....

[2]

2.4 Explain two ways in which particle theory doesn't accurately represent the particles in a substance.

....

....

[2]

[Total 6 marks]

Topic C2 — Bonding, Structure and Properties of Matter

Changing State

1 This question is about the processes by which a material changes state. (Grade 4-6)

1.1 What is the name of the process when a solid becomes a liquid?

....

[1]

1.2 What is the name of the temperature at which a liquid becomes a gas?

....

[1]

1.3 If a liquid turns into a gas at a very high temperature, what does this imply about the strength of the bonds between the particles in the substance?

....

[1]

[Total 3 marks]

2 Use the data in **Table 1** to help you answer the questions that follow: (Grade 7-9)

Table 1

Substance	Sodium Chloride	Water	Copper
Melting Point (°C)	801	0	1083
Boiling Point (°C)	1413	100	2567

2.1 Which substance in **Table 1** would be a liquid at 900 °C?

....

[1]

2.2 Which two substances would be gases at 1500 °C?

....

[2]

2.3 Which process requires the most energy: melting copper or boiling sodium chloride?

....

[1]

2.4 Does the data in **Table 1** suggest that the covalent bonds in a water molecule are weaker than the metallic bonds in copper? Explain your answer.

....

....

....

....

[4]

[Total 8 marks]

Exam Tip

In the exam, you might be given melting and boiling points for compounds that you've never heard of. Don't panic though, it's always the same — solid below the melting point, gas above the boiling point, and liquid in between.

Topic C2 — Bonding, Structure and Properties of Matter

Topic C3 — Quantitative Chemistry

Relative Formula Mass

1 Match up the following formulas with the correct relative formula mass of the substance.

F_2 38

C_2H_6 40

CaO   30

NaOH   56

[Total 2 marks]

2 Magnesium oxide is a salt with the molecular formula MgO.

2.1 Calculate the percentage, by mass, of magnesium ions in magnesium oxide.
Relative atomic masses (A_r): O = 16, Mg = 24

Percentage by mass of magnesium = ... %

[2]

2.2 A chemist is making a mixture that needs to contain 15% magnesium ions by mass.
Calculate the mass of magnesium in 200 g of this mixture.

Mass of magnesium = ... g

[1]

2.3 All the magnesium ions in the mixture come from magnesium oxide.
Using your answers to 2.1 and 2.2, calculate the mass of magnesium oxide needed to provide the correct mass of magnesium ions in 200 g of the mixture.
(If you failed to get an answer to 2.1 or 2.2, you should use the percentage mass of magnesium as 40% and the mass of magnesium ions in the mixture as 20 g. These are **not** the correct values.)

Mass of magnesium oxide = ... g

[1]

[Total 4 marks]

The Mole

1   Carbon dioxide (CO_2) and carbon monoxide (CO) can both be made by reacting carbon and oxygen. Relative atomic masses (A_r): C = 12, O = 16   **Grade 4-6**

1.1   Calculate the relative formula mass (M_r) of carbon dioxide.

M_r of carbon dioxide = ...
[1]

1.2   Calculate the number of moles in 110 g of carbon dioxide.

.... mol
[1]

1.3   Which would weigh more: 1 mole of carbon dioxide or 1 mole of carbon monoxide? Explain your answer using ideas about relative formula mass.

....

....
[2]

[Total 4 marks]

2   Iron and sulfur react together to form iron sulfide in the following reaction: **Grade 7-9**

$$Fe + S \rightarrow FeS$$

2.1   Calculate the mass of 2 moles of sulfur. Relative atomic mass (A_r): S = 32

Mass = ... g
[1]

2.2   Calculate the number of moles in 44 g of iron sulfide.
Relative atomic masses (A_r): Fe = 56, S = 32

.... mol
[2]

2.3   Which is greater, the number of atoms in 3 moles of sulfur or the number of molecules in 2 moles of iron sulfide? Explain your answer.

....

....

....
[2]

[Total 5 marks]

Topic C3 — Quantitative Chemistry

Conservation of Mass

1 A student burned 12 g of magnesium in oxygen to produce magnesium oxide. *(Grade 4-6)*

1.1 Which of the following is the correctly balanced equation for the reaction between magnesium and oxygen? Tick **one** box.

$Mg + O \rightarrow MgO$ ☐ $\quad\quad$ $2Mg + O_2 \rightarrow 2MgO$ ☐

$Mg + O_2 \rightarrow 2MgO$ ☐ $\quad\quad$ $Mg + O_2 \rightarrow MgO$ ☐

[1]

1.2 The student measured the mass of magnesium oxide produced. The mass was 20 g. Calculate the mass of oxygen that reacted with the magnesium.

Mass of oxygen = ... g

[2]

[Total 3 marks]

2 This question is about conservation of mass. *(Grade 6-7)*

2.1 Explain what is meant by the term 'conservation of mass'. Give your answer in terms of the atoms that take part in a chemical reaction.

....

....

....

....

....

[3]

2.2 A student heated zinc powder in air. The equation for the reaction that happened is shown below.

$$2Zn_{(s)} + O_{2(g)} \rightarrow 2ZnO_{(s)}$$

The student weighed the mass of the powder before and after the reaction. Describe the change that would happen to the mass of the powder during the reaction. Explain this change using ideas from the particle model.

....

....

....

....

[3]

[Total 6 marks]

3 A student took some sodium carbonate powder and heated it in an open crucible. $\boxed{\text{Grade 7-9}}$
The equation for the reaction is: $Na_2CO_3 \rightarrow Na_2O + CO_2$

3.1 The student measured that the mass of the powder decreased during the reaction.
She concluded that the measurement must be wrong because mass is conserved during a reaction.
Explain whether the student's measurement or conclusion is likely to be correct.

....

....

....

....

....
[3]

3.2 The student calculated the relative formula masses (M_r) of the reactants and products.
The M_r of sodium carbonate was 106 and the M_r of carbon dioxide was 44.

Use these values to calculate the M_r of sodium oxide.

M_r of sodium oxide = ...
[1]

3.3 In the experiment, the student started with 53 g of sodium carbonate.
Calculate the mass of carbon dioxide that was produced.

Mass of carbon dioxide = ... g
[3]

3.4 Using the law of conservation of mass, calculate the mass of sodium oxide produced.

Mass of sodium oxide = ... g
[1]

[Total 8 marks]

Exam Tip

There's a good chance that if you're given an equation in the exam and asked to do a calculation, you'll probably need to use the molar ratios in the equation. For example, in Q3.3, you need to work out the number of moles in 53 g of Na_2CO_3 and then use the molar ratios in the equation to work out the mass of CO_2.

Topic C3 — Quantitative Chemistry

Target AO3

4   Two students carried out experiments to measure the change in mass when a compound, X, is heated. **Table 1** and **Table 2** show the results of each student's experiment.

		Table 1					Table 2	

Repeat	Initial mass (g)	Final mass (g)	Decrease in mass (g)
1	4.00	2.62	1.38
2	4.00	2.58	1.42
3	4.00	2.69	1.31
4	4.00	2.95	~~1.05~~
		Mean:	1.37

Repeat	Initial mass (g)	Final mass (g)	Decrease in mass (g)
1	7.50	4.81	2.69
2	7.50	4.76	2.74
3	7.50	4.75	2.75
4	7.50	4.84	2.66
		Mean:	2.71

4.1   The first student did not include her result from repeat 4 when she calculated the mean decrease in mass in her experiment. Suggest an explanation for the anomalous result in this repeat.

....

....

[1]

4.2   Calculate the percentage uncertainty in the mean decrease in mass for each set of results.
Percentage uncertainty = (uncertainty ÷ mean) × 100

Percentage uncertainty of the mean for Table 1 = ± .... %

Percentage uncertainty of the mean for Table 2 = ± .... %

[4]

4.3   Compare the results of the two experiments in terms of uncertainty.

....

....

....

....

[3]

[Total 8 marks]

Exam Tip

Somewhere in your exam, you're likely to get a question on an experiment — either one you know, or one that you haven't seen before — where you have to think about things like uncertainty, precision and accuracy. You don't just need to know what these words mean, but also how making tweaks to the design of the experiment can change these factors.

The Mole and Equations

How many moles of O_2 are shown to be reacting in the equation below? Tick **one** box.

$$4Fe + 3O_2 \rightarrow 2Fe_2O_3$$

6 ☐   5 ☐   2 ☐   3 ☐

1   1 mole of sulfuric acid reacts with 2 moles of sodium hydroxide
to form 1 mole of sodium sulfate and 2 moles of water.
Which of the following equations shows the reaction? Tick **one** box.

$2H_2SO_4 + NaOH \rightarrow 2Na_2SO_4 + H_2O$ ☐

$HCl + NaOH \rightarrow NaCl + H_2O$ ☐

$H_2SO_4 + 2NaOH \rightarrow Na_2SO_4 + 2H_2O$ ☐

$Mg + H_2SO_4 \rightarrow MgSO_4 + H_2$ ☐

[Total 1 mark]

2   9.2 g of sodium (Na) was reacted with 7.2 g of water (H_2O)
to form sodium hydroxide (NaOH) and hydrogen (H_2).
Relative atomic masses (A_r): Na = 23, H = 1, O = 16

2.1   Calculate the number of moles of sodium that reacted with water.

.... mol
[1]

2.2   Calculate the number of moles of water that reacted with sodium.

.... mol
[2]

2.3   0.4 mol of sodium hydroxide and 0.2 mol of hydrogen were produced in the reaction.
Give the balanced symbol equation for the reaction between sodium and water.

Balanced symbol equation: .... + ... → .... + ...

[3]

[Total 6 marks]

3 Methane (CH_4) reacts with oxygen (O_2) to form carbon dioxide and water.
Relative formula masses (M_r): $CH_4 = 16$, $O_2 = 32$, $CO_2 = 44$, $H_2O = 18$

3.1 A student carried out this reaction, reacting 8 g of methane with 32 g of oxygen,
producing 22 g of carbon dioxide and 18 g of water.

Use these masses to work out the balanced equation for the
reaction between methane and oxygen. Show your working.

Balanced symbol equation: .... + ... → .... + ...
[3]

3.2 The student repeated the reaction with 48 g of oxygen.
Calculate the number of moles of carbon dioxide that were produced.

.... mol
[3]

3.3 Another student carried out the reaction using 4 mol of methane.
Calculate the number of moles of water produced in this reaction.

.... mol
[1]

3.4 Calculate the mass of water produced in the reaction using 4 mol of methane.

Mass of water = ... g
[1]

[Total 8 marks]

Exam Tip

If you're given the mass of a substance then you can use the formula linking mass, M_r and moles to calculate the number
of moles. But remember, you can rearrange the formula too — so if you know how many moles of something you have,
you can work out its mass, or if you know the mass and the number of moles you can work out its M_r. Cool eh?

Topic C3 — Quantitative Chemistry

Limiting Reactants

1 A student reacted excess calcium with hydrochloric acid. **Grade 4-6**

1.1 Explain why calcium was added in excess.

....

....

[1]

1.2 In this reaction, the hydrochloric acid is called the 'limiting reactant'.
Explain what this term means.

....

....

[2]

[Total 3 marks]

2 A student reacted copper oxide with sulfuric acid to make copper sulfate and water. **Grade 7-9**

$$CuO + H_2SO_4 \rightarrow CuSO_4 + H_2O$$

2.1 The student used 0.50 mol of sulfuric acid and an excess of copper oxide.
What mass of copper sulfate would be produced by the reaction?

Relative atomic masses (A_r): $Cu = 63.5$, $S = 32$, $O = 16$, $H = 1$

Mass of copper sulfate = ... g

[3]

2.2 The student decides to double the quantity of the sulfuric acid and use an excess of copper oxide.
Describe how this would affect the mass of the copper sulfate. Explain your answer.

....

....

[2]

2.3 The student found that only 0.4 mol of copper oxide was available
to react with the doubled quantity of sulfuric acid in question 2.2.
Explain the effect this would have on the amount of product obtained.

....

....

....

....

[3]

[Total 8 marks]

Topic C3 — Quantitative Chemistry

Concentrations of Solutions

1   28 g of calcium chloride was dissolved in 0.4 dm³ of water.   Grade 4-6

1.1 Calculate the concentration of the solution and give the units.

Concentration = ... Units = ...
[2]

1.2 Explain the term 'concentration of a solution'.

....

....
[1]

[Total 3 marks]

2   A student is preparing two solutions, A and B to use in an experiment.   Grade 6-7

2.1 To make solution A, he dissolves 40.0 g of a substance in 500 cm³ of a solvent.
     Calculate the concentration of solution A.

Concentration = ... g/dm³
[2]

2.2 Solution B needs to have a concentration of 60.0 g/dm³. What mass of the substance will the
     student need to dissolve in 500 cm³ to make solution B?

Mass = ... g
[1]

2.3 In the experiment, the student finds the concentration of a third solution, C.
     He repeats the experiment four times. The results of these repeats are
     18.2 g/dm³, 18.1 g/dm³, 18.4 g/dm³ and 18.5 g/dm³.
     Calculate the mean concentration of solution C.

Concentration = ... g/dm³
[1]

2.4 Estimate the uncertainty of your answer to 2.3.

Uncertainty = ± .... g/dm³
[2]

[Total 6 marks]

Exam Tip

When you're working out the mean from a set of results, you should ignore any anomalous results. So if you get a
question in your exam asking you to work out a mean, make sure you check for anomalous results before you start
plugging numbers into your calculator. The question might help you out by reminding you to ignore anomalous results,
but it might not, so make sure you're on the ball with it — don't get caught out.

Topic C3 — Quantitative Chemistry

Acids and Bases

Warm-Up

Fill in the gaps for the following paragraph on techniques to measure pH.

red   neutral
                        less
        purple
green
                more

Universal indicator will turn .... in strongly acidic solutions and .... in strongly alkaline solutions. In a .... solution, Universal indicator will be green. A pH probe attached to a pH meter is .... accurate than Universal indicator as it displays a numerical value for pH.

1 This question is about acids and bases. **Table 1** shows some everyday substances. *Grade 4-6*

Table 1

Substance	pH
Beer	4
Bicarbonate of soda	9
Milk	7

1.1 Write the name of the substance in **Table 1** that is an acid.

....

[1]

1.2 What colour would you expect to see if Universal indicator was added to bicarbonate of soda solution?

....

[1]

1.3 Which ion is produced by an acid in aqueous solution?
Tick **one** box.

☐ Cl⁻   ☐ H⁺   ☐ OH⁻   ☐ OH⁺

[1]

1.4 State the range of the pH scale.

....

[2]

[Total 5 marks]

2 Acids and alkalis react together in neutralisation reactions. *Grade 4-6*

2.1 Write the general word equation for a neutralisation reaction between an acid and an alkali.

....

[1]

2.2 In terms of hydrogen ions and hydroxide ions, write an ionic equation for a neutralisation reaction.

....

[1]

[Total 2 marks]

Strong Acids and Weak Acids

1 Below are some acids listed in order of strength. (Grade 7-9)

Strongest ↑ Hydrochloric Acid

Nitric Acid

Citric Acid

Ethanoic Acid

Weakest ↓ Carbonic Acid

1.1 Hydrochloric acid is a strong acid while carbonic acid is a weak acid.
Explain the difference between a strong acid and a weak acid.

....

....

[2]

1.2 Describe and explain the difference you would expect to find in the pH value of a 1 mol/dm³
solution of nitric acid and a 1 mol/dm³ solution of ethanoic acid.

....

....

....

[3]

1.3 A 0.01 mol/dm³ solution of hydrochloric acid has a pH of 2.
Predict the pH of a 0.001 mol/dm³ solution of hydrochloric acid.

....

[1]

1.4 A solution of citric acid in a beaker has a pH of 3. Which of the following would increase the pH?
Tick **three** boxes that apply .

Adding citric acid with a higher concentration to the beaker. ☐

Adding water to the beaker. ☐

Adding ethanoic acid to the beaker at the same concentration as the citric acid. ☐

Adding hydrochloric acid to the beaker at the same concentration as the citric acid. ☐

Changing the citric acid to nitric acid of the same concentration. ☐

Changing the citric acid to carbonic acid of the same concentration. ☐

[3]

[Total 9 marks]

Exam Tip

Make sure you understand what pH is and how it relates to the strength of an acid. It will also be jolly useful to
understand how the concentration of H⁺ changes with pH. Remember, don't confuse strong acids with concentrated ones.

Reactions of Acids

1   Acids can react with bases and alkalis.   (Grade 4-6)

1.1   What type of reaction occurs when an acid reacts with an alkali?
Tick **one** box.

☐ Oxidation   ☐ Decomposition   ☐ Neutralisation   ☐ Precipitation

[1]

1.2   A student adds 2 spatulas of zinc carbonate into a beaker of dilute hydrochloric acid.
Draw **one** line to connect the observation you would expect during this reaction
with the explanation for that observation.

Observation	**Explanation**
Fizzing	Carbon dioxide is produced
A colour change	Hydrogen is produced
A white solid forming	A salt is made
No change	The zinc dissolves

[1]

[Total 2 marks]

2   Acids can react with metal oxides and metal hydroxides to give a metal salt and water.   (Grade 6-7)

2.1   Write a word equation for the reaction of sulfuric acid and lithium hydroxide.

....

[2]

2.2   Complete and balance the symbol equation for the reaction of sulfuric acid and lithium hydroxide.

$$H_2SO_4 + ... LiOH \rightarrow .... + ... H_2O$$

[2]

2.3   Acids can also react with metal carbonates. Compare the products of the reaction between
sulfuric acid and lithium carbonate with the products of the reaction between sulfuric acid and
lithium hydroxide.

....

....

[2]

[Total 5 marks]

Topic C4 — Chemical Changes

3 Soluble metal salts can be made from the reactions of acids and metal oxides.

Grade 6-7

PRACTICAL

3.1 Zinc chloride can be made from the reaction of zinc oxide and hydrochloric acid.
Describe a laboratory method to produce pure crystals of zinc chloride using this reaction.

....

....

....

....

....

....

[4]

3.2 Suggest an alternative to zinc oxide that would also react with hydrochloric acid to form the desired product.

....

[1]

[Total 5 marks]

4* A student is given three different unlabelled solutions. One contains sodium hydroxide, one contains sodium carbonate and one contains a sodium salt. Use your knowledge of chemical reactions to describe experiments that the student could do to decide which solution is which. Explain how your experiments would allow the student to identify the solutions. Clearly describe the reactants and products of any reactions you include.

Grade 7-9

....

....

....

....

....

....

....

....

....

[Total 6 marks]

Exam Tip

There will almost certainly be an exam question about acid reactions. Luckily for you, they're really easy to memorise, as they always produce the same products. Learn how an acid reacts with each type of base and you'll be ready to go.

The Reactivity Series

1   Metals can be placed in order of reactivity based on how vigorously they react with acids.   (Grade 4-6)

1.1 Write a word equation for the reaction of magnesium with hydrochloric acid.

....
[1]

1.2 What does the reaction of magnesium with hydrochloric acid produce? Tick **one** box.

Positive chloride ions   ☐

Positive hydrogen ions   ☐

Positive magnesium ions   ☐

Negative magnesium ions   ☐
[1]

1.3 Explain why iron reacts less vigorously with hydrochloric acid than magnesium does.

....
[1]

1.4 Name **one** metal that would react more vigorously with hydrochloric acid than magnesium does.

....
[1]

[Total 4 marks]

2   Some metals can react with water.   (Grade 4-6)

2.1 Write the general word equation for the reaction of a metal and water.

....
[1]

2.2 Complete the symbol equation below, for the reaction of
calcium and water. Include state symbols.

$$Ca_{(s)} + 2H_2O_{(l)} \rightarrow \text{.................} + \text{.................}$$
[2]

2.3 Suggest a metal which will react more vigorously with water than calcium. Explain your answer.

....

....
[2]

2.4 Put the metals sodium, zinc and potassium in order, based on how vigorously you think they
would react with water.

Most vigorous .... Least vigorous
[1]

[Total 6 marks]

Topic C4 — Chemical Changes

3   A student investigated the reactions of some metals and found the results shown in **Table 1**.

Table 1

Reaction	Observation
Lithium + water	Very vigorous reaction with fizzing, lithium disappears
Calcium + water	Fizzing, calcium disappears
Magnesium + water	No fizzing, a few bubbles on the magnesium
Copper + water	No fizzing, no change to copper
Iron + water	No fizzing, no change to iron
Lithium + dilute acid	Very vigorous reaction with fizzing, lithium disappears
Magnesium + dilute acid	Fizzing, magnesium disappears
Zinc + dilute acid	Fizzing, zinc disappears
Copper + dilute acid	No fizzing, no change to copper

3.1   Use the results in **Table 1**, along with your knowledge of the general reaction between an acid and a metal, to explain whether lithium or magnesium forms positive ions more easily.

....

....

....

[3]

3.2   Predict what the student would have seen if they had added sodium to water.

....

....

[2]

3.3   Put the metals calcium, copper and lithium in order from most reactive to least reactive.

....

[1]

3.4   Explain why it would be difficult to decide the order of reactivity of magnesium and zinc using these experiments. Suggest an experiment that could be used to decide which is most reactive.

....

....

[2]

[Total 8 marks]

Exam Tip

Learning the order of the reactivity series could be really useful when it comes to answering questions in the exams. Try learning this mnemonic to help you remember... Papa Smurf Likes Calling My Clarinet Zany — Isn't He Cute. (You don't have to use my Booker prize winning concoction, though. You could also make up your own.)

Topic C4 — Chemical Changes

Separating Metals from Metal Oxides

1 Most metals are found as compounds in ores in the earth. Some of the metals can be extracted from their ores by reduction with carbon. *(Grade 4-6)*

1.1 Name a metal that can be found in the ground as an element.

....

[1]

1.2 Why are most metals found in the earth as compounds?

....

[1]

1.3 Define reduction in terms of the loss and gain of oxygen.

....

[1]

1.4 Explain why magnesium **cannot** be extracted from magnesium oxide by reduction with carbon.

....

....

[1]

[Total 4 marks]

2 Iron can be extracted by heating iron oxide, Fe_2O_3, with carbon. The reaction releases large amounts of heat so there is no need to continuously heat the reaction. *(Grade 6-7)*

2.1 Write a symbol equation for a reaction between carbon and iron(III) oxide, Fe_2O_3.

....

[2]

2.2 For the reaction of iron(III) oxide and carbon to form iron, identify whether carbon has been reduced or oxidised. Explain your answer in terms of the transfer of oxygen.

....

....

[2]

2.3 Magnesium is extracted from magnesium oxide by reaction with silicon.
A temperature of 1200 °C is required together with a reduced pressure.

Suggest why magnesium extraction is very costly when compared with iron extraction.

....

....

....

[2]

[Total 6 marks]

Topic C4 — Chemical Changes

Redox Reactions

1 In a metal displacement reaction the least reactive metal is reduced. (Grade 6-7)

1.1 Define reduction in terms of electron transfer.

....

[1]

1.2 Which of the following reactions shows zinc being reduced?
Tick **one** box.

Copper nitrate + zinc → copper + zinc nitrate ☐

Zinc + oxygen → zinc oxide ☐

Zinc chloride + sodium → zinc + sodium chloride ☐

Zinc + hydrochloric acid → zinc chloride + hydrogen ☐

[1]

1.3 The equation shows the reaction of zinc with hydrochloric acid.

$$Zn_{(s)} + 2HCl_{(aq)} \rightarrow ZnCl_{2(aq)} + H_{2(g)}$$

Does hydrogen lose or gain electrons in this reaction?

....

[1]

1.4 What happens to chlorine in the reaction in 1.3?
Tick **one** box.

Chlorine is oxidised ☐

Chlorine is released ☐

Chlorine is reduced ☐

Chlorine is neither oxidised nor reduced ☐

[1]

[Total 4 marks]

2 A student reacts magnesium with an aqueous solution of iron chloride to produce magnesium chloride and iron. (Grade 7-9)
$$Mg_{(s)} + FeCl_{2(aq)} \rightarrow MgCl_{2(aq)} + Fe_{(s)}$$

2.1 Write an ionic equation for this reaction.

....

[1]

2.2 A student repeats the experiment with copper instead of magnesium.
State whether a reaction would still occur. Explain your answer.

....

....

[2]

[Total 3 marks]

☹ ☐   ☺ ☐   ☺ ☐

Electrolysis

Place the labels on the correct label lines to identify the parts of an electrochemical cell.

Anode   Electrolyte

D.C. power supply

Cathode

Anions

Cations

1   Lead bromide can be electrolysed, using molten lead bromide as the electrolyte.   (Grade 4-6)

1.1   What is an electrolyte?

....

[1]

1.2   Write the word equation for the electrolysis of lead bromide.

....

[1]

1.3   Explain why lead ions move towards the cathode and not the anode.

....

....

[2]

1.4   What ions move towards the anode? Give the chemical formula and charge of the ion.

....

[1]

1.5   Is the reaction at the anode oxidation or reduction?

....

[1]

1.6   Why does the lead bromide need to be molten? Tick **one** box.

So the ions can move to the electrodes ☐   So the electrodes don't corrode ☐

So the electrons can be conducted
through the substance ☐   So there is enough heat
for the reaction to occur ☐

[1]

[Total 7 marks]

2   **Figure 1** shows the extraction of aluminium. Aluminium oxide is mixed with cryolite. This mixture is then melted and electrolysed. Metallic aluminium is made at the cathode.

Figure 1

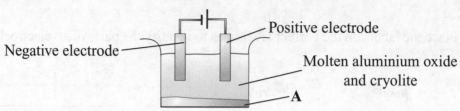

2.1 What is the liquid labelled **A**?

....

[1]

2.2 What is the purpose of mixing the aluminium oxide with cryolite?

....

[1]

2.3 Why do the graphite electrodes need to be replaced regularly?

....

....

[2]

[Total 4 marks]

3   Aqueous iron chloride solution can be electrolysed using inert electrodes. Grade 6-7

3.1 Write the names of the ions present in iron chloride solution.

....

[2]

3.2 Draw **one** line to connect the correct products at each electrode when iron chloride is electrolysed.

At the cathode

Iron is discharged

Hydrogen is discharged

Chlorine is discharged

At the anode

Iron is discharged

Oxygen is discharged

Chlorine is discharged

[1]

3.3 What is discharged at the anode when iron sulfate solution is electrolysed with inert electrodes?

....

[1]

3.4 Iron can be extracted from iron solutions by electrolysis but this is not the usual method. Why is electrolysis not the usual method of extracting iron?

....

....

[2]

[Total 6 marks]

Topic C4 — Chemical Changes

4 A student investigated the products of electrolysis of a variety of aqueous solutions using inert electrodes.

 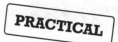

4.1 Draw a labelled diagram of suitable apparatus that could be used for these experiments.

[4]

4.2 Complete **Table 1** by predicting the products at the anode and cathode for each of the solutions.

Table 1

Solution	Product at cathode	Product at anode
$CuCl_2$		
KBr		
H_2SO_4		

[6]

4.3 When potassium nitrate solution is electrolysed neither potassium nor nitrogen are discharged. Explain why and state what is produced instead.

....

....

....

[4]

4.4 Write two half equations for the reaction that occurs when water is electrolysed.

Cathode: ....

Anode: ....

[2]

[Total 16 marks]

Exam Tip

Electrolysis can be a hard subject to get your head around, and adding the electrolysis of aqueous solutions in to the mix doesn't make it any easier. But remember, in aqueous solution, different ions can be discharged depending on their reactivity. Make sure you know the different ions that can be removed from solution, and in what situations that will happen — it really isn't too complicated once you know what you are doing, but you do need to learn the rules.

Topic C4 — Chemical Changes

Exothermic and Endothermic Reactions

1   Which one of the following statements about exothermic and endothermic reactions is correct? Tick **one** box.   (Grade 4-6)

In an exothermic reaction, energy is transferred from the surroundings so the temperature of the surroundings goes down. ☐

In an endothermic reaction, energy is transferred from the surroundings so the temperature of the surroundings goes down. ☐

In an exothermic reaction, energy is transferred from the surroundings so the temperature of the surroundings goes up. ☐

In an endothermic reaction, energy is transferred from the surroundings so the temperature of the surroundings goes up. ☐

[Total 1 mark]

2   During a reaction between solutions of citric acid and sodium hydrogen carbonate, the temperature of the reaction mixture fell from 18 °C to 4 °C.   (Grade 4-6)

2.1   Is this reaction exothermic or endothermic?

....

[1]

2.2   Complete the reaction profile for this reaction to show how the energy changes as the reactants form the products. Mark the overall energy change on the diagram.

[2]

2.3   Where is the energy being transferred from in this type of reaction?

....

[1]

2.4   What happens to the amount of energy in the universe after the reaction?

....

[1]

2.5   Give a practical use of this type of reaction.

....

[1]

[Total 6 marks]

Exam Tip

Just like with wordy answers, the marks for graphs and diagrams tell you how much you need to do. Look at Q2.2 here — there are 2 marks for it, so you know you'll need to do two things. In this case, it's pretty clear what each mark is for, because it's all there in the question. There's one mark for completing the curve, and one for marking the energy change.

3   A company is trying to find a reaction with a low activation energy to use in a hand warmer. The reaction profiles for the reactions being investigated are shown in **Figure 1**.

Figure 1

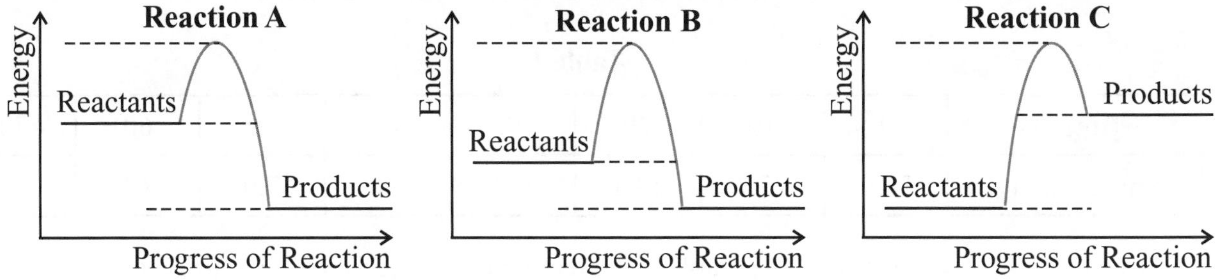

3.1 Define 'activation energy' and describe how activation energy is shown on a reaction profile.

    ....

    ....

    ....

    [2]

3.2 Suggest which reaction would be most suitable for using in a hand warmer. Explain your answer.

    ....

    ....

    ....

    [3]

    [Total 5 marks]

4   A student wanted to investigate how the choice of metal affects the temperature change of the reaction between a metal and an acid. Powdered samples of zinc, magnesium and copper are supplied, along with a solution of hydrochloric acid.

PRACTICAL

Grade
7-9

4.1 Suggest **three** essential pieces of apparatus needed for the investigation.

    ....

    ....

    [3]

4.2* Describe a method for how the testing could be carried out.

    ....

    ....

    ....

    ....

    ....

    ....

    ....

    [6]

    [Total 9 marks]

Topic C5 — Energy Changes

Target AO3

5 The data in **Table 1** shows the temperature of an endothermic reaction over time.

Table 1

Time (s)	0	10	20	30	40	50	60	70
Temperature (°C)	20.0	17.7	14.1	9.7	7.6	7.0	8.1	8.6

5.1 Use the data in **Table 1** to plot a graph of the temperature over time on the grid below, and draw two straight lines of best fit on your graph.

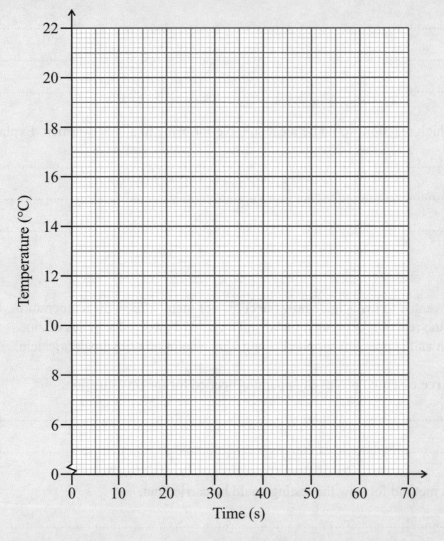

[3]

5.2 Use the intersection of your lines to estimate the maximum temperature change.

maximum temperature change = ... °C

[2]

[Total 5 marks]

Topic C5 — Energy Changes

Bond Energies

1 Methane and chlorine can react together as shown in **Figure 1**.
The bond energies of the substances in this reaction are shown in **Table 1**.

Figure 1

$$H-\underset{\underset{H}{|}}{\overset{\overset{H}{|}}{C}}-H \ + \ Cl-Cl \ \longrightarrow \ H-\underset{\underset{H}{|}}{\overset{\overset{H}{|}}{C}}-Cl \ + \ H-Cl$$

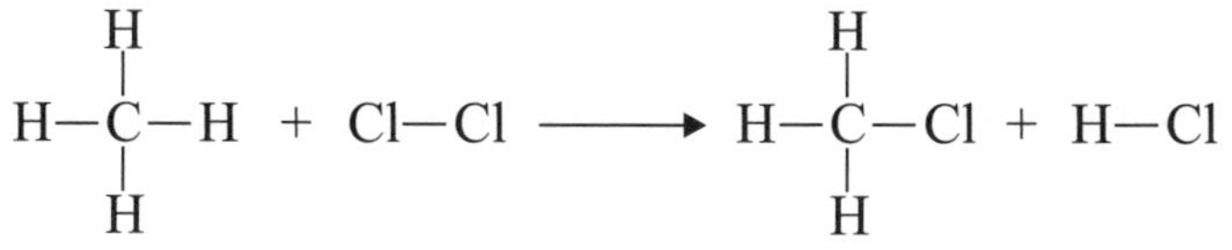

Table 1

Bond	Energy (kJ/mol)
C–H	413
Cl–Cl	243
C–Cl	346
H–Cl	432

1.1 Using the data in **Table 1**, calculate the energy change for the reaction.

Energy change of the reaction = ... kJ/mol

[3]

1.2 Explain, in terms of bond energies, whether the reaction is endothermic or exothermic.

....

....

[2]

[Total 5 marks]

2 Hydrogen and fluorine react together in the following way: $H_2 + F_2 \rightarrow 2HF$.
The overall energy change of the reaction is –542 kJ/mol.
The H–H bond energy is 436 kJ/mol and the F–F bond energy is 158 kJ/mol.

Calculate the energy of the H–F bond.

H–F bond energy = ... kJ/mol

[Total 3 marks]

Exam Tip

The maths for bond energy calculations isn't too tricky — it's usually just simple addition, subtraction and multiplication, and you might need to rearrange an equation. But it's really, really easy to make a mistake — so take your time, work through the question carefully, and, if you've got time at the end of the exam, go back and check your answers.

Topic C5 — Energy Changes

Rates of Reaction

1   This question is about the rate of a chemical reaction between two reactants, one of which is in solution, and one of which is a solid.

Grade 4-6

1.1   Which of the following changes would **not** cause the rate of the chemical reaction to increase?
Tick **one** box.

Increasing the concentration of the solutions. ☐

Heating the reaction mixture to a higher temperature. ☐

Using a larger volume of the solution, but keeping the concentration the same. ☐

Grinding the solid reactant so that it forms a fine powder. ☐

[1]

1.2   What is the name given to the minimum amount of energy
which particles must have if they are to react when they collide?

....

[1]

1.3   Explain why adding a catalyst to the reaction mixture, without changing any other condition,
can cause the rate of the reaction to increase.

....

[1]

[Total 3 marks]

2   **Figure 1** shows how the mass of gas lost from a reaction vessel
changes over time, for the same reaction under different conditions.

Grade 6-7

Figure 1

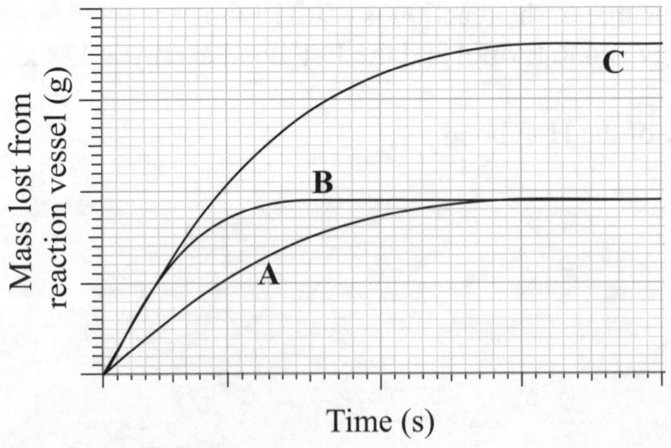

State which of the reactions, **A**, **B** or **C**:

Produced the most product: ....

Finished first: ....

Started at the slowest rate: ....

[Total 3 marks]

3 This question is about the rate of the reaction between magnesium and hydrochloric acid. The chemical equation for the reaction is:

$$Mg_{(s)} + 2HCl_{(aq)} \rightarrow MgCl_{2(aq)} + H_{2(g)}$$

3.1 The graph in **Figure 2** shows how the volume of hydrogen produced changes over the course of the reaction when a small lump of magnesium is added to excess hydrochloric acid.

On the same axes, sketch a curve to show how the volume of hydrogen produced would change over time if an identical piece of magnesium was added to excess hydrochloric acid with a higher concentration.

Figure 2

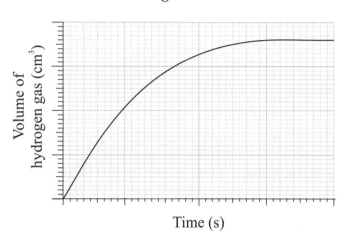

[3]

3.2 State **two** properties of the collisions between particles that affect the rate of a reaction.

....

....

[2]

3.3 Use collision theory to explain why increasing the concentration of a reactant increases the rate of the reaction.

....

....

[2]

3.4 How would you expect the reaction rate to change if the magnesium was cut into smaller pieces?

....

[1]

3.5 Explain why cutting the magnesium into smaller pieces affects the rate of this reaction.

....

....

[2]

3.6 State **one** change that could be made to change the rate of the reaction, other than changing the concentration and the size of the magnesium pieces.

....

[1]

[Total 11 marks]

Topic C6 — The Rate and Extent of Chemical Change

4 A student carries out a reaction between hydrogen gas and iodine gas to form hydrogen iodide (HI).

4.1 The student wants to increase the rate of the reaction, and decides to try two techniques:

1. Increasing the volume of the reaction vessel.
2. Increasing the temperature at which the reaction is carried out.

Explain, using collision theory, whether or not these changes will increase the rate of the reaction.

....

....

....

....

....

....

[5]

4.2 When cerium oxide is mixed with the hydrogen and iodine gases, the rate of the reaction increases. What does this suggest about cerium oxide?

....

[1]

4.3 State whether the reaction equation will change if cerium oxide is present in the reaction vessel. Explain your answer.

....

....

[2]

4.4 Sketch and label **two** reaction profiles on the axes below to show the difference between the reaction of hydrogen and iodine with and without cerium oxide. The energy of the products is lower than the energy of the reactants.

Energy

Progress of
Reaction

[3]

[Total 11 marks]

Exam Tip

The key to explaining questions about reaction rates is usually collision theory. So if these questions are making you bang your head against your desk, have a read up on how collisions affect the rate of a reaction, and on how different reaction conditions influence these collisions. You'll thank me for it later, I can promise you.

Topic C6 — The Rate and Extent of Chemical Change

Measuring Rates of Reaction

Warm-Up

Use the words on the left below to fill in the blanks of the passage on the right below.
No word is used more than once, but you may not need to use all the words.

products   mass

tangent

gradient   temperature

reactants

time   intercept

The rate of a reaction can be measured by dividing the amount of .... used up or the amount of .... formed by the .... To find the rate at a particular time from a graph with a curved line of best fit, you have to find the .... of the .... at that time.

---

1 To find the rate of a reaction you need to take measurements. Which of the following could you take measurements of to work out the rate of a reaction?

Grade 4-6

Tick **two** boxes.

Mass ☐   Volume of solution ☐

Volume of gas ☐   Frequency ☐

[Total 2 marks]

---

2 A student wants to investigate how the rate of a particular reaction is affected by temperature. The reaction produces a precipitate, so she plans to time how long it takes for the solution to go cloudy at each temperature.

Grade 4-6

2.1 What is the dependent variable in this experiment?

....

[1]

2.2 What is the independent variable in this experiment?

....

[1]

2.3 Suggest **one** variable that would have to be controlled in this experiment to make it a fair test.

....

[1]

2.4 The reaction also produces a gas. State whether it would be more accurate to measure the rate of the reaction by timing how long it takes for the solution to go cloudy, or by timing how long it takes a volume of gas to be produced. Explain your answer.

....

....

[2]

[Total 5 marks]

Topic C6 — The Rate and Extent of Chemical Change

3 The rate of a reaction was investigated by measuring the volume of gas produced at regular intervals. The results are shown in **Table 1**.

Table 1

Time (s)	0	60	120	180	240	300	360
Volume of gas (cm³)	0.0	10.5	15.5	17.4	18.0	18.0	18.0

3.1 Name a piece of equipment that could be used to measure the volume of gas produced.

....

[1]

3.2 Plot the data in **Table 1** on the axes below. Draw a line of best fit onto the graph.

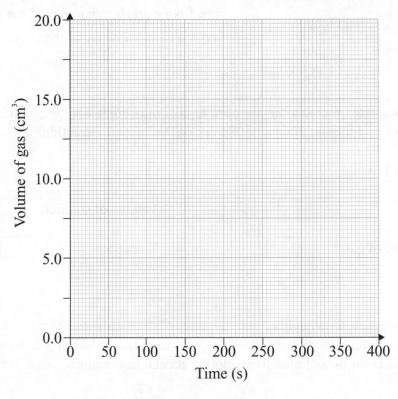

[3]

3.3 At what time does the reaction stop, according to your graph?

....

[1]

3.4 Calculate the mean rate of the reaction.

Mean rate of reaction = ...cm³/s

[2]

3.5 Suggest how you could check whether the results are repeatable.

....

....

[2]

[Total 9 marks]

Exam Tip

When drawing your lines of best fit, don't worry too much about your line going right through loads of points. Your line for this question should look like a smooth, continuous curve, not like you've drawn a line from dot-to-dot.

Topic C6 — The Rate and Extent of Chemical Change

4 The rate of a reaction between two solutions was investigated by monitoring the amount of one of the reactants, A, at regular intervals. A graph of the results is shown in **Figure 1**.

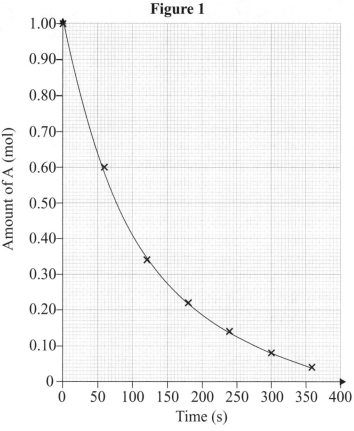

Figure 1

4.1 Use **Figure 1** to calculate the rate of the reaction at exactly 50 s after the start of the reaction. Give this rate to two significant figures. Include units in your answer.

rate = ... units = ...

[4]

4.2 In the same way calculate the rate of the reaction at exactly 200 s after the start of the reaction.

rate = ... units = ...

[4]

4.3 Describe and explain, with reference to collision theory, how the rate changes during the reaction.

....

....

[2]

[Total 10 marks]

Topic C6 — The Rate and Extent of Chemical Change

Reversible Reactions

1 This question is about the chemical reaction that is used to make ammonia from nitrogen and hydrogen. The equation for this reaction is: $N_2 + 3H_2 \rightleftharpoons 2NH_3$

Grade 4-6

1.1 What does the symbol '$\rightleftharpoons$' mean in this reaction?

....

[1]

1.2 When this reaction is carried out in a sealed container, it reaches equilibrium. Which of the following statements about equilibrium is true?
Tick **one** box.

At equilibrium, all the reactants have reacted to form products. ☐

At equilibrium, the amount of products equal the amount of reactants. ☐

At equilibrium, the rate of the forward reaction
is equal to the rate of the backwards reaction. ☐

At equilibrium, both the forwards and the backwards reactions stop. ☐

[1]

[Total 2 marks]

2 An aqueous solution of blue copper(II) ions can react with chloride ions to form a yellow copper compound. The ionic equation for this reaction is: $Cu^{2+} + 4Cl^- \rightleftharpoons [CuCl_4]^{2-}$

Grade 7-9

2.1 The forward reaction is endothermic. What two things can you say about the enthalpy change for the reverse reaction?

....

....

[2]

2.2 A solution containing copper(II) ions is mixed with a solution containing chloride ions in a flask. The solution quickly turns green. When observed for a few minutes no further change in colour can be seen. Explain these observations.

....

....

....

[2]

2.3 Suggest **two** changes that could be made to the mixture that would change its colour.

....

....

[2]

[Total 6 marks]

Target AO3

3 A scientist investigated the gas phase reaction between carbon monoxide and hydrogen.
The equation for this reversible reaction is: $CO_{(g)} + 2H_{2\,(g)} \rightleftharpoons CH_3OH_{(g)}$.
Figure 1 shows how the concentration of carbon monoxide and methanol change with time.

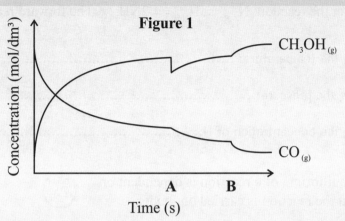

3.1 Suggest what happened to cause the change in concentration of CH_3OH at time **A** and shortly after.

....

....
[2]

3.2 Increasing the temperature of the reaction causes the amount of CH_3OH produced by
the reaction to decrease. Use this information to determine whether the forward reaction
is endothermic or exothermic, and justify your answer.

....

....

....
[2]

3.3 State whether the pressure was decreased or increased at time **B**. Explain your answer.

....

....

....
[2]

3.4 Sketch a graph of the concentrations of carbon
monoxide and methanol versus time for
the **reverse** reaction, $CH_3OH_{(g)} \rightleftharpoons CO_{(g)} + 2H_{2\,(g)}$,
assuming the reaction takes place in a
closed system with constant conditions.

[2]

[Total 8 marks]

Exam Tip

As well as asking you to draw graphs, the examiner may ask you to interpret and explain what a graph tells you about
a reaction. Make sure you understand how the key changes in the graph relate to the reaction in the question.

Topic C6 — The Rate and Extent of Chemical Change

Le Chatelier's Principle

Predict whether the changes below would result in there being more reactants or more products at equilibrium for the reaction: $N_{2(g)} + 3H_{2(g)} \rightleftharpoons 2NH_{3(g)}$. The forward reaction is exothermic.

Increasing the temperature: ....

Decreasing the pressure: ....

Increasing the concentration of N_2: ....

1 The position of equilibrium of a reaction is dependent on the conditions that the reaction is carried out under. **Grade 4-6**

1.1 What does Le Chatelier's Principle say about the effect of changing the conditions of a reversible reaction at equilibrium?

....

[1]

1.2 State **two** conditions you could change in order to alter the position of equilibrium of a reaction that happens in solution.

....

....

[2]

[Total 3 marks]

2 A mixture of iodine monochloride (ICl) and chlorine is sealed in a gas syringe. The gases react in a reversible reaction to form iodine trichloride (ICl_3) and eventually reach an equilibrium. The equation for the reaction is: $ICl_{(l)} + Cl_{2(g)} \rightleftharpoons ICl_{3(s)}$. **Grade 6-7**

2.1 Given that the forward reaction is exothermic, explain how the relative quantities of ICl and ICl_3 would change if the mixture was heated, and all other conditions remained the same.

....

....

....

[2]

2.2 Explain how the relative quantities of ICl and ICl_3 would change if the plunger were pushed into the syringe, and the temperature was kept constant.

....

....

....

[3]

[Total 5 marks]

Topic C6 — The Rate and Extent of Chemical Change

3 Dinitrogen tetroxide (N_2O_4) is a colourless gas. It decomposes in a reversible reaction to form the brown gas, nitrogen dioxide (NO_2). The reaction equation is: $N_2O_{4(g)} \rightleftharpoons 2NO_{2(g)}$. *(Grade 7-9)*

3.1 When a sample of N_2O_4 is left to decompose in a sealed tube, a pale brown colour can be seen. If this mixture is heated, the colour becomes a darker brown. Explain this observation and predict whether the forward reaction is exothermic or endothermic.

....

....

....

[3]

3.2 Explain how you would expect the colour of the equilibrium mixture to change if the pressure of the mixture is decreased, and all other conditions are kept the same.

....

....

....

[3]

[Total 6 marks]

4 Yellow iron(III) ions and colourless thiocyanate ions react reversibly in solution to form dark red iron thiocyanate: $Fe^{3+}_{(aq)} + SCN^-_{(aq)} \rightleftharpoons FeSCN^{2+}_{(aq)}$ *(Grade 7-9)*

The following observations are made about this reaction:
1. When a yellow solution containing Fe^{3+} ions and a colourless solution containing SCN^- ions are mixed, a pale red colour forms which initially grows darker but then stays constant.
2. When more Fe^{3+} ions are added to the solution it initially becomes more orangey in colour but then grows darker red than before the Fe^{3+} was added and remains like this.
3. If $FeSCN^{2+}$ ions are added to the solution it initially becomes darker in colour but then becomes more orangey.

Explain what is happening in each of these observations.

Observation 1: ....

....

Observation 2: ....

....

Observation 3: ....

....

[Total 6 marks]

Exam Tip

Working out what happens to the position of an equilibrium when you change the conditions can be a bit of a brain twister. Just remember that for any change that's made, the reaction will try to do the opposite. So if you increase the temperature, more of the endothermic reaction will happen, if you increase the pressure, the equilibrium will move to the side where there are fewer moles of gas, and if you increase the concentration of a reactant, you'll get more products.

Topic C6 — The Rate and Extent of Chemical Change

Hydrocarbons

Place each of the compounds on the left, below in the correct column of the table depending on whether or not they are hydrocarbons.

propane

ethene

butanoic acid

C_2H_6

CH_3CH_2Cl

C_2H_4 hydrochloric acid

Hydrocarbon	Not a hydrocarbon

1   Alkanes are a family of hydrocarbons.   Grade 4-6

1.1 What is a hydrocarbon?

....
[1]

1.2 Which of the following shows the first four alkanes in order of decreasing carbon chain length? Tick **one** box.

Propane, ethane, butane, methane   ☐

Methane, ethane, propane, butane   ☐

Ethane, methane, butane, propane   ☐

Butane, propane, ethane, methane   ☐

[1]

1.3 Write the general formula of alkanes in terms of n, where n is the number of carbon atoms.

....
[1]

1.4 Complete the word equation for the complete combustion of a hydrocarbon.

hydrocarbon + oxygen → .... + ...
[1]

1.5 During a combustion reaction, are the atoms in the hydrocarbon oxidised or reduced?

....
[1]

[Total 5 marks]

2 The molecular formulas for five hydrocarbons, **A** to **E**, are shown below. (Grade 4-6)

    A C_4H_8 **B** C_4H_{10} **C** C_5H_{10} **D** C_5H_{12} **E** C_6H_{14}

2.1 Which hydrocarbon is butane?

....

[1]

2.2 Which of the hydrocarbons are alkanes? Explain your answer.

....

....

[2]

2.3 Which of the hydrocarbons is likely to have the highest boiling point? Explain your answer.

....

....

[2]

[Total 5 marks]

3 Petrol and diesel are both fuels containing mixtures of hydrocarbons. The average chain length of the hydrocarbons in petrol and diesel are different, which causes diesel to have a higher boiling point than petrol. (Grade 6-7)

3.1 Compare the viscosity of petrol and diesel.
Explain your answer with reference to the information above.

....

....

[2]

3.2 Predict whether petrol or diesel will be more flammable.
Explain your answer with reference to the information above.

....

....

[2]

3.3 Diesel contains alkanes that have 20 carbon atoms.
Give the molecular formula of an alkane with 20 carbon atoms.

....

[1]

3.4 Petrol contains alkanes with 8 carbon atoms.
Finish and balance the equation for the complete combustion of this hydrocarbon

.... C_8H_{18} + ... $O_2 \rightarrow$ .... + ...

[2]

[Total 7 marks]

Topic C7 — Organic Chemistry

Fractional Distillation

1 Crude oil is a finite resource. *(Grade 4-6)*

1.1 What is crude oil formed from?

....
[1]

1.2 What does 'finite resource' mean?

....

....
[1]

1.3 What type of substance does crude oil mainly consist of?
Tick **one** box.

Alkenes ☐   Alcohols ☐

Alkanes ☐   Water ☐

[1]
[Total 3 marks]

2 Fractional distillation is used to separate the mixture of molecules in crude oil into fractions such as petrol and diesel oil. *(Grade 6-7)*

2.1 What property of the molecules in crude oil is used to separate them into different fractions?

....
[1]

2.2 Explain how a fractionating column separates the molecules in crude oil into different fractions.

....

....

....

....
[3]

2.3 Fractions boil over a range of temperatures much narrower than the original crude oil.
What does this suggest about the structures of the hydrocarbons in a fraction?

....
[1]
[Total 5 marks]

Exam Tip

Question 2.2 is a good example of a question where you're asked to explain how a process works. Questions like these are usually worth more marks, so make sure you include at least the same number of points in your explanation as there are marks available. When marking your answers, have a proper look at what each mark has been awarded for.

Topic C7 — Organic Chemistry

Uses and Cracking of Crude Oil

1 Crude oil is processed to be used for a variety of purposes. *Grade 4-6*

1.1 Suggest **two** types of useful material produced from crude oil fractions.

....

[2]

1.2 Long-chain hydrocarbons can be processed to produce short-chain hydrocarbons.
What is the name of this process?
Tick **one** box.

Fractional distillation ☐

Thermal reduction ☐

Thermal oxidation ☐

Cracking ☐

[1]

1.3 Why do we break up long chain hydrocarbons into shorter chain hydrocarbons?

....

[1]

[Total 4 marks]

2 Some hydrocarbons from crude oil undergo processing by the petrochemical industry. For instance, decane, $C_{10}H_{22}$, can undergo cracking as shown in the following equation: *Grade 6-7*

$$C_{10}H_{22} \rightarrow C_8H_{18} + C_2H_4$$

2.1 What type of reaction is cracking?

....

[1]

2.2 Describe how cracking is carried out.

....

....

[2]

2.3 Cracking can form a variety of products.
Write an alternative balanced equation for the cracking of decane.

....

[1]

[Total 4 marks]

3 When large alkanes are cracked, smaller alkanes and alkenes are produced. An example of cracking is given in **Figure 1**.

Figure 1

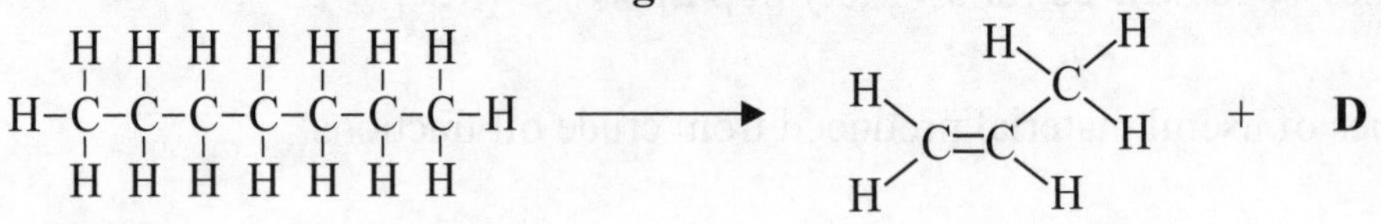

3.1 Write the chemical formula of the reactant.

....

[1]

3.2 Draw the displayed formula of **D**.

[2]

3.3 Suggest a use for the alkene, **C**.

....

[1]

[Total 4 marks]

4* Explain why and how some fractions of crude oil are processed by cracking, giving chemical equations where relevant. You should state some uses of the products of this process.

....

....

....

....

....

....

....

....

....

....

[Total 6 marks]

Exam Tip

When balancing cracking equations, make sure that there's at least one alkane and alkene in the products. Also, just like any chemical equation, remember to check that the number of each atom on both sides of the equations is the same.

Topic C7 — Organic Chemistry

Target AO3

5   A group of students conducted an experiment to measure the volume of gas produced when they crack a long-chain hydrocarbon. The students' set-up is shown in **Figure 2**.

 Grade 7-9

Figure 2

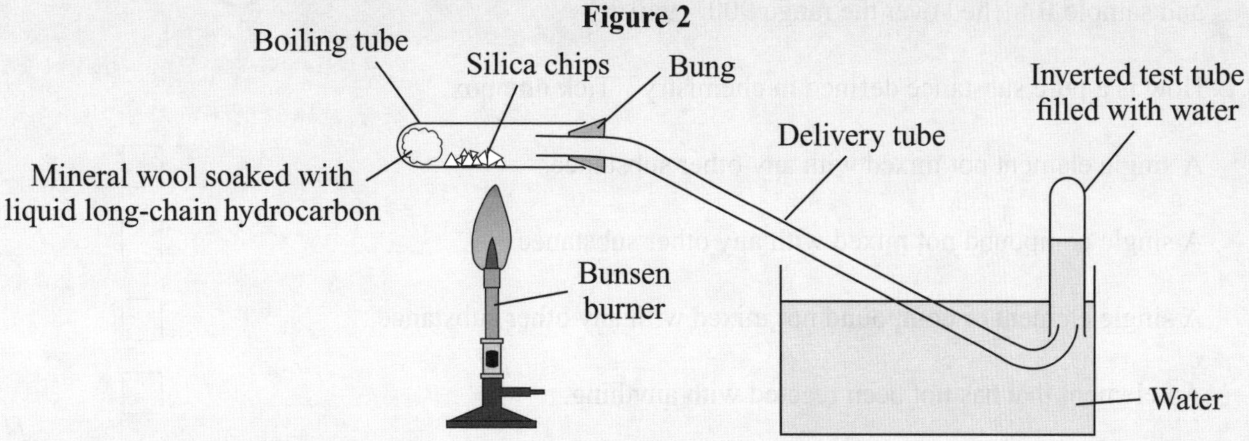

Boiling tube   Silica chips   Bung

Inverted test tube filled with water

Delivery tube

Mineral wool soaked with liquid long-chain hydrocarbon

Bunsen burner

Water

5.1   Explain why the bung is an important safety precaution when using a Bunsen burner to heat the boiling tube.

....

....
[2]

5.2   One of the students had a lot more gas in their test tube than the others at the end of the experiment. Suggest an error that the student could have made that would cause this to occur.

....

....

....
[2]

5.3   The students want to improve the accuracy of their results.
Suggest **one** part of the set-up that could be changed in order to produce more accurate results.

....
[1]

5.4   During the experiment, some water was sucked back into the delivery tube.
Suggest why it is important to remove the apparatus from the water when this happens.

....
[1]

5.5   Suggest why it would not be possible to carry out this experiment in a laboratory without a catalyst.

....

....
[1]

[Total 7 marks]

Exam Tip

In the exam, you might be asked about experiments and reactions that you've never seen before. Firstly — don't panic. Secondly — think about the information you've been given and if you can link it to your existing knowledge in some way.

Topic C7 — Organic Chemistry

Purity and Formulations

1 Copper can be made extremely pure. The melting point of two samples of copper were measured. Sample **A** had a melting point of 1085 °C and sample **B** melted over the range 900 – 940 °C.

1.1 How is a pure substance defined in chemistry? Tick **one** box.

A single element not mixed with any other substance. ☐

A single compound not mixed with any other substance. ☐

A single element or compound not mixed with any other substance. ☐

An element that has not been reacted with anything. ☐

[1]

1.2 Suggest which of the samples was the most pure? Explain your answer.

....

....
[2]

1.3 The boiling point of copper is 2,562 °C. Which of the samples is likely to have a boiling point closer to that of pure copper?

....
[1]

[Total 4 marks]

2 A paint was composed of 20% pigment, 35% binder, 25% solvent, and 20% additives.
Grade 6-7

2.1 Explain why the paint is a formulation.

....

....

....
[3]

2.2 How would a manufacturer of the paint ensure that each batch had exactly the same properties?

....
[1]

2.3 Other than paint, name **one** other example of a formulation.

....
[1]

[Total 5 marks]

Exam Tip

A formulation is a mixture but a mixture isn't always a formulation. For the exam, you may need to identify formulations based on information about their ingredients and how they've been designed to make the product fit for purpose.

Paper Chromatography

Warm-Up

Complete the diagram by correctly labelling the different parts of the chromatography apparatus using the labels on the left, below.

Sample

Watch glass   Filter paper

Baseline

Solvent

Spots of chemicals

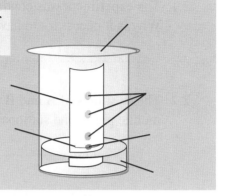

1   Paper chromatograms were produced for three dyes, **D**, **E** and **F**, using a variety of solvents. The chromatogram produced using ethanol as a solvent is shown in **Figure 1**.

Grade 6-7

Figure 1

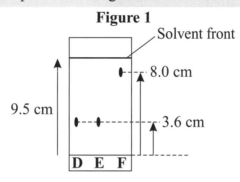

Solvent front

9.5 cm

8.0 cm

3.6 cm

D E F

1.1 Calculate the R$_f$ values for **E** and **F** in ethanol, using the chromatogram shown in **Figure 1**.

R$_f$ of **E** = ...

R$_f$ of **F** = ...
[4]

1.2 Why do the substances travel different distances?

....

....
[1]

1.3 In all solvents, each dye only has one spot.
     What does this imply about the composition of the dyes?

....
[1]

1.4 State which of the dyes could be the same.

....
[1]

[Total 7 marks]

Topic C8 — Chemical Analysis

2 A paper chromatography experiment was used to identify the compounds in a mixture, **W**, as shown in **Figure 2**. Three known compounds, **A**, **B** and **C** were spotted alongside **W**. Water was used as the solvent.

Grade 6-7

2.1 The experiment was conducted in a beaker with a watch glass functioning as a lid. Why is it necessary to have a lid while conducting a paper chromatography experiment?

....

[1]

2.2 The R_f values of **A** and **B** were found to be 0.9 and 0.1 respectively. With reference to the mobile phase and stationary phase, suggest why A has a much larger R_f value than **B**.

....

[1]

2.3 A diagram of the chromatogram from the experiment can be seen in **Figure 2**. State which of the known compounds could be found in **W**.

Figure 2

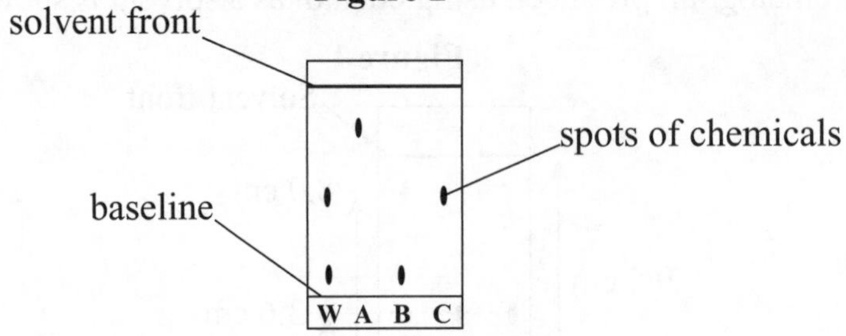

....

[1]

2.4 A student suggested that if the solvent was changed, the R_f value of compounds **A**, **B** and **C** would stay the same. Explain whether the student was correct.

....

....

....

[2]

2.5 The experiment was repeated again using a different solvent. The mixture **W** had three spots on the resultant chromatogram. What does this suggest about the mixture **W**?

....

[1]

2.6 Suggest why only two spots were shown on the chromatogram shown in **Figure 2**.

....

....

[1]

[Total 7 marks]

Topic C8 — Chemical Analysis

3   A student set up a chromatography experiment to investigate a sample of ink which contained a mixture of several different compounds.

3.1   The chromatogram from the student's experiment is shown in **Figure 3**.

Figure 3

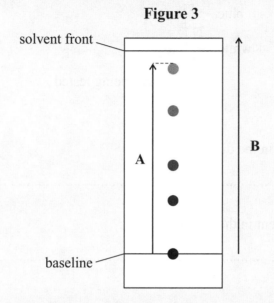

What **two** conclusions could the student make about the compounds in the ink?
Explain your answers.

....

....

....

....

[4]

3.2   The student used distances **A** and **B** to calculate the R_f value for one of the compounds.
Explain the **two** mistakes that the student has made and what they should have done instead.

....

....

....

....

[4]

[Total 8 marks]

Tests for Gases

1   A student wants to identify a gaseous product.

The diagram below shows the gas being tested.

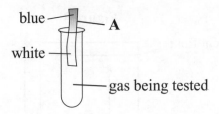

blue — A
white
gas being tested

1.1   Identify the item labelled **A** in the diagram.

....

[1]

1.2   Suggest which gas was present in the test tube.

....

[1]

[Total 2 marks]

2   A student performs an experiment that produces a colourless gas. She does not know what the gas is, so she collects it and tests it in order to identify it.

2.1   Suggest why the student should perform the experiment in a fume cupboard.

....

[1]

2.2   Describe how she could test the gas to see if it was carbon dioxide.

....

....

[2]

2.3   When a lighted splint is placed into a sample of the gas, it was **not** accompanied by a popping sound. What does this tell you about the gas?

....

[1]

2.4   When the student placed a glowing splint into a sample of the gas, the splint relighted. Identify the gas that was produced by her experiment.

....

[1]

[Total 5 marks]

The Evolution of the Atmosphere

Warm-Up

Circle whether each of the following sentences is **true** or **false**.

1) Earth's early atmosphere contained mainly nitrogen.   True   or   False

2) Earth's early atmosphere formed from gases released by volcanoes.   True   or   False

3) Earth's early atmosphere contained very little oxygen.   True   or   False

4) The oceans formed when oxygen reacted with hydrogen to form water.   True   or   False

1   The composition of gases in the atmosphere has varied during Earth's history.   (Grade 4-6)

1.1   What are the approximate proportions of oxygen and nitrogen in the atmosphere today?
      Tick **one** box.

One-fifth oxygen and four-fifths nitrogen.   □

Two-fifths oxygen and three-fifths nitrogen.   □

Three-fifths oxygen and two-fifths nitrogen.   □

Four-fifths oxygen and one-fifth nitrogen.   □

[1]

1.2   Other than oxygen and nitrogen, name **two** other gases in the atmosphere today.

      ....
[2]

1.3   How was the oxygen in the atmosphere produced?

      ....
[1]

1.4   How was nitrogen in the atmosphere produced?

      ....
[1]

1.5   For approximately how long has the atmosphere had a composition similar to what it is today?
      Tick **one** box.

5 million years □   30 million years □   200 million years □   1 billion years □

[1]

[Total 6 marks]

Exam Tip

The Earth's early atmosphere developed in three phases. If you're struggling with the questions on this topic, it might be helpful to break your revision up into these phases and make sure you understand one before moving on to the next.

2 During the Earth's first billion years, the percentage of carbon dioxide in the atmosphere was probably much higher than it is today. The formation of sedimentary rocks and fossil fuels helped to decrease the percentage of carbon dioxide.

(Grade 6-7)

2.1 Suggest **one** reason, other than sedimentary rock and fossil fuel formation, why the percentage of carbon dioxide in the atmosphere is thought to have decreased.

....

[1]

2.2 Outline how sedimentary rocks are formed.

....

....

[1]

2.3 State what the sedimentary rocks coal and limestone are formed from.

Coal: ....

Limestone: ....

[2]

[Total 4 marks]

3 There are several theories about how Earth's atmosphere evolved to its current composition. One theory suggests that the proportion of oxygen in Earth's early atmosphere was similar to the proportion in Mars' atmosphere today, which is 0.13%. The theory then suggests that, about 2.7 billion years ago, the proportion of oxygen in Earth's atmosphere started increasing.

(Grade 7-9)

3.1 Suggest why it's difficult to come up with a conclusive theory about how the atmosphere evolved.

....

[1]

3.2 Write a balanced symbol equation for the reaction that is thought to have caused the proportion of oxygen in Earth's atmosphere to increase.

....

[1]

3.3 Suggest why there is such a small amount of oxygen in the atmosphere of Mars.

....

....

[2]

3.4 Red beds are rocks that contain iron oxide. They form when other iron compounds from older rocks come into contact with oxygen in the atmosphere, and react. The oldest red beds formed about 2 billion years ago.

Suggest how this provides evidence for when the amount of oxygen in Earth's atmosphere started increasing.

....

....

[1]

[Total 5 marks]

Topic C9 — Chemistry of the Atmosphere

Greenhouse Gases and Climate Change

1 Greenhouse gases in the atmosphere help maintain life on Earth. (Grade 4-6)

1.1 Which of the following is **not** a greenhouse gas?
Tick **one** box.

Carbon dioxide ☐   Methane ☐

Nitrogen ☐   Water vapour ☐

[1]

1.2 State how greenhouse gases help to support life on Earth.

....

[1]

1.3 Give **two** examples of types of human activity which are leading to an increase in the concentration of greenhouse gases in the atmosphere.

....

....

[2]

[Total 4 marks]

2 An increase in the amount of greenhouse gases in the atmosphere may cause the climate to change. (Grade 6-7)

2.1 Explain how greenhouse gases help to keep the Earth warm.
Your answer should make reference to the interaction of greenhouse gases with radiation.

....

....

....

[3]

2.2 An increase in global temperatures could cause sea levels to rise.
Give **two** potential consequences of rising sea levels.

....

....

[2]

2.3 Other than rising sea levels, give **one** other potential consequence of climate change.

....

[1]

[Total 6 marks]

Exam Tip

Examiners love to provide unfamiliar data and then ask questions about whether it shows a link between two factors, especially when it comes to greenhouse gases and climate change. Make sure you know how to interpret data in both graph and table form, and how to use the data to support your answer — if not for the exam, then for the next page...

Topic C9 — Chemistry of the Atmosphere

3* The global temperature anomaly is the difference between current temperature and an average value. The graph in **Figure 1** shows how the global temperature anomaly and the concentration of CO_2 in the atmosphere have varied over time. Describe the trends in the data and suggest reasons for them.

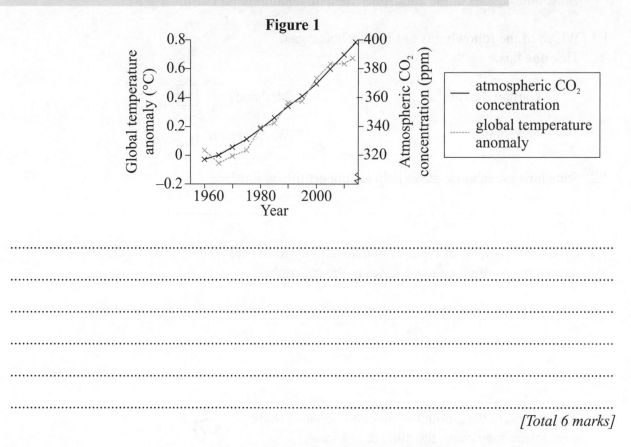

Figure 1

....

....

....

....

....

....

[Total 6 marks]

4 **Table 1** shows some data about atmospheric greenhouse gases. The global warming potential measures the impact of the gas on global warming compared to carbon dioxide.

Table 1

Gas	Formula	Current atmospheric level (%)	Lifetime in atmosphere (years)	Global warming potential
Carbon dioxide	CO_2	0.040	100-300	1
Methane	CH_4	0.00019	12	28
CFC-12	CCl_2F_2	5.3×10^{-7}	100	10 200

4.1 Use the table to suggest why methane is an important greenhouse gas, despite currently being at a lower level than carbon dioxide.

....

[1]

4.2 Use data from the table to explain why CFC-12 could have a significant impact on global warming.

....

....

[2]

[Total 3 marks]

Topic C9 — Chemistry of the Atmosphere

Target AO3

5 Scientists in Antarctica use ice cores to measure how the Earth's atmosphere and temperature have changed over time.

5.1 Antarctic ice contains bubbles of gas that were trapped when the ice first froze. Suggest how these bubbles can be used to work out how the Earth's atmosphere has changed.

....

....

[1]

5.2 **Table 2** shows the carbon dioxide concentration from one Antarctic ice core, as well as the global temperature anomaly for the same period. The global temperature anomaly is the temperature difference from the average temperature for the 20th century.

Table 2

Year	CO$_2$ concentration (ppm)	Global temperature anomaly (°C)
1960	319	0.1
1970	324	0.1
1980	340	0.3
1990	355	0.5
2000	374	0.6

A scientist states that the data shows a link between carbon dioxide concentration and global temperature. Is their conclusion supported by the data in **Table 2**? Explain your answer.

....

....

....

[2]

5.3 Suggest how increasing carbon dioxide levels might affect the scientists' ability to collect new ice cores in the future.

....

....

....

[3]

5.4 Scientists are able to collect large ice cores from deep inside ice sheets. These cores can be up to 3 km long, and can contain ice from hundreds of thousands of years ago. Collecting these cores takes a long time. Suggest **one** other limitation to collecting large ice cores.

....

....

[1]

[Total 7 marks]

Topic C9 — Chemistry of the Atmosphere

Carbon Footprints

1 Individuals have an annual carbon footprint. One of the factors that contributes to each person's carbon footprint is the amount of electrical energy they use each year. *(Grade 4-6)*

1.1 What is meant by the term 'carbon footprint'?

....

....

[2]

1.2 Suggest **two** ways that the carbon footprint resulting
from an individual's electricity usage could be reduced.

....

....

[2]

1.3 Suggest why an individual might not try to reduce their carbon footprint.

....

[1]

[Total 5 marks]

2 In recent years, some businesses have tried to reduce their carbon footprint by capturing the carbon dioxide they produce and storing it, rather than releasing it into the atmosphere. *(Grade 6-7)*

2.1 Suggest **two** disadvantages for companies of capturing and storing carbon dioxide.

....

....

[2]

2.2 Discuss **two** ways in which governments can encourage businesses to reduce their carbon footprints and explain why some countries may be resistant to using these methods.

....

....

....

....

....

[4]

[Total 6 marks]

Exam Tip

Learning the definitions for all the different terms that crop up in GCSE Science may be a bit of a bore, but it might be really useful in the exams. Learning all the itty bitty details is worth it if it means you get all the marks available.

Air Pollution

1   A variety of pollutants can be released when fuels burn, with a range of consequences.   (Grade 4-6)

1.1   Why can the combustion of coal produce sulfur dioxide?

....

[1]

1.2   Name one pollutant that can lead to each of the following consequences:

Acid rain: ....

Global dimming: ....

[2]

1.3   State **two** ways in which acid rain can be damaging.

....

....

[2]

[Total 5 marks]

2   Combustion of fuel in cars is a major contributor to air pollution.   (Grade 6-7)

2.1   Explain how cars produce nitrogen oxides.

....

....

[2]

2.2   Give **two** problems caused by nitrogen oxides in the environment.

....

....

[2]

2.3   Fuel combustion can produce particulates. What impact do particulates have on human health?

....

[1]

2.4   Combustion of fuels can also produce a gas that prevents blood from carrying oxygen around the body. Inhaling it can cause health problems, and sometimes death.

Name the gas and state why it is difficult to detect it.

....

....

[2]

[Total 7 marks]

Topic C9 — Chemistry of the Atmosphere

Finite and Renewable Resources

1   This question is about sustainable use of the Earth's resources.
Table 1 shows the time it takes to form various materials.

Table 1

Material	Time to form (years)
Wood	2-20
Coal	3×10^8
Cotton	0.5

1.1   Using the data in **Table 1**, state **one** finite resource. Explain your answer.

....

....

[2]

1.2   What is meant by the term 'renewable resource'?

....

[1]

[Total 3 marks]

2   Humans have developed items made from both natural and synthetic materials.

2.1   Give **one** example of how agriculture is used to increase
the supply of an otherwise natural resource.

....

....

[1]

2.2   Give **one** example of a synthetic product which has replaced
or is used in addition to a natural resource.

....

[1]

[Total 2 marks]

3   The mining of metals has economic, environmental and social impacts.

Give **one** advantage and **one** disadvantage of metal mining.

....

....

[Total 2 marks]

Exam Tip

Table 1 contains a number in standard form. Scientists use this as an easy way of writing numbers that are either tiny
or massive. To convert it into a normal number, move the decimal point right the number of times shown by the power,
so 1.0×10^3 would become 1000. If the power is negative, move the decimal point to the left, so 1.2×10^{-2} equals 0.012.

Reuse and Recycling

1 This question is on sustainable development. (Grade 6-7)

1.1 What is sustainable development?

....

....

[2]

1.2 How do chemists play a role within sustainable development?
Explain your answer using an example.

....

....

....

[2]

[Total 4 marks]

2 Carrier bags can be made from a number of different materials. Two possible materials are jute and poly(ethene). **Table 1** gives some information about these materials. (Grade 6-7)

Table 1

	Poly(ethene)	Jute
Source	Crude oil	Plant fibre
Energy of Production	Moderate energy production	High energy production
Biodegradability	Not biodegradable	Biodegradable
Recyclability	Can be recycled	Possible but not widely done, likely to be reused

2.1 Using the information in **Table 1**, compare the sustainability
of the raw materials needed to make the bags.

....

....

[2]

2.2 Using the information in **Table 1**, compare the sustainability of the production of the bags.

....

....

[2]

2.3 Using the information in **Table 1**, compare the sustainability of the disposal of both bags.

....

....

....

[3]

[Total 7 marks]

Topic C10 — Using Resources

3 This question is on recycling. **Grade 6-7**

3.1 Give **two** reasons why recycling can be more sustainable than making new materials.

....

....

[2]

3.2 Name a material that is commonly recycled and briefly describe the process.

....

....

[2]

3.3 State **one** alternative to recycling that also improves sustainability.

....

[1]

[Total 5 marks]

4 This question is about the sustainability of copper. **Grade 7-9**

4.1 Explain how the process of phytomining is used to produce a substance
which contains copper compounds.

....

....

....

....

[4]

4.2 Describe **two** ways in which copper metal can be extracted from the product of phytomining.

....

....

[2]

4.3 Explain why phytomining cannot ultimately provide a sustainable source of copper metals.
Suggest **one** thing that can be done to make use of copper more sustainable.

....

....

....

[3]

[Total 9 marks]

Exam Tip

Make sure you understand how reuse and recycling are used to make the materials we use in our daily lives
more sustainable. You should also get to grips with the different biological methods of extracting copper,
and the advantages in terms of sustainability of using these methods compared to traditional mining techniques.

Topic C10 — Using Resources

Life Cycle Assessments

Draw one line between each stage of a product's life and the correct example of that stage.

Life cycle stage	Example
Getting the Raw Materials	Coal being mined from the ground.
Manufacturing and Packaging	Plastic bags going on to landfill.
Using the Product	A car using fuel while driving.
Product Disposal	Books being made from wood pulp.

1 Life cycle assessments are carried out on products as a way of finding out what their environmental impact is. *(Grade 6-7)*

1.1 State **two** potential impacts of a product on the environment when it is disposed of at the end of its useful life.

....

....

[2]

1.2 Suggest **one** environmental consideration of a product which can be easily quantified while carrying out a life cycle assessment.

....

[1]

1.3 Suggest why some pollutant effects are less straightforward to quantify.

....

[1]

1.4 If two different assessors carried out a life cycle assessment on identical products, would you expect the results to be exactly the same? Explain your answer.

....

....

....

[3]

1.5 Some life cycle assessments can be selective in assessing the effects of a product on the environment. Explain how and why selective life cycle assessments could be misused.

....

....

[2]

[Total 9 marks]

Target AO3

2   **Table 1** contains life cycle assessment data for two types of soft drink container.

Table 1

	Glass Bottles	Aluminium Cans
Raw Materials	Sand, soda ash and limestone	Aluminium ore
Manufacturing	• Have to be produced at very high temperatures • Their production releases greenhouse gases	• Require large amounts of electricity to extract aluminium from the ore • Their production releases greenhouse gases
Usage	Can be refilled and reused	Usually only used once
Disposal	Widely recycled and used to produce new glass	Can be continually recycled as a source of aluminium

2.1 Use information from **Table 1** to suggest **one** way in which glass bottles are more environmentally friendly than aluminium cans.

....

[1]

2.2 Recycling aluminium cans saves large amounts of energy compared to producing new cans. Does this positively or negatively affect their life cycle assessment? Explain your answer.

....

....

....

[2]

2.3 Certain glass objects cannot be recycled with the glass bottles. Explain why this negatively affects the life cycle assessment of the glass bottles.

....

....

[2]

2.4 Suggest another useful comparison that could be added to the disposal section of this LCA.

....

....

[1]

[Total 6 marks]

Exam Tip

An important skill in the exam is to consider potential impacts that haven't been given as part of the life cycle assessment. Companies may produce assessments that make their products look great when they are actually environmentally damaging. This is why it's important to consider all the information you can before answering.

Topic C10 — Using Resources

Potable Water

Warm-Up

For each of the statements below circle whether the statement is **true** or **false**.

1) Potable water does not contain any dissolved substances.   True   or   False

2) Potable water is the same as drinking water.   True   or   False

3) Potable water can only be produced from fresh water found in rivers, streams and reservoirs.   True   or   False

1 This question is about potable water. (Grade 4-6)

1.1 Which of the following is **not** a correct description of potable water? Tick **one** box.

Pure water ☐

Water containing a small number of microbes ☐

Water that is safe to drink ☐

Water with a low concentration of salt ☐

[1]

1.2 Fresh water is used to produce potable water. In the UK, where is the majority of fresh water sourced from during the production of potable water?

....

[1]

1.3 Draw **one** line between each treatment of water and the substances removed by the process.

Passing water through filter beds		Solid Waste
		Microbes
Sterilisation		Chemicals

[2]

1.4 Name **three** things that can be used to sterilise fresh water.

....

....

[3]

[Total 7 marks]

2   Distillation can be used to desalinate sea water. **Figure 1** shows a set of equipment that could be used to desalinate sea water.

Figure 1

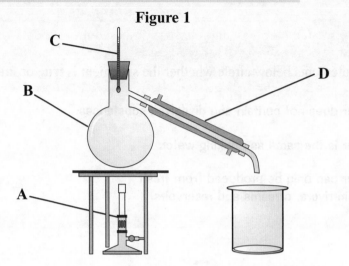

2.1 Name the components labelled **A** to **D** in the diagram.

A ....   **B** ....

C ....   **D** ....

[4]

2.2 Plan a method for using this equipment to produce a sample of potable water from seawater. You should include in your plan enough detail to allow someone to carry out the procedure safely and effectively.

....

....

....

....

....

[5]

2.3 Suggest a method, other than distillation, that could be used to desalinate water.

....

[1]

2.4 Explain why we do not use desalination to produce large quantities of potable water in the UK.

....

....

....

[2]

[Total 12 marks]

Exam Tip

Some water costs a lot to make potable, some not so much. Make sure you understand the different processes that salty water and fresh water undergo to make it safe to drink and why the different processes are chosen.

Topic C10 — Using Resources

Waste Water Treatment

1 Waste water must be treated before being reused or released into the environment. (Grade 4-6)

1.1 Which **two** of the following pollutants must be removed
from sewage and agricultural waste water?

Calcium ions, Ca^{2+} ☐

Organic matter ☐

Harmful microbes ☐

Sodium ions, Na^+ ☐

[2]

1.2 Industrial waste water must have further treatment compared to
sewage and agricultural waste water. Suggest why this.

....

[1]

[Total 3 marks]

2 This question is about the treatment of waste water in the form of sewage. (Grade 4-6)
Figure 1 shows a schematic diagram of a sewage treatment facility.

Figure 1

Waste Water → Screening → Sedimentation → **B** → aerobic digestion → released into rivers

Sedimentation → **A** → **X** → natural gas / fertiliser

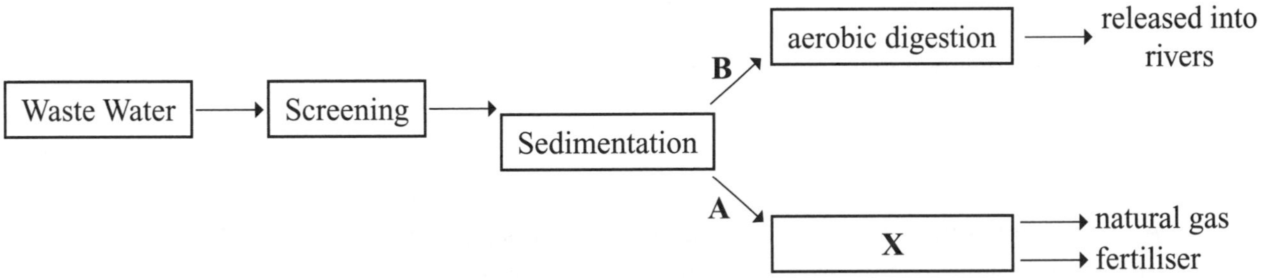

2.1 What is the purpose of the stage described as 'screening'?

....

....

[2]

2.2 What are the names given to the two substances produced by sedimentation?

Substance **A**: ....

Substance **B**: ....

[2]

2.3 What is the name of process **X**?

....

[1]

[Total 5 marks]

Topic C10 — Using Resources

Energy Stores and Systems

1 **Figure 1** shows an apple on a tree. **Figure 2** shows a filament bulb connected to a battery. Both **Figure 1** and **Figure 2** show systems.

Figure 1

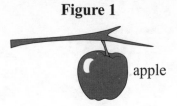

Figure 2

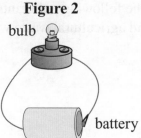

1.1 Define the term 'system'.

....

[1]

1.2 The apple in **Figure 1** falls from the tree.
Give **two** energy stores that energy is transferred between when this happens.

Energy is transferred from: ....

Energy is transferred to: ....

[2]

1.3 In **Figure 2**, energy is transferred from the chemical energy store of the battery to the thermal energy store of the bulb. State how energy is transferred between these two stores.

....

....

[1]

[Total 4 marks]

2* A cyclist allows his bike to roll down a hill without pedalling. Towards the bottom of the hill he applies his brakes. The bike comes to a stop. Applying the brakes causes the brakes to warm up. Describe the energy transfers that have occurred. State the forces doing work that cause each of these energy transfers. You can ignore any friction between the bike and the ground and any air resistance.

....

....

....

....

....

[Total 4 marks]

Exam Tip

Make sure you know the different types of energy store and remember that energy transfers can occur mechanically (because of a force doing work, like above), electrically, by heating or by radiation (e.g. light and sound waves).

Kinetic and Potential Energy Stores

1 A student is tuning his guitar. He stretches the string by 10 mm so it produces the right note when played. The string has a spring constant of 20 N/m.

Calculate the energy stored in the elastic potential energy store of the string as it is stretched. You can assume that the limit of proportionality was not exceeded whilst it was being stretched. Use an equation from the Equations List.

Energy = ... J

[Total 2 marks]

2 A 0.1 kg toy contains a compressed spring. When the spring is released, the toy flies 0.45 m upwards from ground level, before falling back down to the ground.

Assuming there's no air resistance, calculate the speed of the toy when it hits the ground. Gravitational field strength = 9.8 N/kg.

Speed = ... m/s

[Total 5 marks]

3 Two children, A and B, fire identical 10.0 g ball bearings from a catapult. The elastic band of each catapult is elastically extended by 0.10 m and then released to fire the ball bearings.

3.1 Child A's elastic band has a spring constant of 144 N/m. Calculate the energy transferred to the kinetic energy store of child A's ball bearing. Use an equation from the Equations List.

Energy = ... J

[2]

3.2 The initial speed of child B's ball bearing is twice as fast as child A's ball bearing. Calculate the spring constant of child B's elastic band. Give your answer to 2 significant figures.

Spring constant = ... N/m

[5]

[Total 7 marks]

Topic P1 — Energy

Specific Heat Capacity

Which of the following is the correct definition of specific heat capacity? Tick **one** box.

The energy transferred when an object is burnt. ☐

The maximum amount of energy an object can store before it melts. ☐

The energy needed to raise 1 kg of a substance by 10 °C. ☐

The energy needed to raise 1 kg of a substance by 1 °C. ☐

PRACTICAL

1   **Figure 1** shows the apparatus used by a student to investigate the specific heat capacities of various liquids. She measured out 0.30 kg of each substance, then supplied 15 kJ of energy to each sample using an immersion heater. She then recorded her results, shown in **Table 1**.

Figure 1

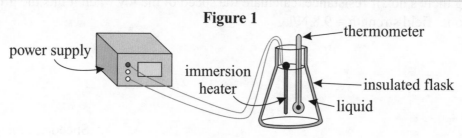

Table 1

Liquid	Mass (kg)	Temperature change (°C)	Specific heat capacity (J/kg °C)
A	0.30	12	4200
B	0.30	23	2200
C	0.30	25	....

1.1   Complete **Table 1** by calculating the specific heat capacity of Liquid C.
Use an equation from the Equations List.

[3]

1.2   Describe the energy transfers that occur when a liquid is heated using the equipment in **Figure 1**.

....

....

....

....

[4]

[Total 7 marks]

Target AO3

2 A student is testing three materials, A, B and C, to find their specific heat capacities. **Grade 7-9**

He heats a 100 g block of each material using an electric heater. The heater is connected to a joulemeter, which measures the amount of energy transferred to the block.
The student measures the temperature of each block for every 250 J of energy transferred.
Each block of material is wrapped in a layer of silicone foam while it is heated.

2.1 The student says, "Putting foam around the blocks while they are heated will improve the accuracy of my results." State whether the student is correct. Explain your answer.

....

....

....
[2]

A graph of the student's results for the three materials is shown in **Figure 3**.

Figure 3

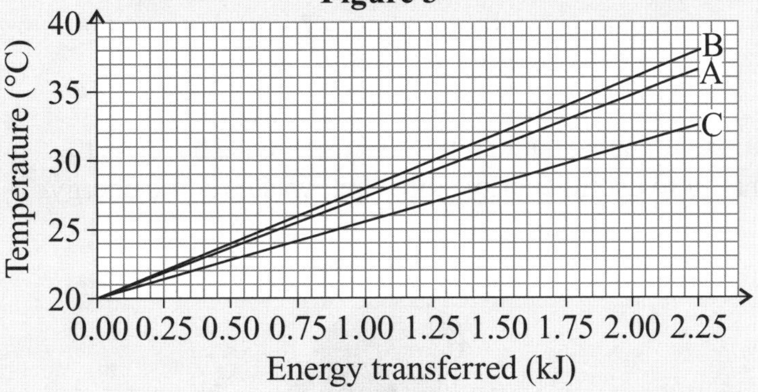

2.2 Using the graph, determine the material with the greatest specific heat capacity. Explain your answer.

....

....

....

....

....
[3]

2.3 Explain how the student can determine whether his results are valid.

....

....

....
[2]

[Total 7 marks]

Exam Tip

You may be asked to analyse the effect that using a particular piece of equipment, or method of measurement, will have on the quality of the experiment. It might help to think through how you've seen it used in other experiments.

Topic P1 — Energy

Conservation of Energy and Power

Choose from the words on the left to fill in the blanks in the sentences on the right. You do not need to use all of the words.

joules   work done

total   minimum

energy lost   rate of   watts

Power is the .... energy transfer or

.... It is measured in ....

1   An electric fan wastes some energy by transferring it to the thermal energy stores of its surroundings. Describe what is meant by 'wasted energy'.

Grade 4-6

....

....

....

[Total 1 mark]

2   **Figure 1** shows a rechargeable battery-powered shaver. The shaver transfers some energy to useful energy stores and wastes some energy.

Grade 4-6

Figure 1

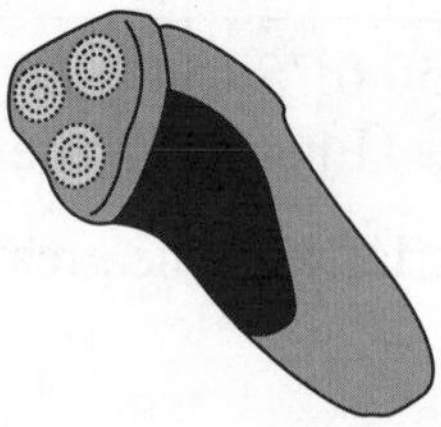

2.1   Which statements about energy are false? Tick **two** boxes.

Energy can be transferred usefully. ☐

Energy can be created. ☐

Energy can be stored. ☐

Energy can be dissipated. ☐

Energy can be destroyed. ☐

[1]

2.2   Give **one** example of a useful energy store and **one** of a wasted energy store that the shaver transfers energy to.

Useful energy store: ....

Wasted energy store: ....

[2]

2.3   Describe what effect increasing the power of the shaver would have on the shaver's battery life.

....

[1]

[Total 4 marks]

3 A student is investigating the insulating properties of various materials. He surrounds a beaker of water with each material, before heating the water using an electric immersion heater with a constant power of 35 W.

Grade 6-7

3.1 Write down the equation that links power, work done and time.

....
[1]

3.2 Calculate the work done by the immersion heater when it is operated for 600 s.

Work done = ... J
[2]

3.3 Whilst investigating the insulating properties of cotton wool, the student forgets to measure the time that he leaves the immersion heater on for. Calculate the time that the heater was on for, if it transferred 16 800 J of energy to the system.

Time = ... s
[2]

[Total 5 marks]

4 A car contains a worn out engine with a power of 32 000 W. The car takes 9.0 s to accelerate from rest to 15 m/s. A mechanic replaces the engine with a more powerful but otherwise identical one. The new engine has a power of 62 000 W.

Grade 7-9

4.1 Explain how the new engine will affect the time it takes for the car to accelerate from rest to 15 m/s.

....

....

....

....
[3]

4.2 Calculate how long it will take for the car to accelerate to 15 m/s now. You can assume that the total amount of energy wasted whilst the car is accelerating is the same for both engines.

Time = ... s
[3]

[Total 6 marks]

Exam Tip

For really big powers, you might see the unit kW, which stands for kilowatt. Don't let this put you off though, you just need to remember that 1000 W = 1 kW. You might see this in a few other units too, for example 1000 m = 1 km.

Topic P1 — Energy

Reducing Unwanted Energy Transfers

1 **Figure 1** shows a thermal image of a house. Different parts of the outside of the house are at different temperatures. The owner wants to keep the inside of the house as warm as possible.

Figure 1

Key

14 °C

5 °C

1.1 Suggest where the highest rate of unwanted energy transfer occurs in the house.

....

[1]

1.2 Suggest **one** way to reduce this unwanted energy transfer.

....

....

[1]

1.3 A second house is tested and it is found that the majority of its unwanted energy transfers occur around the doors and windows. Suggest **two** ways to reduce these energy transfers.

1. ....

2. ....

[2]

[Total 4 marks]

2 A builder is building an energy-efficient house.

She has four brick brands to choose from for the walls, shown in **Table 1**.

Table 1

Brand	Thermal conductivity (m²/s)	Brick thickness (cm)
A	5.2×10^{-7}	10
B	5.2×10^{-7}	15
C	2.7×10^{-7}	10
D	2.7×10^{-7}	15

Based on the information in **Table 1**, explain which brick brand she should use.

....

....

....

....

[Total 4 marks]

Exam Tip

Some questions, like those in Question 1, will ask you to give a specific number of answers to that question. It's worth remembering that you won't get more marks for giving extra information. Give the answers you need to and move on.

Topic P1 — Energy

3 **Figure 2** shows an old-fashioned well. The handle is turned, which rotates the axle. This causes the rope attached to the bucket to wrap around the axle, raising the bucket from the well.

Figure 2

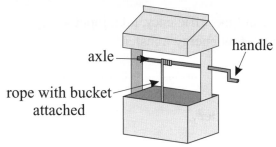

A student measures the time taken to raise a bucket of water from the well. After lubricating the axle of the well, the student repeats the test and finds the time taken is shorter. Explain why.

....

....

....

....

....

[Total 3 marks]

4 A student investigates which type of window is the best at reducing unwanted energy transfers. The student places different samples of windows on a hot plate and measures how long it takes for the top surface of the window sample to reach 30 °C.

Figure 3

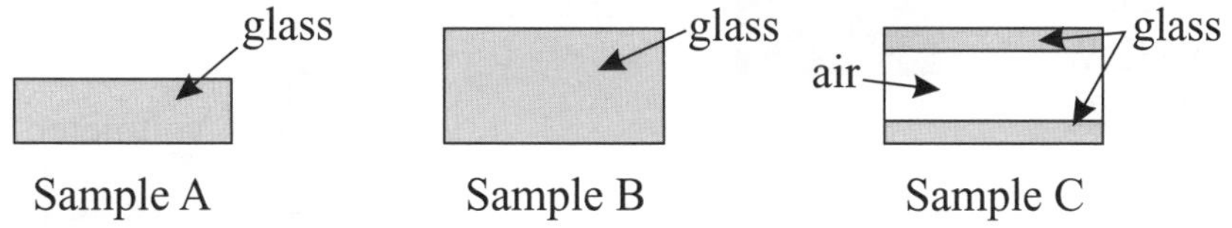

glass   glass   glass   Thermal conductivity

air   glass = 0.2 W/mK

Sample A   Sample B   Sample C   air = 0.03 W/mK

Figure 3 shows the cross-sections of each window sample. Rank them from best to worst for reducing unwanted energy transfers from a house. Explain your choices.

Best: ....   Second best: ....   Worst: ....

....

....

....

....

....

....

[Total 5 marks]

Topic P1 — Energy

Efficiency

1   20 kJ of energy is transferred to a mobile phone battery to fully charge it once it has lost all charge. It transfers 16 kJ of useful energy during use until it needs to be recharged.   *(Grade 4-6)*

1.1   Write down the equation that links efficiency, total input energy transfer and useful output energy transfer.

....

[1]

1.2   Calculate the efficiency of the battery.

Efficiency = ...

[2]

[Total 3 marks]

2   An electric motor has a useful power output of 57 W and an efficiency of 75%. Calculate the total power input for the motor.   *(Grade 4-6)*

Input power = ... W

[Total 3 marks]

3   A student investigates the efficiency of a scale model of an electricity generating wind turbine using the equipment in **Figure 1**.   *(Grade 6-7)*

The student changes the number of sails on the turbine and measures the power output from the turbine's generator. The air blower is supplied with 533 W and has an efficiency of 0.62.

Figure 1

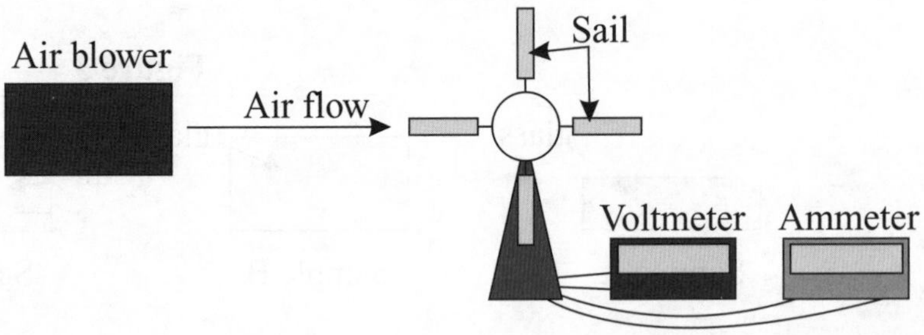

3.1   When using two sails, the efficiency of the turbine was 13%. Calculate the power generated. Give your answer to 2 significant figures.

Output power = ... W

[4]

3.2   Suggest **two** ways the student could increase the efficiency of the turbine.

1. ....

2. ....

[2]

[Total 6 marks]

Target AO3

4 A student is investigating whether the efficiency of a kettle varies with the volume of water in the kettle.

The kettle automatically switches off when the water in the kettle reaches its boiling point.
The student carries out the following method:
1. Fill the kettle with 500 ml of 20 °C water.
2. Calculate the mass of the water, and calculate the energy that should be required to raise the temperature of the water from 20 °C to 100 °C (the useful energy output).
3. Turn on the kettle, and allow it to boil the water and automatically switch off.
4. Measure and record the energy transferred to the kettle whilst it was on using a joulemeter.
5. Allow the kettle to cool, and then repeat steps 1-4 for different volumes of water.

4.1 Suggest **one** way the student could improve the experiment.

....

....

[1]

4.2 At one point during the experiment, the student forgets to allow the kettle to cool before carrying out a measurement for a new volume of water. Explain how this will affect their results.

....

....

....

[2]

The student records the useful energy output from the kettle for each volume of water and the energy transferred to the kettle (the total energy input) in **Table 1**.

Table 1

Volume of water (cm³)	660	1000	1330	1660	2000
Total energy input (MJ)	0.212	0.302	0.388	0.474	0.547
Useful energy output (MJ)	0.168	0.252	0.336	0.420	0.504

4.3 Before the experiment, the student predicted that the kettle would be more efficient for smaller volumes of water. Are the results consistent with this prediction? Explain your answer.

....

....

....

....

....

[4]

[Total 7 marks]

Exam Tip

For experiments with a detailed method, take the time to read through the individual steps before you tackle the question. You might also find it helpful to underline key information and data so that you can find it more easily later on.

Topic P1 — Energy

Energy Resources and Their Uses

Write the resources below in the correct place in the table to show whether they are renewable or non-renewable energy resources.

bio-fuel   oil

        coal

                hydroelectricity

    solar

            wind

                    nuclear fuel

    tidal   geothermal

                        gas

        wave power

Renewable	Non-renewable

1 Describe the difference between renewable and non-renewable energy resources. `Grade 4-6`

....

....

[Total 2 marks]

2 Most cars run on petrol or diesel, which are both derived from fossil fuels. `Grade 4-6`

2.1 Name the **three** fossil fuels.

....

[1]

2.2 Give **two** other everyday uses for fossil fuels.

1. ....

2. ....

[2]

2.3 Some modern cars are powered by bio-fuels. What are bio-fuels?

....

....

[1]

2.4 Suggest **one** reason why car manufacturers are developing cars that are powered by alternative fuels to petrol and diesel.

....

....

[1]

[Total 5 marks]

3   A UK university is considering ways to reduce their energy bills. They are considering building either a single wind turbine nearby, or installing solar panels on top of their buildings. By commenting on the change of seasons throughout the year, suggest why the university may decide to install both wind turbines and solar panels.

Grade 6-7

....

....

....

....

[Total 5 marks]

4   An energy provider is looking to replace their old fossil fuel power plant. They are eligible for a government grant, so the initial building costs are negligible.

Grade 7-9

4.1* The energy provider is interested in building a power plant that uses renewable energy resources. They have narrowed their choice to either a hydroelectric power plant or a tidal barrage. Compare generating electricity from hydroelectricity and tides, commenting on their reliability and their impact on the environment.

....

....

....

....

....

....

[4]

4.2* An alternative is replacing the old power plant with a new power plant that is run on fossil fuels. Discuss the advantages and disadvantages of using fossil fuels to generate electricity.

....

....

....

....

....

....

....

....

....

[6]

[Total 10 marks]

Topic P1 — Energy

Trends in Energy Resource Use

1   **Figure 1** shows the energy resources used to generate electricity in a country.

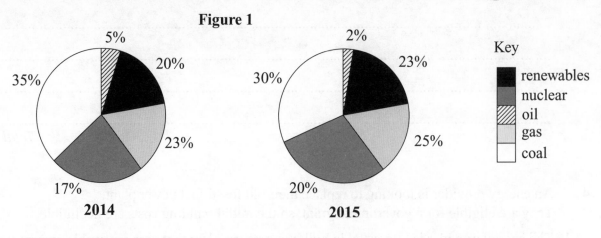

Figure 1

2014

2015

Key

- ■ renewables
- ▨ nuclear
- ▨ oil
- ▨ gas
- □ coal

1.1   Determine what percentage of the country's electricity was generated by fossil fuels in 2014.

.........................%

[2]

1.2   Suggest **one** trend you can determine from the graphs in **Figure 1**.

....

[1]

[Total 3 marks]

2*   In the UK, the use of renewable energy resources is increasing, but many say it is not increasing at a fast enough rate. Suggest reasons for this increase in the use of renewable energy resources. Suggest and explain the factors that may affect the speed at which we use more renewable energy resources.

....

....

....

....

....

....

....

....

....

....

....

[Total 6 marks]

Current and Circuit Symbols

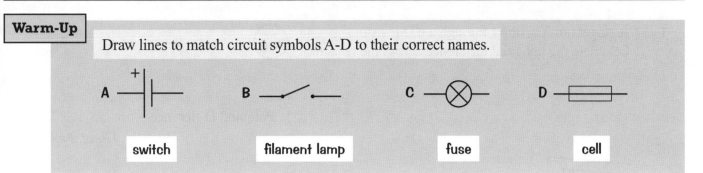
Figure 1

1   **Figure 1** shows a simple circuit, featuring a 10 Ω resistor.

1.1 Explain why there is no current in the circuit.

....
                                                                                                    [1]

1.2 Use a word from the following list to complete the sentence below:

charge	potential difference	resistance	frequency

Current is the rate of flow of ....

                                                                                                    [1]
                                                                                            [Total 2 marks]

2   **Figure 2** shows two ammeters, A_1 and A_2, in a circuit.
     The reading on A_1 is 0.5 A.

Figure 2

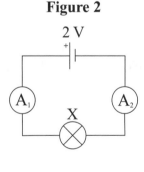

2.1 What is the reading on A_2?

                    Current = ... A
                                        [1]

2.2 State the equation that links electric charge, time and current.

....
                                                                                                    [1]

2.3 Calculate the charge that flows through component **X** in 2 minutes. Give the unit in your answer.

                    Charge = ... Unit = ...
                                                                                                    [3]
                                                                                            [Total 5 marks]

Resistance and V = IR

1   A current of 3 A flows through a 6 Ω resistor.
    Calculate the potential difference across the resistor.

Potential Difference = ...V

[Total 2 marks]

2   A student investigated how the resistance of a piece of wire depends on its length.
    The circuit she used is shown in **Figure 1**. Her results are displayed in **Table 1**.

Figure 1

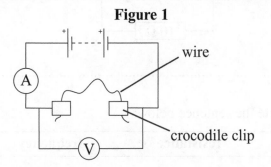

Table 1

Length / cm	Resistance / Ω
10	0.6
20	1.3
30	1.7
40	2.4
50	3.0

2.1   Describe how the student could have used the apparatus in **Figure 1** to obtain the results in **Table 1**.

    ....

    ....

    [2]

2.2   Plot a graph of the data in **Table 1** on the grid
      shown in **Figure 2**. Label the axes correctly.
      Draw a line of best fit on the graph.

      [4]

Figure 2

2.3   State **one** conclusion the student can
      make about the relationship between
      the resistance of a wire and its length.
      Explain how **Figure 2** shows this.

      ....

      ....

      ....

      ....

      [2]

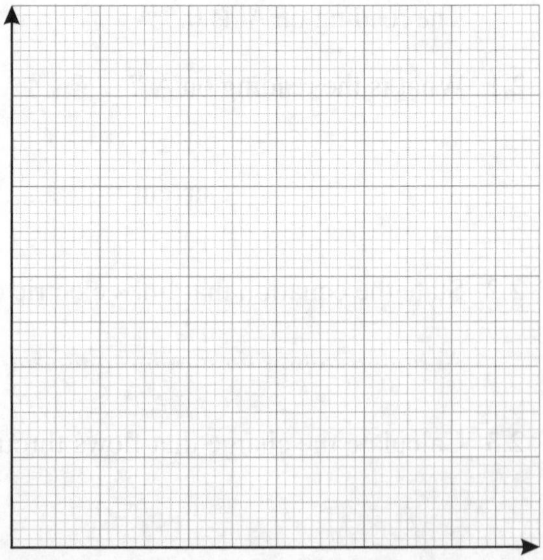

[Total 8 marks]

Exam Tip

Always use a sharp pencil to both plot your data and draw your line of best fit. It will make it easier for you to draw
your line accurately, as well as making it easier for the examiner to check that all of your points are in the right places.

Topic P2 — Electricity

Resistance and I-V Characteristics

1 **Figure 1** shows some graphs of current against potential difference. *(Grade 4-6)*

1.1 Tick the box below the correct graph for a resistor at constant temperature.

Figure 1

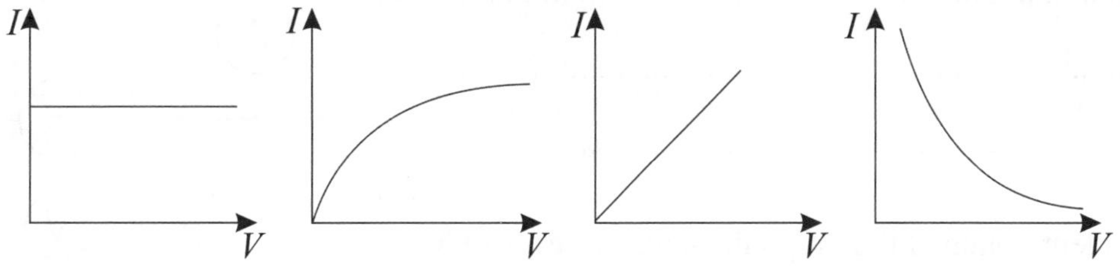

A ☐   B ☐   C ☐   D ☐

[1]

1.2 Name the type of graph shown in **Figure 1**.

....

[1]

1.3 Use words from the following list to complete the sentences below:

linear	non-linear	non-ohmic	ohmic

A resistor at a constant temperature is an example of a(n) ....

conductor. It is also an example of a(n) .... component.

[2]

[Total 4 marks]

2 This question is about diodes. *(Grade 6-7)*

2.1 Draw the standard circuit symbol for a diode.

[1]

2.2 An old name for a diode is a valve. A valve in a bicycle pump only lets air flow through
it in one direction. In what way do diodes behave in a similar way to valves?

....

[1]

2.3 A student measured the resistance of a diode using an electric circuit. He found the resistance
to be 0.02 Ω. The next day he measured the diode again. This time he measured the resistance
to be 100 MΩ. Suggest why the student's measurements were so different.
You may assume that the circuit is working perfectly on both occasions.

....

....

[2]

[Total 4 marks]

PRACTICAL

3   A student used the circuit in **Figure 2** to find the *I-V* characteristic of a filament lamp.

3.1   Explain the purpose of the variable resistor in the circuit.

Figure 2

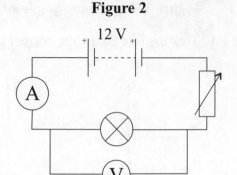

....

....

....

....
                                                                          [2]

3.2   The student obtained the graph displayed in **Figure 3**.
      Use the graph to find the resistance of the lamp at 3 A.

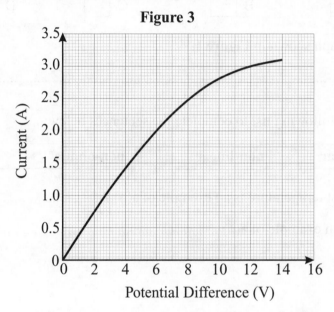

Resistance = ... Ω
                                                                          [4]

3.3   What does the graph tell you about the lamp's resistance as the current increases?
      Explain why the resistance behaves in this way.

....

....
                                                                          [2]

3.4   The student states that the lamp behaves as an ohmic conductor up to a potential difference of
      approximately 3.5 V. Explain what has led the student to this conclusion.

....

....
                                                                          [2]
                                                                [Total 10 marks]

Exam Tip

If you're asked a question about a required practical, think about how you would conduct that experiment in real life.
It won't always be just the method you need to think about too. You should also consider how the experiment should be
set up, what safety precautions you might need to take, or what errors you need to account for as part of the experiment.

Topic P2 — Electricity

Target AO3

4   A student creates a test circuit containing a diode, as shown in **Figure 4**.

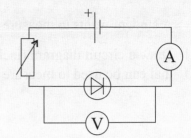

4.1 Describe a method the student could use to investigate how the resistance of the diode changes with current.

....

....

....

....

....

....

....

....

[3]

The student carries out the experiment and plots her results on a graph, shown in **Figure 5**.

Figure 5

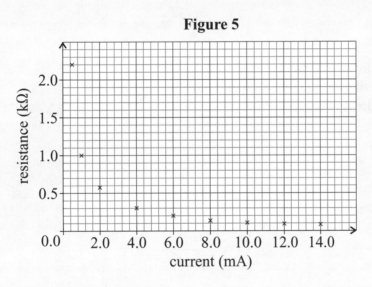

4.2 Draw a curve of best fit on **Figure 5**.

[1]

4.3 The student states, "From my results, I can conclude that the greater the magnitude of the current through the diode, the lower the resistance." Explain why the student cannot make this conclusion from her results.

....

....

....

....

[2]

[Total 6 marks]

Circuit Devices

1 A student wants to measure the resistance of a light dependent resistor.

1.1 Draw a circuit diagram (including an ammeter and a voltmeter)
that can be used to measure the resistance of an LDR.

[3]

The resistance of an LDR changes depending on its surroundings.

1.2 State what happens to the resistance of an LDR as the surrounding light intensity increases.

....

[1]

1.3 Give **one** example of a device that uses a light dependent resistor.

....

[1]

[Total 5 marks]

2 **Figure 2** shows a circuit that can be used for a light
that lights up when the surface of a cooker is hot.
Describe how the circuit works.

Figure 2

12 V

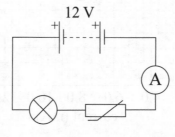

....

....

....

....

....

[Total 4 marks]

Series Circuits

1 **Figure 1** shows a number of circuits.
Tick the box below the diagram that shows **all** the components connected in **series**.

Figure 1

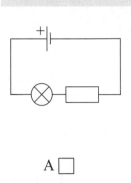 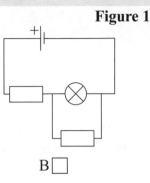 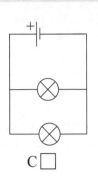 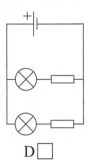

A ☐   B ☐   C ☐   D ☐

[Total 1 mark]

2 In the circuit in **Figure 2**, the reading on the ammeter is 75 mA.

Figure 2

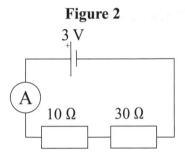

2.1 Calculate the total resistance of the two resistors.

Resistance = ... Ω
[1]

2.2 Find the potential difference across the 30 Ω resistor.

Potential Difference = ... V
[2]

[Total 3 marks]

3 In the circuit in **Figure 3**, the reading on the voltmeter is 2 V.
Component R is a resistor. Find the resistance of R.

Figure 3

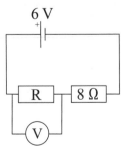

Resistance = ... Ω
[Total 5 marks]

Topic P2 — Electricity

Parallel Circuits

1 Draw a circuit diagram consisting of a cell and two filament lamps connected in parallel. (Grade 4-6)

[Total 1 mark]

2 **Figure 1** shows a circuit with a 6 V supply and 4 Ω and 12 Ω resistors connected in parallel. There are also three ammeters and two voltmeters in the circuit. (Grade 6-7)

Figure 1

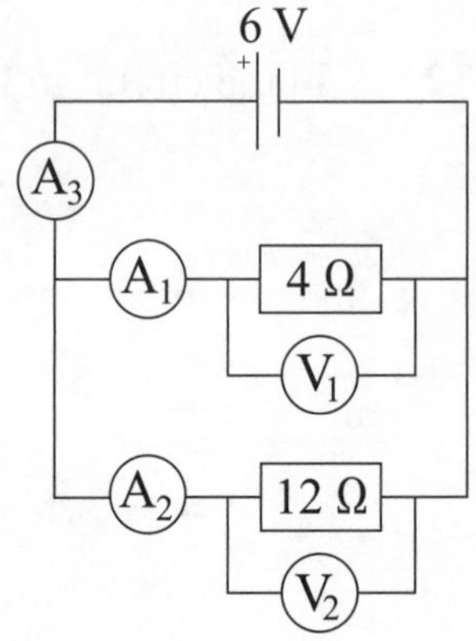

2.1 Determine the readings on voltmeters V_1 and V_2.

Potential difference = ... V
[1]

2.2 Calculate the currents through A_1 and A_2.

A_1 current = ... A, A_2 current = ... A
[5]

2.3 Calculate the current from the supply as measured by A_3.

A_3 = ... A
[1]

[Total 7 marks]

3* Explain why adding resistors in series increases the total resistance, whilst adding resistors in parallel decreases the total resistance. (Grade 7-9)

....

....

....

....

....

....

....

[Total 6 marks]

Exam Tip

It's really easy to accidentally hit a wrong key on your calculator when you're under exam conditions. If you've got the time, it's definitely worth having a few goes at each calculation just to check that you get the same answer each time.

Investigating Resistance

1 A student is investigating how adding identical fixed resistors in series affects the resistance of the circuit. **Figure 1** shows his results.

Figure 1

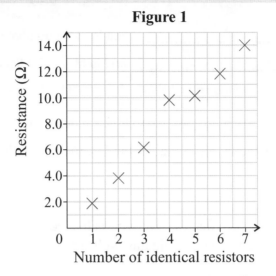

1.1 The student made a mistake when plotting his results. Draw a line of best fit for the student's data on **Figure 1**. Use this to predict the correct resistance for the incorrectly plotted result.

Resistance = ... Ω

[2]

1.2 The student repeats his experiment, this time using 1 Ω resistors.
Draw the predicted line of best fit for the results of this experiment on the axes in **Figure 1**.

[2]

[Total 4 marks]

2* A student wants to investigate how adding fixed resistors in parallel affects the overall resistance of a circuit. Describe an experiment the student could do to investigate this. You may draw a circuit diagram as part of your answer.

....

....

....

....

....

....

....

....

[Total 6 marks]

Electricity in the Home

Warm-Up

Use the words given to complete the sentences about the wires in three-core cables.

| green and yellow | 0 | 230 | brown |

The live wire is .... and is at a potential difference of .... V.

The earth wire is .... and is at a potential difference of .... V.

---

1   A toaster is connected to the mains electricity supply using a three-core cable.   (Grade 6-7)

1.1   State the frequency and potential difference of the UK mains supply.

....

[2]

1.2* The toaster cable has a fault such that the live wire is in electrical contact with the neutral wire. Explain why the toaster will not work while this fault remains.

....

....

....

....

[4]

[Total 6 marks]

---

2   The cable that connects an iron to the mains supply has become worn with use. There is no insulation covering part of the live wire. The iron is plugged in, but switched off.   (Grade 6-7)

2.1   State **two** purposes of the insulation that covers the live wire.

....

....

[2]

2.2   A man switches on the iron and touches the exposed live wire. He receives an electric shock. With reference to the electrical potential of the man, explain why he receives an electric shock.

....

....

....

[3]

2.3   The socket is switched off and the iron is unplugged. Explain whether there is still a danger of the man receiving an electric shock from the plug socket.

....

....

....

[3]

[Total 8 marks]

Power of Electrical Appliances

1 Use the correct words from the following list to complete the sentences below. *(Grade 4-6)*

| current | power | in total | per second | potential difference | safety |

The .... of an appliance is the energy transferred ....

Energy is transferred because the .... does work against the appliance's resistance.

[Total 3 marks]

2 A child is playing with a toy car. The car is powered by a battery and has two speed settings — fast and slow. *(Grade 6-7)*

2.1 The child sets the speed to slow and drives the car for 20 seconds. The power of the car at this speed is 50 W. Write down the formula that links energy, power and time.

....

[1]

2.2 Calculate the energy transferred by the car.

Energy transferred = ... J

[2]

2.3 The child now sets the speed to fast. The power of the car at this speed is 75 W.
Explain why the battery runs down more quickly when the car is set at a higher speed.

....

....

[2]

[Total 5 marks]

3 **Table 1** shows some data for two different cycles of a washing machine. *(Grade 7-9)*

Table 1

Cycle	Power	Time needed
Standard Mode	600 W	125 minutes
Economy Mode	400 W	160 minutes

3.1 Name the **two** main useful energy transfers that take place in the washing machine.

....

....

[3]

3.2 Calculate the work done by the washing machine per minute
when the machine is in Economy Mode.

Work done = ... J

[2]

3.3 Calculate the energy saved per cycle by using Economy Mode instead of Standard Mode.

Energy saved = ... J

[4]

[Total 9 marks]

Target AO3

4   A student wants to measure the useful power output of a motor.

The student has the following equipment she can use in an experiment:
- a motor, attached to an axle
- a power supply and basic circuitry
- a length of string
- a clamp and clamp stand
- a metre ruler
- a stopwatch
- a 1 kg mass

4.1* Describe an experiment that the student could perform to determine
the useful power output of the motor, using the equipment listed.

....

....

....

....

....

....

....

....

....

....

....

[4]

Figure 1 shows the display of the stopwatch when the
student takes a time measurement during her experiment.
The time recorded was 18.5 s.

Figure 1

4.2 State the smallest increment of time the stopwatch can measure.

....

[1]

4.3 Suggest why any errors in the student's time measurements are likely
to be larger than the smallest increment of time that can be measured by the stopwatch.

....

....

[2]

[Total 7 marks]

Exam Tip

Question 4.1 is an example of a question with different levels of response. These questions tend to be worth more marks
than the other questions in the exam, so it's worth learning how to answer them properly. It's a good idea to plan how
you're going to structure your answer first rather than jumping straight in, so you make sure you cover all the key points.

Topic P2 — Electricity

More on Power

Use the words below to fill in the gaps in the passage about energy in a circuit.

work   resistance   energy   decreases

A power source supplies .... to a charge.

When a charge passes through a component with .... ,

it does .... , so the charge's energy ....

---

1   **Figure 1** shows a circuit. The reading on the voltmeter is 6 V and the reading on the ammeter is 2 A. This means 2 coulombs of electric charge pass through the ammeter every second. *(Grade 6-7)*

Figure 1

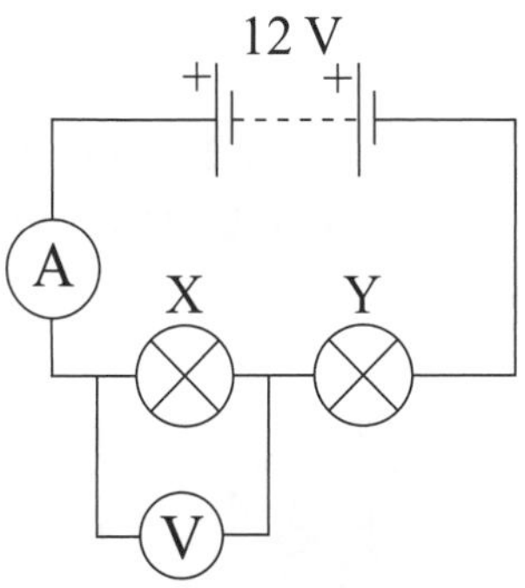

1.1   Write down the equation that links potential difference, charge and energy transferred.

....
[1]

1.2   Calculate the energy transferred to lamp X when 2 C of charge passes through it.

Energy transferred = ... J
[2]

1.3   Explain why multiplying the current through lamp X by the potential difference across it will give you the same value as in 1.2.

....

....

....
[3]

[Total 6 marks]

2   Fans use a motor to turn a set of blades. *(Grade 7-9)*

2.1   A 75 W ceiling fan in an office is powered by the mains supply at 230 V. Calculate the current supplied to the fan.

Current = ... A
[2]

2.2   A smaller fan on someone's desk runs from a computer's USB port. It has a power of 2.5 W, and draws a current of 0.50 A. Calculate its resistance.

Resistance = ... Ω
[2]

[Total 4 marks]

Topic P2 — Electricity

The National Grid

1   The national grid uses **transformers** to transfer energy efficiently.   (Grade 4-6)

1.1   Which **two** of the following quantities are changed by a transformer? (Assume the transformer is 100% efficient.) Put ticks in the boxes next to the correct answers.

☐ Power   ☐ Potential Difference   ☐ Current   ☐ Resistance

[2]

1.2   Describe the difference in the function of a step-up and a step-down transformer.

....

[1]

[Total 3 marks]

2   **Figure 1** shows a diagram of part of the national grid which transfers energy from a power station to a home.   (Grade 6-7)

Figure 1

Power Station → Transformer A → Power Cables → Transformer B → Home

2.1   What types of transformer are transformers A and B?

Transformer A = ...

Transformer B = ...

[2]

2.2* Explain how transformer A helps to improve the efficiency of the national grid.

....

....

....

....

....

....

[4]

2.3   Explain the purpose of transformer B.

....

....

[2]

[Total 8 marks]

Exam Tip

You don't need to understand how a transformer works, just what they're used for and the difference between them.

Topic P2 — Electricity

The Particle Model and Motion in Gases

Warm-Up

The images below show the particles in a substance when it is in three different states of matter.
Label each image to show whether the substance is a solid, a liquid or a gas.

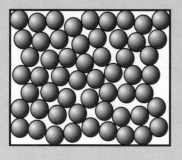   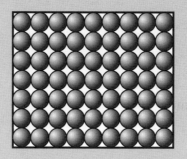   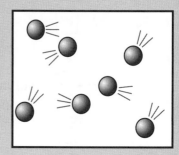

....

1   Use words from the box below to complete the passage. You can use
    each word **more than** once and you do not need to use all the words.

potential	maximum	decreases	kinetic	increases	average

When the temperature of a gas increases, the average energy in the .... energy

stores of the gas molecules increases. This .... the .... speed

of the gas molecules. If the gas is kept at a constant volume, increasing the temperature

.... the pressure.

[Total 3 marks]

2   A tyre is pumped up to its maximum volume.   (Grade 4-6)

2.1 Using the particle model, explain what would happen to the tyre pressure
     if more air were pumped in, but its volume remained the same.

     ....

     ....

     ....

     [3]

2.2 Explain why the tyre pressure would be higher on a hot day compared to a cold day.

     ....

     ....

     ....

     ....

     [4]

     [Total 7 marks]

3 Each container shown has the same mass of gas inside.
Tick the box below the container with the lowest gas pressure.

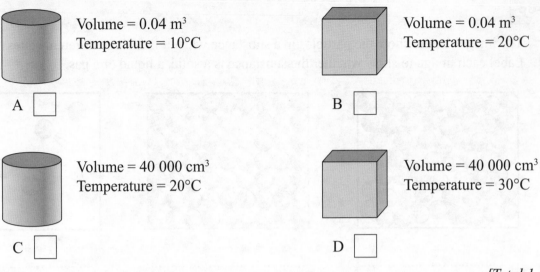

Volume = 0.04 m³
Temperature = 10°C

A ☐

Volume = 0.04 m³
Temperature = 20°C

B ☐

Volume = 40 000 cm³
Temperature = 20°C

C ☐

Volume = 40 000 cm³
Temperature = 30°C

D ☐

[Total 1 mark]

4 **Figure 1** shows a metal box that contains a gas at room temperature. The box has two lids
with different areas, that each require the same force in order to be removed from the box.
The box is heated using a hot plate. The temperature of the gas inside the box keeps rising
until, at a certain temperature, one of the lids will pop off the top of the box.

Figure 1

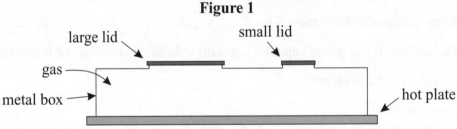

Explain why increasing the temperature of the gas causes a lid to pop off the box.
State which of the two lids will pop off first.

....

....

....

....

....

....

....

....

[Total 5 marks]

Topic P3 — Particle Model of Matter

 ☐ ☐ ☐

Density of Materials

1 A 0.5 m³ block of tungsten has a mass of 10 000 kg. *(Grade 4-6)*

1.1 Write down the equation that links density, mass and volume.

....

[1]

1.2 Calculate the density of tungsten.

Density = ... kg/m³

[2]

1.3 Calculate the mass of a 0.02 m³ sample cut from the tungsten block.

Mass = ... kg

[2]

[Total 5 marks]

PRACTICAL

2* A student has a mass balance, a measuring beaker and some acetic acid. *(Grade 4-6)*

Describe an experiment the student can carry out to calculate the density of acetic acid, using the equipment listed.

....

....

....

....

....

[Total 4 marks]

PRACTICAL

3 A student uses the apparatus in **Figure 1** to calculate the densities of different rings to determine what materials they are made from. *(Grade 6-7)*

Figure 1

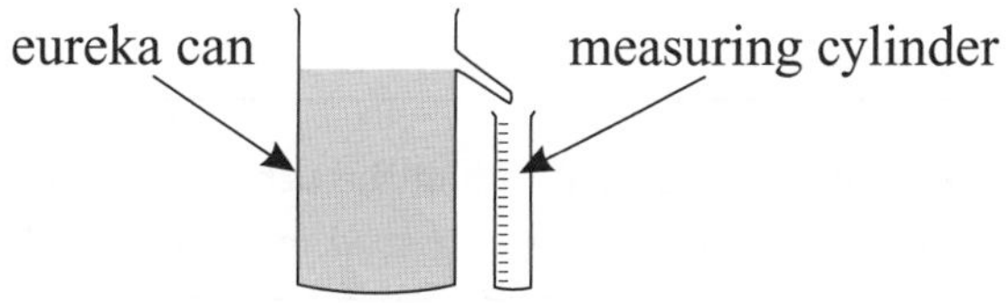

eureka can   measuring cylinder

Topic P3 — Particle Model of Matter

3.1* A eureka can is a beaker with a spout through which overflowing water can escape.
The can is filled up to the spout so that when an object is placed in the can the
displaced water flows into the measuring cylinder.
Describe how the apparatus in **Figure 1** could be used to determine the density of an object.

....

....

....

....

....

[4]

3.2 **Table 1** shows an incomplete table of the student's results.

Table 1

Ring	Mass (g)	Water displaced (ml)	Material
A	5.7	0.30	....
B	2.7	0.60	....
C	3.0	0.30	....

Complete **Table 1** using the following information:
Density of gold = 19 g/cm³   Density of silver = 10 g/cm³   Density of titanium = 4.5 g/cm³

[4]

[Total 8 marks]

PRACTICAL

4   A student investigates the density of an aluminium cola can by submerging it in a
measuring cylinder of water. When completely submerged, a full can of unopened cola
displaces 337 ml of water. The student then empties the can. She finds that it holds
332 ml of cola and that the mass of the empty can is 13.5 g when it is empty.
Calculate the density of aluminium used to make the can.

Grade 6-7

Density = ... g/cm³
[Total 4 marks]

Exam Tip

You might be asked to explain an experiment that's used to find the density of an object. Make sure you know the
different equipment you would need for finding the density of a solid or a liquid and how the results are used.

Topic P3 — Particle Model of Matter

Internal Energy and Changes of State

1 Use words from the box below to complete the passage.
You can only use a word **once** and you do not need to use all the words.

| mass | increases | temperature | density | decreases |

When a system is heated, the internal energy of the system .... This either

increases the .... of the system or causes a change of state. During a change of

state the temperature and .... of the substance remain constant.

[Total 2 marks]

2 A change of state is a physical change. *(Grade 4-6)*

2.1 State the name of the following changes of state:

Gas to liquid: .... Liquid to gas: ....

[1]

2.2 State what is meant by the term 'physical change'.

....

....

[1]

[Total 2 marks]

3 Heating an object increases its internal energy. *(Grade 6-7)*

3.1 State what is meant by the term 'internal energy'.

....

[1]

3.2 Heating an object can increase its temperature.
State **two** things that the increase in a system's temperature depends on.

1. ....

2. ....

[2]

[Total 3 marks]

4 A student fills a test tube with 30 g of water. He heats the water so that it begins to boil
and collects all of the water vapour produced via a tube placed into the bung of the test
tube. After the test tube has cooled, he finds that the mass of the water in the test tube is
now 20 g. State the mass of the water vapour the student collected. Explain your answer. *(Grade 6-7)*

....

....

....

....

[Total 2 marks]

Specific Latent Heat

1 An immersion heater is used to boil 0.50 kg of water in a sealed container. *(Grade 6-7)*

1.1 Define the term 'specific latent heat'.

....

.... *[1]*

1.2 The lid is removed when the water begins to boil. The immersion heater transfers 1.13 MJ of energy to evaporate all of the water. Calculate the specific latent heat of vaporisation of water. Use the equation from the Equations List.

Specific latent heat = ... MJ/kg
[3]

[Total 4 marks]

2 **Figure 1** shows a graph of temperature against time as a substance is heated. *(Grade 7-9)*

2.1 Describe what is happening during the period 3-8 minutes from the beginning of heating.

....

.... *[1]*

2.2 Explain, in terms of particles, why the graph is flat between 3-8 minutes even though the substance is being heated.

....

....

....

.... *[3]*

Figure 1

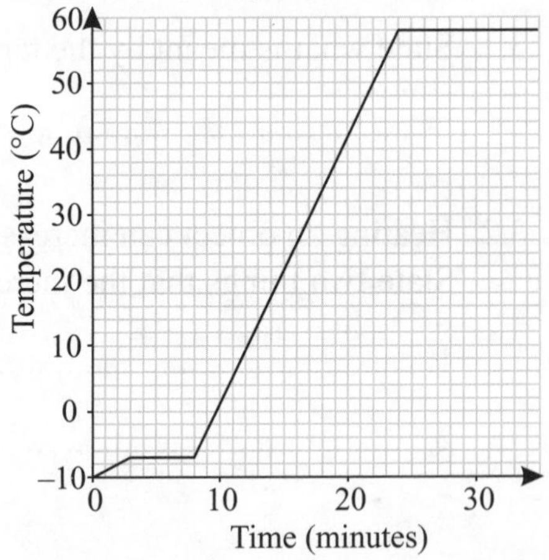

2.3 Give the melting and boiling points of the substance.

Melting point = ... °C   Boiling point = ... °C
[2]

[Total 6 marks]

Exam Tip

Calculation questions in the exam often contain marks for showing your working, such as rearranging equations or converting values into the correct units. This means that, even if your final answer isn't right, you might get a few marks.

Topic P3 — Particle Model of Matter

Target AO3

3   A student is carrying out an experiment to determine how long it takes for ice to melt at room temperature.

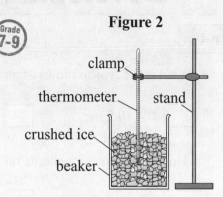

Figure 2

The student used the equipment shown in **Figure 2**. The beaker contains 0.05 kg of crushed ice. He recorded the temperature of the ice every minute. He stopped the experiment when he first recorded a temperature greater than 0 °C. A graph of his results is shown in **Figure 3**.

Figure 3

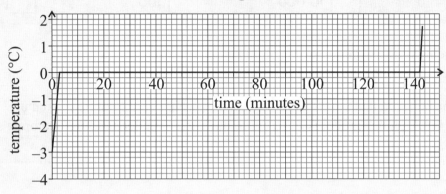

3.1   Give **two** ways the student could improve his experiment.

1. ....

....

2. ....

....

[2]

3.2   The specific latent heat of fusion of water is 334 000 J/kg. Calculate the average rate of energy transfer to the ice from the surroundings while the ice is melting. Use the correct equation from the Equations List.

rate of energy transfer = ... J/s

[4]

3.3   The student repeats the experiment with a single 0.05 kg ice cube and gets different results. He states, "This shows that my original experiment wasn't repeatable." Is the student correct? Explain your answer.

....

....

....

[2]

[Total 8 marks]

Topic P3 — Particle Model of Matter

Developing the Model of the Atom

Warm-Up

What is the typical radius of an atom?

☐ 1×10^{-10} m   ☐ 1×10^{10} m   ☐ 1×10^{-20} m   ☐ 1×10^{-15} m

How many times smaller is the radius of a nucleus than the radius of the atom?

☐ 10   ☐ 10 000   ☐ 100   ☐ 1000

1   Our understanding of the structure of the atom has changed significantly since the early 19th century. *(Grade 4-6)*

1.1   In 1804, Dalton believed that atoms were tiny spheres which could not be broken up. State one way in which this model is different to our current understanding of atomic structure.

....

[1]

1.2   The alpha particle scattering experiment provided evidence for the nuclear model of the atom. Name and describe the model that it replaced.

....

....

[2]

1.3   What did the work of James Chadwick prove the existence of around 20 years after the atomic nucleus became an accepted scientific theory?

....

[1]

[Total 4 marks]

2   Niels Bohr discovered that electrons within an atom can only exist with defined energy levels. *(Grade 4-6)*

2.1   Describe how an electron can move between energy levels.

....

....

....

[2]

2.2   Name the type of particle created when an atom loses or gains electrons.

....

[1]

2.3   What is the charge on one of these particles if it is created by an atom losing an electron?

....

[1]

[Total 4 marks]

3* State **two** discoveries about atomic structure which arose from the alpha particle scattering experiment. In each case, state the observation that led to the discovery.

Grade 6-7

....

....

....

....

....

....

....

[Total 4 marks]

4 **Table 1** is an incomplete table showing the relative charges of the subatomic particles in an atom.

Grade 6-7

Table 1

Particle	Proton	Neutron	Electron
Relative charge	....	....	−1

4.1 Complete **Table 1**.

[2]

4.2 Describe how these subatomic particles are arranged in the atom.

....

....

....

[2]

4.3 An iron atom has 26 protons.
State the number of electrons in the atom and explain your reasoning.

....

....

....

[3]

[Total 7 marks]

Exam Tip

Remember that nothing is ever completely certain — just look at John Dalton and his ideas about atomic structure. New experiments are taking place all the time and they can completely change our models and theories. Make sure you can describe how the nuclear model has changed and how this illustrates the fact that our theories can always change.

Topic P4 — Atomic Structure

Isotopes and Nuclear Radiation

Draw a line from each form of radiation to show how ionising it is.

gamma   alpha   beta

moderately ionising   weakly ionising   strongly ionising

1 Some isotopes are unstable. They decay into more stable isotopes by emitting nuclear radiation. *(Grade 4-6)*

1.1 What is the name of this process?

....
[1]

1.2 Describe what is meant by isotopes of an element.

....

....
[2]

1.3 Some nuclear radiation is ionising. Define ionisation.

....
[1]

1.4 An unstable isotope releases a particle made up of two protons and two neutrons from its nucleus. Name this type of decay.

....
[1]

[Total 5 marks]

2 An isotope which emits alpha radiation is used in the circuit of a house's smoke detector. Ionising radiation can be damaging if the human body is exposed to it. *(Grade 6-7)*

Explain why the use of ionising radiation in the smoke detector does not pose a threat to the health of people living in the house.

....

....

....

....
[Total 2 marks]

3 One isotope of sodium is $^{23}_{11}$Na. **Grade 6-7**

3.1 Write down the mass number of this isotope.

....
[1]

3.2 Calculate the number of neutrons in the sodium nucleus.

Number of neutrons = ...
[1]

3.3 Which of the following is another isotope of sodium? Tick one box.

$^{11}_{23}$Na ☐ $^{11}_{24}$Na ☐ $^{23}_{12}$Na ☐ $^{24}_{11}$Na ☐
[1]

3.4 An isotope of neon is $^{23}_{10}$Ne. Explain whether or not the charge on the neon isotope's nucleus is different to the charge on the nucleus of the sodium isotope.

....

....

....
[2]
[Total 5 marks]

4* Ionising radiation is used to detect leaks in pipes that are buried just below the ground. An unstable isotope is introduced to one end of the pipe and, above the ground, a radiation detector is moved along the path of the pipe. **Grade 7-9**

Explain how this method can be used to identify the location of a leak in the pipe, and suggest what type of radiation the isotope should emit.

....

....

....

....

....

....

....

....

....
[Total 6 marks]

Exam Tip

If you're asked about uses of the different kinds of radiation, then think about their properties (how ionising they are, how far they travel etc.). Then just apply what you know to the situation — if you're trying to detect something from a long way away or through a thick barrier, then you want something which has a long range. Simple really...

Topic P4 — Atomic Structure

Target AO3

5   An engineer is investigating how the thickness of paper placed between a source of beta radiation and a detector affects the amount of radiation that reaches the detector.

The engineer uses a Geiger-Muller tube to measure the amount of radiation emitted from the source that makes it through different thicknesses of paper. The results of the engineer's experiment are recorded in **Table 1**.

Table 1

thickness of paper (mm)	count-rate detected (cps)				Uncertainty (cps)
	Trial 1	Trial 2	Trial 3	Mean (to nearest whole number)	
0.2	161	157	169	162	6.0
0.3	145	150	136	144	7.0
0.4	129	122	142	131	10.0
0.5	99	122	105	109	....
0.6	93	95	98	....	2.5
0.7	85	89	81	85	4.0
0.8	67	69	74	70	3.5

5.1   Complete **Table 1** by filling in the missing values.

[2]

5.2   The engineer states that the count-rate data recorded for 0.6 mm thick paper is the most precise and the most accurate data. State and explain whether the engineer is correct.

....

....

....

[2]

5.3   Write a conclusion for the engineer's experiment based on the data in **Table 1**.

....

....

[1]

5.4   The half-life of a radioactive substance is the time taken for the count-rate from the substance to reduce to half its initial value. Explain why it is important that the source of beta radiation used in this experiment has a half-life that is much longer than the duration of the experiment.

....

....

....

[2]

[Total 7 marks]

Topic P4 — Atomic Structure

Nuclear Equations

1 An electron is emitted from a nucleus. *(Grade 6-7)*

1.1 State the effect this has on the charge of the nucleus.

....

[1]

1.2 Explain the effect that this has on both the mass number and atomic number of the nucleus.

....

....

....

[3]

1.3 After emitting the electron, the atom is excited. It gets rid of excess energy by emitting a gamma ray. What effect does this have on the charge and mass of the nucleus?

....

[1]

[Total 5 marks]

2 A student writes down the following nuclear decay equation: $^{234}_{90}\text{Th} \longrightarrow {}^{234}_{91}\text{Pa} + {}^{0}_{0}\gamma$ *(Grade 7-9)*

2.1 Explain how you know that this equation is incorrect.

....

[1]

2.2 The student has missed out one other particle which is formed during this decay. Write down the symbol for this particle, including its atomic and mass numbers.

....

[1]

2.3 Radium (Ra) has atomic number 88. The isotope radium-226 undergoes alpha decay to form radon (Rn). Write a nuclear equation to show this decay.

....

[3]

2.4 The radon isotope then undergoes alpha decay to form an isotope of polonium (Po), which undergoes alpha decay to form an isotope of lead (Pb). Calculate the number of neutrons in the nucleus of this lead isotope.

Number of neutrons = ...

[3]

[Total 8 marks]

Topic P4 — Atomic Structure

Half-life

1 The graph in **Figure 1** shows how the count-rate of a radioactive sample changes over time.

1.1 Define the term 'half-life' in terms of count-rate.

....

....
[1]

Figure 1

1.2 Using **Figure 1**, determine the half-life of the sample.

Half-life = ... s
[1]

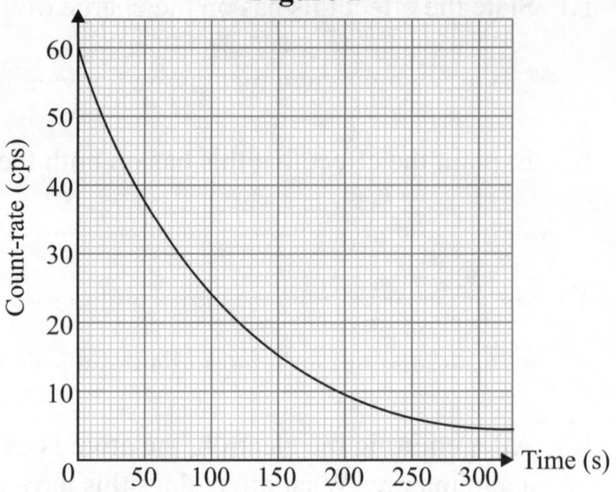

1.3 Initially, the sample contains approximately 800 undecayed nuclei.
Predict how many of these nuclei will have decayed after two half-lives.

Decayed nuclei = ...
[2]

1.4 After two half-lives, what is the ratio of the number of undecayed nuclei left to the initial number of undecayed nuclei? Tick **one** box.

1:2 ☐   2:1 ☐   1:4 ☐   4:1 ☐

[1]

[Total 5 marks]

2 **Table 1** shows data about two radioactive sources.

Table 1

	Isotope 1	Isotope 2
Number of undecayed nuclei	20 000	20 000
Half-life	4 minutes	72 years

Explain which isotope will have the highest activity initially.

....

[Total 1 mark]

Exam Tip

If you come across a half-life question in the exam, and you're given a graph, it should look similar to the one in Figure 1. The numbers will change from example to example, but if you can understand that curve, you'll be halfway there.

3 The activity of a radioisotope is 8800 Bq. After 1 hour and 15 minutes, the activity has fallen to 6222 Bq. A further 1 hour and 15 minutes after that, the activity has fallen to 4400 Bq.

3.1 Calculate the radioisotope's half-life. Give your answer in minutes.

Half-life = ... minutes

[1]

3.2 Calculate the activity of the isotope after a total time of 6 hours and 15 minutes has passed. Give your answer to 2 significant figures.

Activity = ... Bq

[2]

[Total 3 marks]

4 A radioactive sample has a 50 second half-life. The initial activity of the sample is 120 Bq.

4.1 Complete the graph in **Figure 2** to show how the activity will change in the first 150 seconds.

Figure 2

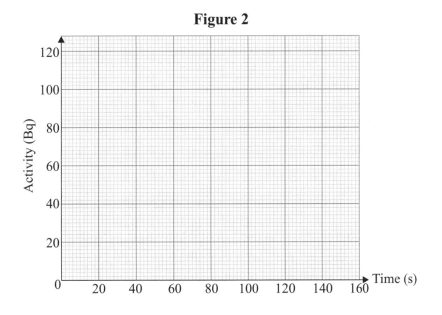

[3]

4.2 Use your graph to predict the activity of the sample after 40 seconds.

Activity = ... Bq

[1]

4.3 Calculate a prediction of the activity after 250 s.
Explain why this prediction is less likely to be correct than your prediction in 4.2.

....

....

....

[3]

[Total 7 marks]

Topic P4 — Atomic Structure

Irradiation and Contamination

1 Workers in a nuclear power station take many precautions to prevent unnecessary exposure to radiation. Suggest **two** methods that could be used to reduce their exposure to radiation when dealing with highly radioactive substances.

(Grade 4-6)

1. ....

2. ....

[Total 2 marks]

2 A scientist is reviewing the safety procedures to be used in her lab. She is concerned about **contamination** and **irradiation**.

(Grade 6-7)

2.1 Explain the difference between contamination and irradiation.

....

....

....

....

[2]

2.2 Give **two** ways in which the scientist can protect herself against contamination when handling a radioactive sample with a low activity.

1. ....

2. ....

[2]

[Total 5 marks]

3* Radium-226 is an alpha source that was used in clocks until the 1960s to make the hands and numbers glow. Explain whether a clockmaker should be more concerned about irradiation or contamination when repairing old clocks that contain radium.

(Grade 7-9)

....

....

....

....

....

....

....

....

[Total 6 marks]

Contact and Non-Contact Forces

Write each word below in the table on the right to show whether it is a scalar or vector quantity.

acceleration   time   temperature

mass   weight   force

Scalar	Vector

1   Which of the following correctly defines a vector? Tick **one** box.   (Grade 4-6)

Vector quantities only have magnitude.   ☐

Vector quantities show direction but not magnitude.   ☐

Vector quantities have both magnitude and direction.   ☐

Vector quantities are a push or pull on an object.   ☐

[Total 1 mark]

2   A child is pulling a toy train along the floor by a piece of string.
State **one** contact force and **one** non-contact force that acts on the toy.   (Grade 6-7)

Contact force: ....

Non-contact force: ....

[Total 2 marks]

3   **Figure 1** shows a pair of identical magnets. There is a force of repulsion between them.   (Grade 6-7)

Figure 1

Magnet A   Magnet B

| S | | N | | N → | | S |

3.1   Complete the diagram in **Figure 1** by drawing another arrow representing the force that magnet B exerts on magnet A.

[2]

3.2   Magnet B is replaced by a much stronger magnet but magnet A remains the same.
Describe how you would redraw the arrows on the diagram to show this new force interaction.

....

....

[2]

[Total 4 marks]

Weight, Mass and Gravity

1   Use words from the box below to complete the passage.
    You can only use a word **once** and you do not need to use all the words. Grade 4-6

| weight   kilograms   mass   directly   inversely   newtons   newton metres |

.... is the amount of matter in an object. .... is

a force due to gravity. Mass is measured in .... whilst weight is

measured in .... The weight of an object is ....

proportional to its mass.

[Total 3 marks]

2   What is meant by the term 'centre of mass'? Grade 4-6

   ....

   ....

[Total 1 mark]

3   The Opportunity rover is a robot which is currently on the surface of the planet Mars. Grade 6-7
    The total mass of the Opportunity rover and its landing parachute is 350 kg.

3.1 Write down the equation that links weight, mass and gravitational field strength.

   ....

[1]

3.2 Calculate the total weight of the Opportunity rover and its parachute when it was on the Earth.
     (The gravitational field strength of the Earth = 9.8 N/kg.)

Weight = ... N

[2]

3.3 When Opportunity landed on Mars it left behind its parachute and moved away to explore.
     The mass of the parachute was 209 kg. Calculate the weight of Opportunity without its
     parachute on Mars. (The gravitational field strength of Mars = 3.8 N/kg.)
     Give your answer to 3 significant figures.

Weight = ... N

[3]

[Total 6 marks]

Exam Tip

Outside of physics, people often use the term weight when they mean mass. Make sure you get the differences straight
in your head. You measure mass in on a set of scales, but weight is a force measured by a spring-balance (newtonmeter).

4 A student is doing an experiment to determine the gravitational field strength on Earth.

To do this, the student intends to measure the weight of a set of iron standard masses.
Each standard mass is labelled with its mass, which is used as the value of mass in the experiment.

4.1 One of the standard masses is heavily rusted.
Suggest why this mass shouldn't be used in the experiment.

....

....

[1]

To measure the weight of a mass, the
mass is placed on a small plastic tray
that is hung from a newtonmeter,
as shown in **Figure 1**. The force
displayed on the newtonmeter is then
recorded as the weight of the mass.

Figure 1

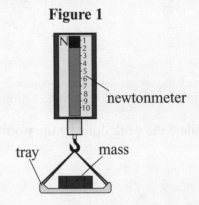

newtonmeter

4.2 State the type of error that is introduced
to the results by using this method.
Explain how this error is caused.

tray   mass

....

....

[2]

4.3 The student carries out the experiment, and records their results in **Table 1**.
Plot the student's results on the grid shown in **Figure 2**, and draw a line of best fit.

Table 1

Mass (kg)	Weight (N)
0.2	2.2
0.3	3.2
0.4	4.2
0.5	5.0
0.6	6.4
0.7	7.2
0.8	8.2

Figure 2

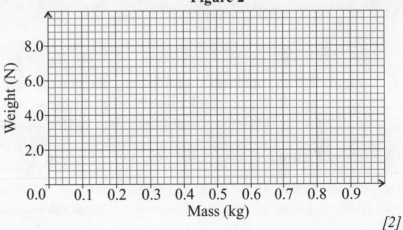

[2]

4.4 Calculate a value for the gravitational field strength using the graph in **Figure 2**.

Gravitational field strength = ... N/kg

[3]

[Total 8 marks]

Topic P5 — Forces

Resultant Forces and Work Done

1   **Figure 1** shows four runners who are running in windy weather.
Tick the box under the runner who is experiencing the largest resultant force.

Figure 1

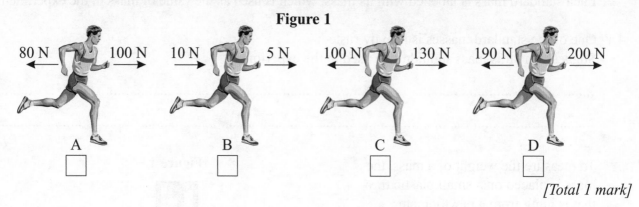

80 N ← → 100 N   A ☐

10 N → 5 N →   B ☐

100 N ← 130 N →   C ☐

190 N ← 200 N →   D ☐

[Total 1 mark]

2   A woman pulls a 20 kg suitcase along a 15 m corridor using a horizontal force of 50 N.

2.1   Calculate the work done by the woman. Give the correct unit.

Work done = ... Unit = ...
[3]

2.2   Work has to be done against frictional forces acting on the wheels of the suitcase.
Explain the effect this has on the temperature of the suitcase.

....

....
[2]

[Total 5 marks]

3   **Figure 2** shows an incomplete free body diagram of a ladder leaning
against a wall. There is no friction between the ladder and the
wall but there is friction between the ladder and the ground.

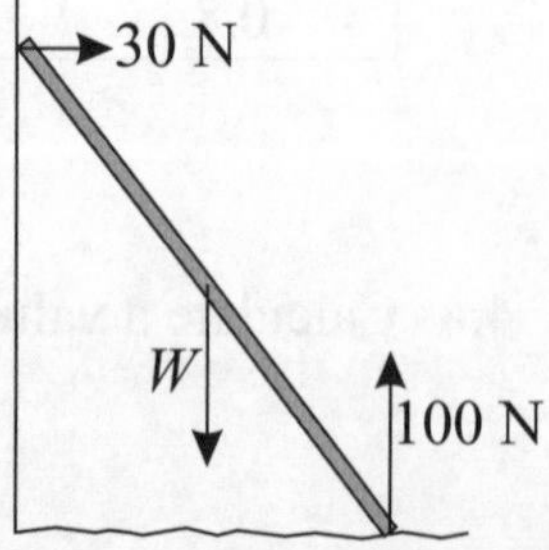

3.1   Using **Figure 2**, determine the weight of the ladder, W.

Figure 2

Weight = ... N
[1]

3.2   Complete **Figure 2** by drawing the missing frictional force.

→30 N

[2]

[Total 3 marks]

W↓   ↑100 N

Calculating Forces

Find the horizontal and vertical components of the force shown on the right. Each side of a square equals 1 N.

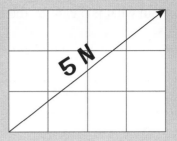

Horizontal component = ... N

Vertical component = ... N

1 **Figure 1** shows a girl on a swing. Her weight of 500 N acts vertically downwards and a tension force of 250 N acts on the ropes at an angle of 30° to the horizontal.

Figure 1

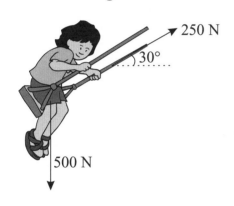

Figure 2

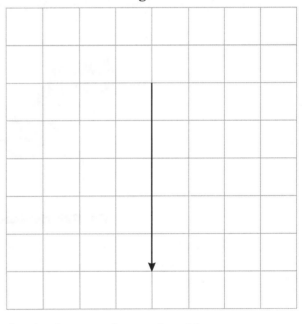

1.1 **Figure 2** shows an incomplete scale drawing for the forces acting on the girl. Only the girl's weight has been drawn so far. Calculate the scale used in the drawing.

.... cm = ... N

[1]

1.2 Complete the scale drawing in **Figure 2** to find the magnitude of the resultant force acting on the girl.

Magnitude = ... N

[2]

[Total 3 marks]

Topic P5 — Forces

Forces and Elasticity

1 Deformations can be elastic or inelastic. **Grade 4-6**

1.1 Explain what is meant by the terms elastic deformation and inelastic deformation.

....

....

....

....

[2]

1.2 Stretching is one way in which forces can deform an object. State **two** other ways.

....

[1]

[Total 3 marks]

2 A student investigates the change in height of a toy horse in a playground, shown in **Figure 1**, when different people sit on it. **Grade 7-9**

Figure 1

2.1 When a child weighing 250 N sits on the toy horse in **Figure 1**, his feet don't touch the floor. The height of the toy horse decreases by 20 cm. Calculate the spring constant of the spring. Give the correct unit.

Spring constant = ... Unit = ...

[3]

2.2 The child gets off and then the student's teacher then sits on the toy horse. Her weight is double that of the child. The student predicts that the height of the toy horse will change by 40 cm. Explain whether or not you agree with the student. State any assumptions you have made.

....

....

....

[2]

[Total 5 marks]

Investigating Springs

1   A student carried out an investigation to study the relationship between the force exerted on and the extension of a spring. He hung different numbers of 1 N weights from the bottom of the spring and measured the extension of the spring with a ruler, as shown in **Figure 1**.

Figure 1

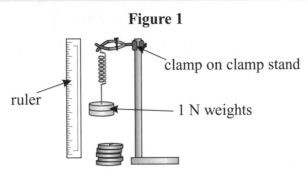

clamp on clamp stand

ruler

1 N weights

Table 1

Force (N)	Extension (cm)
0	0
1	4.0
2	8.0
3	12.0
4	15.9
5	21.6
6	30.0

Figure 2

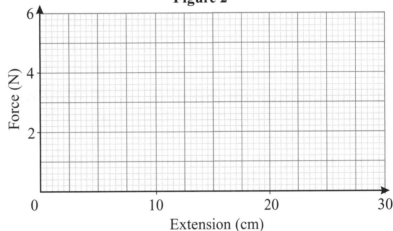

1.1   **Table 1** shows the results that the student obtained in his investigation.
Draw the force-extension graph for the student's results on the axes in **Figure 2**.

[3]

1.2   Using the graph you have drawn, calculate the spring constant of the spring being tested.

Spring constant = ... N/m
[2]
[Total 5 marks]

2   Calculate the work done on a spring when it is extended elastically by 8.0 cm. The spring constant of the spring is 25 N/m.

Work done = ... J
[Total 2 marks]

Topic P5 — Forces

Distance, Displacement, Speed and Velocity

Warm-Up

Choose from the words on the left to fill in the blanks on the right. Use each word once.

distance
velocity
vector
scalar

Displacement and .... are both .... quantities. This means they have both a size and a direction. Speed and .... are both .... quantities. They do not depend on direction.

1 **Figure 1** shows the path taken by a football kicked by a child. When it is kicked at Point A, the ball moves horizontally to the right until it hits a vertical wall at Point B. The ball then bounces back horizontally to the left and comes to rest at Point C. *(Grade 4-6)*

Figure 1

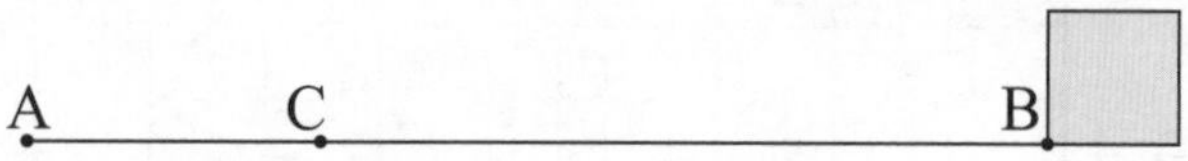

A   C   B   Scale 1 cm = 1 m

1.1 What is the distance that the ball has moved through from A to B?

Distance = ... m

[1]

1.2 What is the total distance that the ball has moved through from A to C?

Distance = ... m

[1]

1.3 Draw a vector arrow on **Figure 1** to show the displacement of the ball.

[1]

1.4 What is the magnitude of the displacement of the ball after it has come to rest?

Displacement = ... m

[1]

[Total 4 marks]

2 The speed of sound varies depending upon the substance it is travelling through. State the speed of sound in air. *(Grade 4-6)*

....

[Total 1 mark]

3 Give **three** factors that can affect a person's walking, running or cycling speed. *(Grade 4-6)*

....

....

[Total 3 marks]

4 Explain whether a satellite orbiting the Earth at 3.07 x 10³ m/s has a constant velocity. **Grade 6-7**

....

....

[Total 2 marks]

5 A man has just got a new job and is deciding whether to walk, cycle or take a bus to get to work. There are two routes he could take. The shorter route is along a 6 km path that only pedestrians and cyclists are allowed to use. The bus takes a longer route along a road. **Grade 6-7**

5.1 Write down the formula that links distance travelled, speed and time.

....

[1]

5.2 Estimate how long it would take the man to walk the pedestrian route.

Time taken = ... s

[3]

5.3 Estimate how much time would be saved if the man cycled this route instead.

Time saved = ... s

[4]

5.4 Travelling to work by bus takes 20 minutes.
The total distance covered during this time is 9.6 km.
Calculate the average speed of the bus.

Average speed = ... m/s

[3]

[Total 11 marks]

6 The speed at which an aircraft flies is often expressed in terms of its Mach number, which describes the speed in relation to the speed of sound. For example, Mach 2 is twice the speed of sound. A commercial airliner on a long-haul flight has a speed of Mach 0.8. The temperature of the air is typically –60 °C. **Grade 7-9**

The speed of sound is temperature dependent and can be found using:

Speed of sound in m/s = 331 + 0.6T, where T is the temperature in °C.

Calculate the distance travelled by the jet over 5.0 × 10⁴ s.

Distance travelled = ... km

[Total 4 marks]

Topic P5 — Forces

Acceleration

Draw one line from each scenario to the typical acceleration for that object.

A sprinter starting a race	10 m/s²
A falling object	2 × 10⁵ m/s²
A bullet shot from a gun	1.5 m/s²

1   Briefly describe the motion of a decelerating object.

....

[Total 1 mark]

2   **Table 1** shows how the speed of a car changes with time as it accelerates uniformly.

Table 1

Time (s)	0	1	2	3
Speed (m/s)	0	4	8	12

2.1 Write down the formula that links acceleration, velocity and time.

....

[1]

2.2 Calculate the acceleration of the car.

Acceleration = ... m/s²
[2]
[Total 3 marks]

3   A car accelerates uniformly at 2.5 m/s² from rest to a speed of 20 m/s. Calculate the time taken for the car to reach 20 m/s.

Time = ... s
[Total 3 marks]

4   A train travelling at 32 m/s slows down to 18 m/s over a distance of 365 m. Calculate the deceleration of the train over this distance. Use an equation from the Equations List.

Deceleration = ... m/s²
[Total 2 marks]

Topic P5 — Forces

Distance-Time and Velocity-Time Graphs

1 A boat is being rowed along a straight canal. Some students use a watch to time how long after setting off the boat passes marker posts spaced 100 metres apart. **Table 1** shows their results.

Table 1

Distance (m)	0	100	200	300	400	500
Time (s)	0	85	165	250	335	420

Figure 1

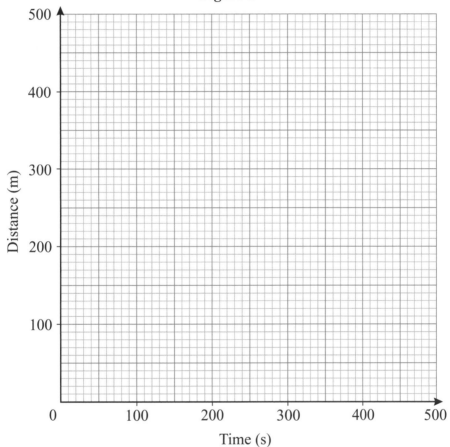

1.1 Draw the distance-time graph for the results in **Table 1** on the axes shown in **Figure 1**.

[3]

1.2 Using the graph in **Figure 1**, determine how far the boat travelled in 300 s.

Distance = ... m

[1]

1.3 Determine how long it took the boat to travel 250 m.

Time = ... s

[1]

1.4 Suggest **one** way to make the timings made by the students more accurate.

....

....

[1]

[Total 6 marks]

Topic P5 — Forces

2 **Figure 2** shows the distance-time graph for a cyclist's bike ride.

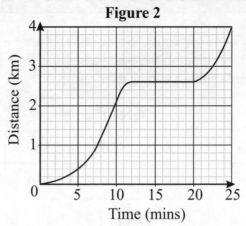

Figure 2

2.1 Use **Figure 2** to determine how long the cyclist rode for before stopping for a rest.

....

[1]

2.2 Describe the cyclist's motion in the first five minutes of her journey.

....

[1]

[Total 2 marks]

3 **Figure 3** shows the distance-time graph for a car's journey.

Figure 3

3.1 Use **Figure 3** to find the speed of the car 5 s into its journey.

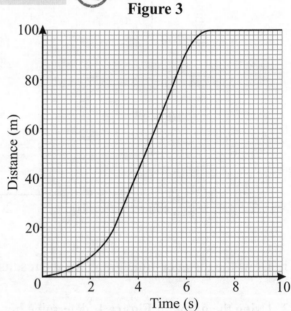

Speed = ... m/s

[3]

3.2 Use **Figure 3** to find the speed of the car 2 s into its journey.

Speed = ... m/s

[3]

[Total 6 marks]

Exam Tip

It's important to be accurate when you're asked to use a graph to find an answer. These questions do tend to include a bit of margin for error, but be careful. A small misread could cause you to end up with a significantly different answer.

4   **Figure 4** shows an incomplete velocity-time graph for a roller coaster ride.

Figure 4

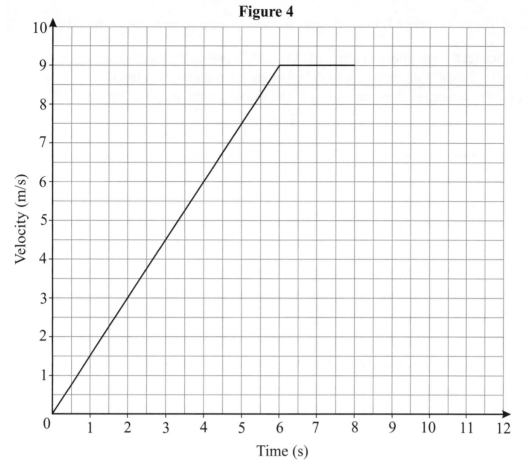

4.1 After 8 seconds, the roller coaster decelerates at an increasing rate.
     It comes to rest 4 seconds after it begins decelerating.
     Complete the velocity-time graph in **Figure 4** to show this.

[2]

4.2 Calculate the acceleration of the roller coaster during the first 6 seconds of the ride.

Acceleration = ... m/s^2

[2]

4.3 Calculate the distance travelled by the ride between 0 and 8 s.

Distance = ... m

[4]

4.4 Calculate the distance travelled during the entire ride to the nearest metre.

Distance = ... m

[5]

[Total 13 marks]

Topic P5 — Forces

Target AO3

5 A teacher did an experiment to investigate the top speed of a remote-controlled car.

The teacher set the car going in a straight line at full power, and measured
the speed of the car with time as it travelled along a straight 120 m track.
The results of his experiment are shown in the velocity-time graph in **Figure 5**.

Figure 5

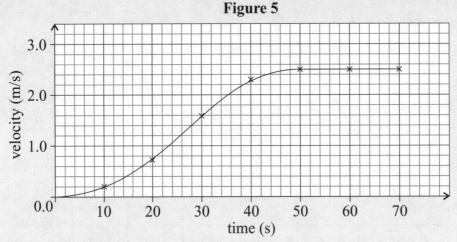

5.1 Using the graph in **Figure 5**, determine the acceleration of the car at 26 s.

Acceleration = ... m/s²

[3]

5.2 A student wants to repeat the teacher's experiment on a smaller scale. She has a 5 m track,
and a lower powered remote-controlled car. She is considering two different methods
for determining the speed of the car as it travels along the track:

- Connect light gates to a data logger. Position a light gate every
  50 cm along the track, and attach a 5 cm square card to the top
  of the car so that it is able to break the light beam of the light gates.
- Attach a ticker tape to the back of the car. The ticker tape is held in a dispenser which marks
  the tape at its opening every 2 s. As the car moves, it pulls the tape out of the dispenser.

Give **one** advantage and **one** disadvantage of **each** method.

....

....

....

....

....

....

....

[4]

[Total 7 marks]

Terminal Velocity

1   Any object falling (in a fluid) for long enough reaches its terminal velocity.   (Grade 4-6)
Which statements correctly describe terminal velocity? Tick **two** boxes.

Terminal velocity is the minimum velocity an object can fall at. ☐

The resultant vertical force on an object falling at its terminal velocity is zero. ☐

The resultant vertical force on an object falling at its terminal velocity equals its weight. ☐

Terminal velocity is the maximum velocity an object can fall at. ☐

[Total 1 mark]

2   A fish is accelerating as it swims through water.   (Grade 4-6)
Which of the following statements about its motion is true?

The resistive force from the water acting on the fish is constant. ☐

The resistive force from the water acting on the fish is increasing. ☐

The resistive force from the water acting on the fish is decreasing. ☐

There is no resistive force from the water acting on the fish. ☐

[Total 1 mark]

3   A student drops a large book and a cricket ball that   (Grade 7-9)
both have the same weight from a tall building.

3.1 Explain why both objects eventually fall at a constant velocity.

....

....

....

....

[3]

3.2 Explain why the terminal velocity of the book is lower than the terminal velocity of the ball.

....

....

....

....

[2]

[Total 5 marks]

Exam Tip

Remember that the acceleration of a falling object is continuously decreasing due to air resistance until it reaches zero.
That means you won't be able to use any of those fancy equations for uniform acceleration that you're used to.

Topic P5 — Forces

Newton's First and Second Laws

1   State Newton's First Law for a stationary object.   (Grade 4-6)

....

....

[Total 1 mark]

2   Use words from the box below to complete the passage. You can only use a word **once** and you do not need to use all of the words.   (Grade 4-6)

area	mass	inversely	directly	resistive	resultant

Newton's Second Law states that the acceleration of an object is ....

proportional to the .... force acting on the object and

.... proportional to the .... of the object.

[Total 3 marks]

3   **Figure 1** shows the horizontal forces acting on a motorbike travelling at a constant velocity.   (Grade 6-7)

Figure 1

3.1   There are two resistive forces acting on the bike.
Suggest what these forces may be.

....

....

[2]

3.2   The engine provides a driving force of 5.0 kN. One of the resistive forces has a magnitude of 3.85 kN. Calculate the size of the second resistive force.

Force = ... N

[1]

[Total 3 marks]

4 A 5.0 kg vase is knocked from a shelf.

4.1 Write down the formula that links force, mass and acceleration.

....

[1]

4.2 Calculate the resultant force acting on the vase as it begins to fall.
Acceleration due to gravity, $g = 9.8$ m/s².

Force = ... N

[2]

[Total 3 marks]

5 A 1450 kg car accelerates uniformly from rest. It reaches 24 m/s in 9.2 s.
Calculate the force needed to cause this acceleration.

Force = ... N

[Total 4 marks]

6 **Figure 2** shows a 7520 kg lorry. The driver spots a hazard ahead and applies
the brakes. The lorry decelerates uniformly and comes to a stop 50 m after
the brakes are applied. Estimate the braking force needed to stop the lorry.

Figure 2

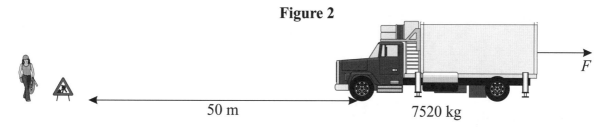

50 m   7520 kg

Force = ... N

[Total 5 marks]

Exam Tip

Watch out for questions talking about constant or uniform acceleration over a distance. They can be tricky and require a
lot of steps. If you're struggling, read the question carefully, pick out the key bits of information and write them all down.
Then look on the equation sheet to see if there are any equations you can use to find the values the question is asking for.

Topic P5 — Forces

Inertia and Newton's Third Law

Which of the following is Newton's Third Law? Tick **one** box.

A non-zero resultant force is needed to cause a change in speed or direction. ☐

A resultant force is inversely proportional to the mass of an object. ☐

When two objects interact, they exert equal and opposite forces on each other. ☐

A resultant force of zero leads to an equilibrium situation. ☐

1 **Figure 1** shows the forces acting on a gymnast in equilibrium balancing on two beams. Grade 4-6

Figure 1

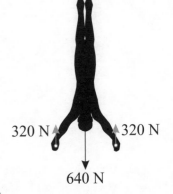

1.1 State the force exerted by each of the gymnast's hands on the balance beams.

Force = ... N
[1]

1.2 State the name of this force.

....
[1]

1.3 State the size of the attractive force exerted on the Earth by the gymnast.

Force = ... N
[1]

[Total 3 marks]

2 Define the following terms: Grade 6-7

2.1 Inertia

....
[1]

2.2 Inertial mass

....
[1]

[Total 2 marks]

Investigating Motion

1   **Figure 1** shows the apparatus used by a student to investigate the effect of varying force on the acceleration of a trolley. The trolley is on a frictionless, flat surface.

Figure 1

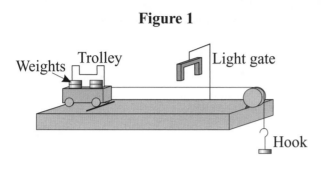

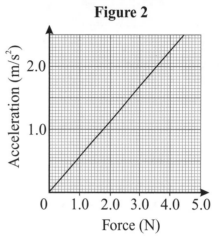

When the hook is allowed to fall, the trolley accelerates. The force acting on, and the acceleration of, the trolley are recorded. The student repeats this process, each time moving a 1.0 N weight from the trolley to the hook. **Figure 2** is a graph of acceleration against force for the trolley.

1.1 Give **one** conclusion that can be made from **Figure 2**.

....

[1]

1.2 Write down the formula that links force, mass and acceleration.

....

[1]

1.3 Calculate the mass of the system from **Figure 2**.

Mass = ... kg

[3]

[Total 5 marks]

2   A second student investigates how the mass of a trolley affects its motion down a fixed ramp. The accelerating force on the trolley is the component of the trolley's weight that acts along the ramp. The student adds masses to the trolley and each time measures its final speed at the bottom of the ramp to calculate its acceleration. Explain why this experiment will not correctly show the relationship between the mass and acceleration of the trolley.

....

....

....

....

....

[Total 2 marks]

Topic P5 — Forces

Stopping Distances

1 Define the following terms: (Grade 4-6)

1.1 Thinking distance

....

[1]

1.2 Braking distance

....

[1]

[Total 2 marks]

2 The thinking distance for a driver in a car travelling at 40 mph is 12 m. The braking distance is 24 m. Calculate the car's stopping distance when it is travelling at 40 mph. (Grade 4-6)

Stopping Distance = ... m

[Total 1 mark]

3 When a vehicle's brakes are applied, energy is transferred away from the kinetic energy stores of the wheels. State what causes this and describe the effect it has on the brakes. (Grade 6-7)

....

....

....

....

[Total 2 marks]

4* Explain the importance of a car having brakes and tyres that are in good condition and the effect this will have on stopping distance and safety. (Grade 6-7)

....

....

....

....

....

....

....

....

....

[Total 6 marks]

Topic P5 — Forces

Reaction Times

1 What is the typical reaction time for a person? (Grade 4-6)

☐ 1.3 – 1.8 s ☐ 0.2 – 0.9 s ☐ 0.01 – 0.02 s ☐ 2.0 – 3.0 s

[Total 1 mark]

2 Give three things that could affect a person's reaction time. (Grade 4-6)

1. ....

2. ....

3. ....

[Total 3 marks]

3 A teacher tests the reaction times of two of her students by measuring (Grade 4-6) how far a ruler falls vertically before the student catches it.

3.1 Describe **one** other method that can be used to test people's reaction times.

....

[1]

3.2 **Table 1** shows the results. The values in the table show the distance the ruler falls in cm during each attempt. Complete the table by working out the average distance fallen by the ruler for each student.

Table 1

	Attempt 1	Attempt 2	Attempt 3	Average
Student A	7.0	7.1	6.9	....
Student B	8.4	8.2	8.3	....

[2]

3.3 Which student has the fastest average reaction time? Give a reason for your answer.

....

[1]

3.4 Suggest **two** ways the teacher could make the experiment a fair test.

....

....

[2]

3.5 The teacher then repeats the experiment. This time, she has a third student talk to the student being tested. Predict how this will affect the reaction times of both students A and B.

....

[1]

[Total 7 marks]

4 Describe the steps involved when using the ruler drop experiment to investigate reaction times. (Grade 6-7)

....

....

....

....

....

....

[Total 5 marks]

5* A man is driving home late at night. He listens to loud music as he drives to keep himself alert. He is impatient to get home so drives quickly. Explain the safety implications of the man's actions. (Grade 6-7)

....

....

....

....

....

....

[Total 4 marks]

6 A student tests his reaction time with a metre ruler using a ruler drop experiment. He catches the metre ruler after it has fallen 45.0 cm. Calculate his reaction time. (Grade 7-9)

The acceleration due to gravity is 9.8 m/s².

Reaction time = ... s

[Total 4 marks]

Exam Tip

For long explanation answers make sure you cover every point mentioned in the question. You won't get all of the marks if you miss out part of what they're asking for, no matter how much you write for the rest of your points.

Topic P5 — Forces

Momentum

Warm-Up

The snippets below show the parts of a description of momentum.
Number each snippet 1 to 5 to show the correct order. The first one has been done for you.

| ...vector quantity and is equal to... | **1** Momentum is a property of... |

| ...moving objects. | ...mass × velocity. | It is a... |

1 A motorbike is travelling at 25 m/s and has 5500 kg m/s of momentum. Grade 4-6

1.1 Write down the equation that links momentum, mass and velocity.

....
[1]

1.2 Calculate the mass of the motorbike.

Mass = ... kg
[3]
[Total 4 marks]

2 **Figure 1** and **Figure 2** show a Newton's cradle. Grade 6-7
All of the balls on the cradle have the same mass.

When a ball is lifted and allowed to hit the
others as shown in **Figure 1**, it causes the last
ball in the line to move outwards, as shown
in **Figure 2**. The balls in between appear to
remain stationary. The velocity of the first
ball when it hits the second ball is equal to the
velocity of the final ball when it starts to move.
Using conservation of momentum, explain this behaviour.

Figure 1   **Figure 2**

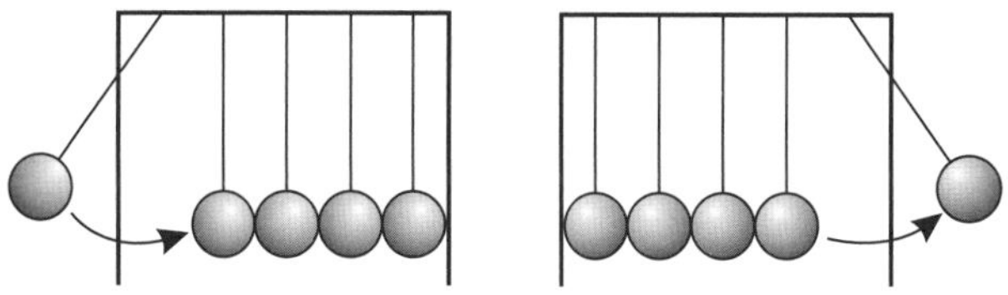

....

....

....

....

....

....
[Total 4 marks]

Exam Tip

Like a lot of topics in Forces, remembering how momentum is calculated can help you to describe and explain it.

Topic P5 — Forces

Transverse and Longitudinal Waves

1   A student produces two types of waves on a spring, A and B, as shown in **Figure 1**.

Figure 1

A 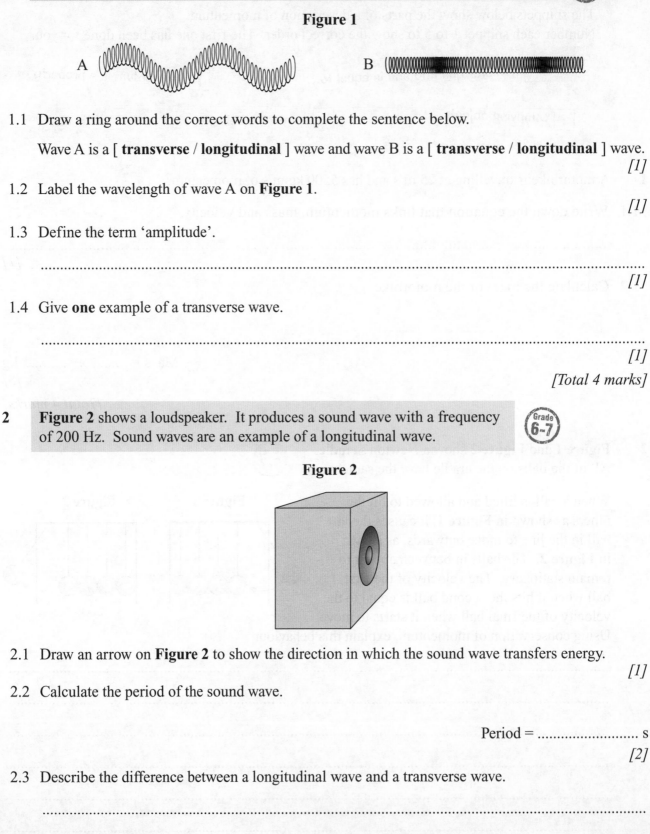   B

1.1   Draw a ring around the correct words to complete the sentence below.

     Wave A is a [**transverse** / **longitudinal**] wave and wave B is a [**transverse** / **longitudinal**] wave.

[1]

1.2   Label the wavelength of wave A on **Figure 1**.

[1]

1.3   Define the term 'amplitude'.

     ....

[1]

1.4   Give **one** example of a transverse wave.

     ....

[1]

[Total 4 marks]

2   **Figure 2** shows a loudspeaker. It produces a sound wave with a frequency of 200 Hz. Sound waves are an example of a longitudinal wave.

Figure 2

2.1   Draw an arrow on **Figure 2** to show the direction in which the sound wave transfers energy.

[1]

2.2   Calculate the period of the sound wave.

                                       Period = ... s

[2]

2.3   Describe the difference between a longitudinal wave and a transverse wave.

     ....

     ....

     ....

[2]

[Total 5 marks]

Experiments with Waves

1 **Figure 1** shows ripples on the surface of some water in a ripple tank. The signal generator producing the ripples is set to a frequency of 12 Hz. A student measures the distance between the first and last visible ripple as 18 cm, as shown in **Figure 1**.

Figure 1

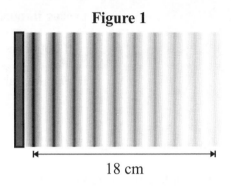

18 cm

1.1 The student finds it difficult to measure the distance because the ripples are moving. Suggest and explain what the student could do to make the measurement easier.

....

....

....

[2]

1.2 Calculate the speed of the ripples in the water.

Speed = ... m/s

[3]

[Total 5 marks]

2* Describe a method to measure the speed of waves on a string. **Grade 7-9**

....

....

....

....

....

....

....

....

....

[Total 6 marks]

Wave Behaviour and Electromagnetic Waves

Warm-Up

At the boundary with a new material, a wave can be reflected, absorbed or transmitted.
Draw a line to match each option to the correct definition.

wave is reflected   it passes through the material unaffected

wave is absorbed   it bounces back off the material

wave is transmitted   it transfers all energy to the material

1   Electromagnetic waves form a continuous spectrum.

1.1   Use words from the box below to complete the following sentences.

a vacuum	glass	sound	longitudinal	transverse	water

All waves in the electromagnetic spectrum are ....

All electromagnetic waves travel at the same speed in ....

[2]

1.2   **Figure 1** shows a graph of intensity against wavelength for two objects at different temperatures.

Name the part of the electromagnetic spectrum that the peak wavelength of object B lies in.

....
[1]

Figure 1

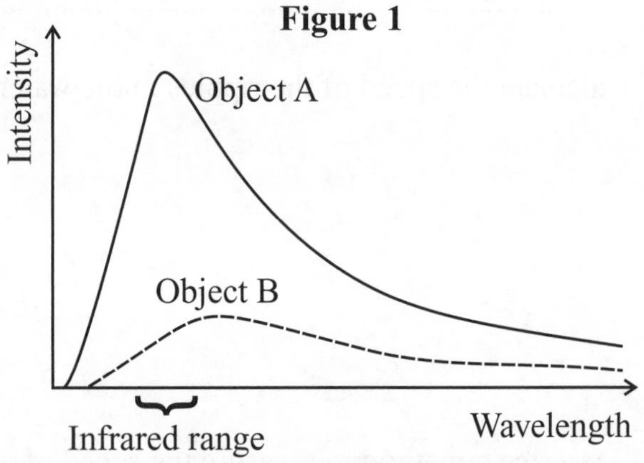

Object A

Object B

Intensity

Infrared range   Wavelength

1.3   The peak wavelength for object A lies within the infrared range of the electromagnetic spectrum.
Describe an example of infrared radiation transferring energy from a source to an absorber.

....

....
[2]

[Total 5 marks]

2   A man is wearing mirrored sunglasses. Anyone looking at him can see their reflection in the glasses but cannot see his eyes. The man can still see through the glasses.

State what happens to the light as it passes from the surroundings to the mirrored sunglasses.

....

....
[Total 2 marks]

Topic P6 — Waves

Refraction

1   **Figure 1** shows wave fronts of light passing from air into glass. As the wave fronts enter the glass they slow down.

Figure 1

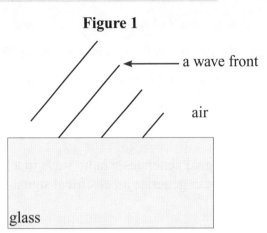

1.1   Complete the diagram in **Figure 1** by completing the wave fronts inside the glass.

[2]

1.2   Draw a ray on **Figure 1** to show how a light ray is refracted as it passes from air into glass. On your diagram, label the incident ray, refracted ray, and normal line.

[3]

[Total 5 marks]

2   A light ray crosses the boundary between two blocks, as shown in **Figure 2**.

Figure 2

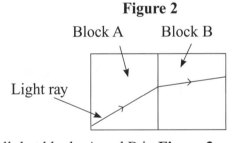

2.1   Explain how you can tell that blocks A and B in **Figure 2** are made from different materials.

....

[1]

2.2   Block B is a made from a type of glass. The light ray passes out of block B into a vacuum. Explain what happens to the direction and speed of the ray as it leaves block B.

....

....

....

[2]

[Total 3 marks]

Exam Tip

Remember — each wave front represents the same point on a wave, so the distance between each is equal to a wavelength.

Topic P6 — Waves

Radio Waves

Tick the appropriate boxes to sort the radio-wave facts from the fiction.

	True	False
Long-wave radio can be transmitted across long distances.	☐	☐
Long-wave radio uses diffraction to follow the curve of the Earth's surface.	☐	☐
Short-wave radio can only be used over short distances.	☐	☐
Radio waves with very short wavelengths do not travel well through obstacles.	☐	☐

1* Describe how an electrical signal generates a radio wave in a TV signal transmitter. Explain how this radio wave can generate an electrical signal in a distant TV aerial. (Grade 6-7)

....

....

....

....

....

....

[Total 4 marks]

2* A family from northern England are on holiday in France. They are unable to listen to their local FM radio station from back home. However, they are still able to listen to the same long-wave radio broadcasts as they do at home. Explain why. (Grade 7-9)

....

....

....

....

....

....

....

....

....

....

[Total 6 marks]

EM Waves and Their Uses

1 A student uses a microwave oven to cook a jacket potato. **(Grade 6-7)**

1.1 Describe how microwaves cook the potato in the microwave oven.

....

....

....

[3]

1.2 The potato is placed in the microwave oven on a glass plate.
Explain why the glass plate does not get hot when the microwave oven is used.

....

....

....

[2]

1.3 State the other type of electromagnetic radiation which is commonly used to cook food.

....

[1]

1.4 Microwaves can also be used to communicate with satellites. Explain why the microwaves used
for communications must have different wavelengths to those used in microwave ovens.

....

....

....

....

....

[4]

[Total 10 marks]

2 A police helicopter has an infrared camera attached to its base. The camera
can be used to detect people trying to hide in the dark. Explain the advantages
of using an infrared camera rather than a normal camera for this purpose. **(Grade 7-9)**

....

....

....

....

[Total 3 marks]

Exam Tip

Describe questions can be worth quite a few marks, so it's important to know how to tackle them in the right way.
Be careful to include all of the key points in your description, otherwise you could throw away crucial marks.

Topic P6 — Waves

More Uses of EM Waves

Sort the EM uses below into the table. Some of the uses may appear in more than one column.

Uses of EM waves

A artificial suntanning

B fibre optic data transmission

C energy efficient light bulbs

D revealing invisible ink

E medical imaging of bones

F cancer treatment

UV Rays	Visible Light	X-rays	Gamma Rays

1 X-rays and gamma rays can both be used in medical imaging. *Grade 6-7*

1.1 Briefly describe how a medical tracer can be used to create an internal body image.

....

....

....

[2]

1.2 Explain why gamma rays are suitable for medical imaging.

....

....

[1]

1.3 Explain how X-rays are used to form images of a patient's skeleton.

....

....

....

....

[3]

1.4 Exposure to both X-rays and gamma rays can be dangerous to humans. Suggest **one** precaution taken by medical workers who use X-rays or gamma rays when imaging patients.

....

[1]

[Total 7 marks]

You may be asked to explain why a given electromagnetic wave is suited to a particular use. So make sure you understand the properties of the different electromagnetic wave types, and know some of their most common uses.

Investigating Infrared Radiation PRACTICAL

1 A student uses a Leslie cube, shown in **Figure 1**, to investigate how different materials radiate energy.
A Leslie cube is a hollow cube whose faces are made out of different materials.

Figure 1

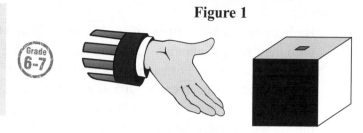

The student fills the cube with hot water and places his hand near to each surface.
He records how warm his hand feels in front of each surface.
The four sides of the cube are matte black, shiny black, matte white and shiny white.

1.1 Predict which side the student's hand would feel warmest in front of.

....

[1]

1.2 Predict which side the student's hand would feel coolest in front of.

....

[1]

1.3 Suggest **one** way to improve the student's experiment.

....

[1]

[Total 3 marks]

2* A student wants to investigate how effective different surfaces are at absorbing radiation. Describe a method the student could use to do this.
Your answer should include ways the student can make his investigation a fair test.

....

....

....

....

....

....

....

....

....

....

....

[Total 6 marks]

Topic P6 — Waves

Target AO3

3 A student is investigating the rate of cooling due to the emission of infrared radiation.

He is investigating 3 different steel cans, A, B and C, of equal size and shape. Can A is painted with matt navy blue paint. Can B is painted with glossy navy blue paint. Can C is painted in glossy white paint. For each can, the student uses the equipment shown in **Figure 2**.
The student fills each can with 500 g of hot water.
Once the water in the can reaches 50 °C,
the student records the temperature of the water.
He then records the temperature of the water
every 30 seconds, for 4 minutes.

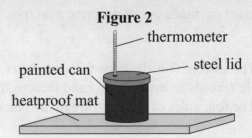

Figure 2

thermometer — steel lid — painted can — heatproof mat

3.1 Identify **three** ways that the student has made sure that the results of the experiment will be valid.

1. ....

....

2. ....

....

3. ....

....

[3]

3.2 Predict the can in which the water will cool fastest. Justify your prediction.

....

....

....

[2]

3.3 The student's results for one can are shown in **Table 1**. His results for the other cans are shown in the graph in **Figure 3**. Plot the results in **Table 1** on **Figure 3**, and draw a curve of best fit.

Table 1

Time (s)	Temperature of water in can (°C)
0	50.0
30	47.0
60	44.5
90	42.5
120	40.5
150	39.5
180	39.0
210	38.5
240	38.0

Figure 3

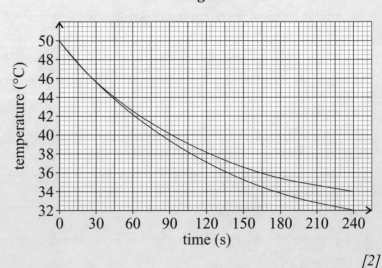

[2]

[Total 7 marks]

Topic P6 — Waves

Dangers of Electromagnetic Waves

1   Some types of electromagnetic wave can be harmful to people.   (Grade 6-7)

1.1   Describe how X-rays and gamma rays can cause cancer.

....

....

[2]

1.2   Another type of harmful electromagnetic radiation is ultraviolet radiation.
Give two damaging effects of ultraviolet light.

....

....

[2]

[Total 4 marks]

2   **Table 1** lists the radiation doses for some common medical procedures.   (Grade 7-9)

Table 1

Procedure	Typical effective dose (mSv)	Lifetime additional risk of fatal cancer per examination
X-ray image of skull	0.07	1 in 300 000
X-ray image of lower spine	1.3	1 in 15 000
CT scan of head	2	1 in 10 000

2.1   The lifetime additional risk of fatal cancer from a CT scan of the chest is 1 in 2500.
Use **Table 1** to estimate the typical effective dose of a CT scan of the chest.

Typical effective dose = ... mSv

[2]

2.2*   Nuclear medicine scans use gamma rays to create images of internal organs, but have a high
effective radiation dosage. Discuss the risks involved in performing this type of scan, and why
the procedure might go ahead despite the risks.

....

....

....

....

....

....

....

....

[6]

[Total 8 marks]

Permanent and Induced Magnets

Complete the sentence using one of the words below.

non-contact   contact   nuclear

Magnetic force is an example of a .... force.

1   Magnets have magnetic fields.   (Grade 4-6)

1.1 Define the term magnetic field.

....

....

[1]

1.2 Name **two** magnetic materials.

1. ....

2. ....

[2]

1.3 **Figure 1** shows a bar magnet. Draw the magnetic field lines onto the diagram in **Figure 1**.

Figure 1

| N   S |

[2]

1.4 Which of the following statements are correct for magnets? Tick **two** boxes.

Like poles attract each other. ☐

The magnetic field at the north pole of a magnet is always stronger than at the south pole. ☐

The closer together the magnetic field lines, the stronger the magnetic field. ☐

Magnetic field lines point from the north pole to the south pole of a magnet. ☐

The force between a magnet and a magnetic material can be attractive or repulsive. ☐

[2]

[Total 7 marks]

2 A block of cobalt is held in place near to a bar magnet, as shown in **Figure 2**.

Figure 2

bar magnet   cobalt

2.1 A steel paperclip is placed against the block of cobalt at point P, shown on **Figure 2**.
The paperclip sticks to the block of cobalt. State why this is the case.

....

....

....
[2]

2.2 The bar magnet is removed. Explain what happens to the paperclip.

....

....
[2]

[Total 4 marks]

Figure 3

3 A student wants to investigate the magnetic field of a horseshoe magnet, shown in **Figure 3**.

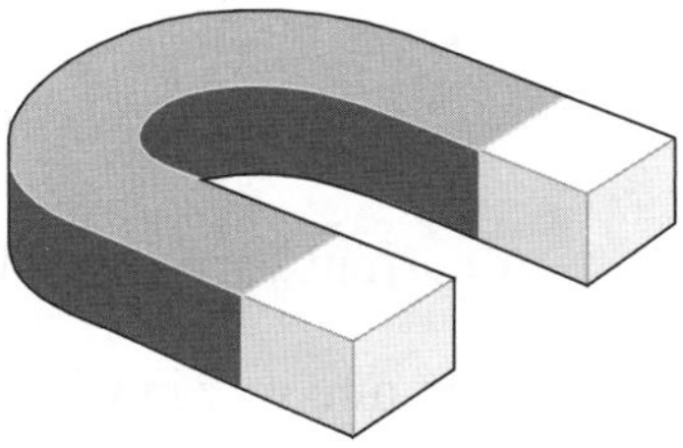

3.1* Explain how a compass could be used to determine the magnetic field of the magnet.

....

....

....

....

....

....

....
[4]

3.2 State what would happen to the compass if you were to move it far away from any magnets.
Explain why this would happen.

....

....
[2]

[Total 6 marks]

Exam Tip

If you're asked to sketch out a diagram, don't be afraid to use all the space that's given to you. It's far, far better to draw a diagram that looks weirdly gigantic than one that's tiny and tricky for the examiner to read properly.

Topic P7 — Magnetism and Electromagnetism

Electromagnetism

1 **Figure 1** shows a wire which has a current flowing through it. The arrow shows the direction of the current.

Figure 1

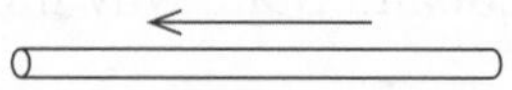

1.1 The flow of charge creates a magnetic field around the wire.
On **Figure 1**, draw field lines showing the direction of the magnetic field created.

[2]

1.2 The direction of the current is reversed. State the effect this will have on the magnetic field.

....

[1]

1.3 State **one** way in which the magnetic field strength around the wire could be increased.

....

[1]

[Total 4 marks]

2 A current-carrying solenoid has a magnetic field outside it similar to a bar magnet. (Grade 7-9)

2.1 State **one** way in which the magnetic field strength of a solenoid can be increased.

....

[1]

2.2 The north pole of a magnet is brought near to the current-carrying solenoid as shown in **Figure 2**.
State whether the north pole is **attracted** or **repelled** by the solenoid. Explain why.

Figure 2

N

....

....

....

[3]

[Total 4 marks]

Exam Tip

A current carrying-wire will always produce a magnetic field around it. No matter what position the wire is in, or what shape it's been bent into, the magnetic field around it will always depend on the direction of the current.

Topic P7 — Magnetism and Electromagnetism

The Motor Effect

1 A 0.75 m section of wire, carrying a current of 0.4 A, is placed into a magnetic field. When the wire is perpendicular to the field, it experiences a force of 1.2 N. Calculate the magnetic flux density of the field, using an equation from the Equations List. Give the correct unit in your answer.

Magnetic flux density = ...

Unit = ...

[Total 3 marks]

2 A student carries out an experiment using a horseshoe magnet and an iron bar connected in a circuit. Part of the set-up is shown in **Figure 2**.

Figure 2

Birds-eye view of experiment set-up.

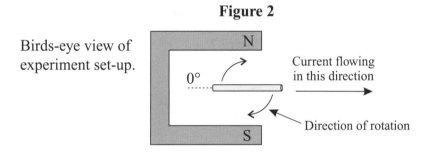

The student rotates the iron bar 90° clockwise and measures the force acting on the bar as she does so. She then plots her results on a graph of force, *F*, against angle of rotation, *θ*.

Which of the following graphs shows a sketch of her results? Tick **one** box.

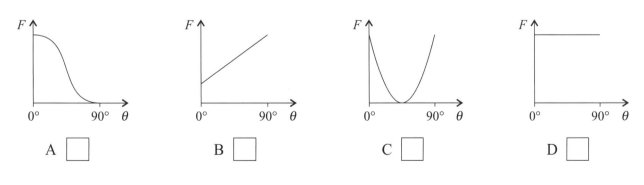

[Total 1 mark]

Topic P7 — Magnetism and Electromagnetism

Electric Motors

1 A wire is placed between two magnets, as shown in **Figure 1**. A current is flowing through the wire, in the direction shown.

Grade 4-6

Figure 1

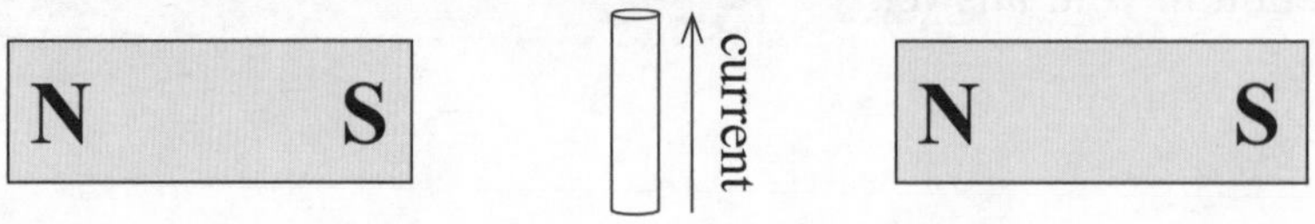

N S   current   N S

What will happen to the wire? Tick **one** box.

It will move to the left.   ☐

It will move away from you, into the paper.   ☐

It will move towards you, out of the paper.   ☐

It will remain stationary.   ☐

[Total 1 mark]

2 **Figure 2** shows part of a basic dc motor. A coil of wire is positioned between two magnetic poles and allowed to rotate.

Grade 6-7

Figure 2

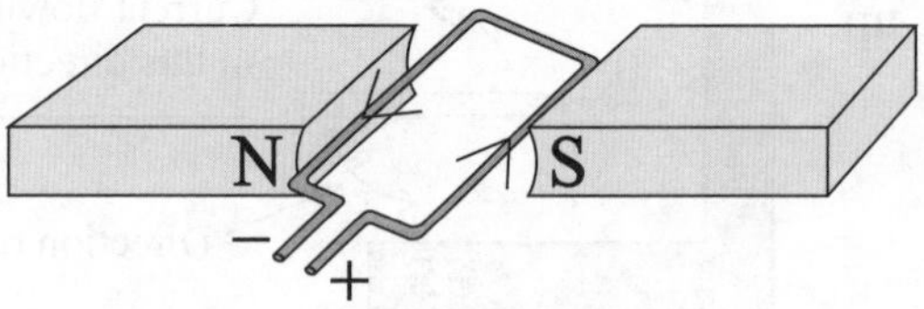

N S
− +

2.1 State the direction in which the coil will turn (**anticlockwise** or **clockwise**).

....

[1]

2.2 Explain why the coil turns.

....

....

....

[2]

2.3 Explain how a dc current can be used to make the coil in **Figure 2** continue to rotate in the same direction.

....

....

....

....

[2]

[Total 5 marks]

Topic P7 — Magnetism and Electromagnetism

Biology Mixed Questions

1   Alcohol is metabolised in the liver using alcohol dehydrogenase enzymes.   *(Grade 4-6)*

1.1   State **one** function of the liver, other than alcohol metabolism.

....

[1]

1.2   Which of the following sentences about enzymes is **true**? Tick **one** box.

☐ Enzymes speed up chemical reactions in living organisms.

☐ Enzymes are used up in chemical reactions.

☐ Enzymes are products of digestion.

☐ Enzymes are the building blocks of all living organisms.

[1]

A scientist was investigating the effect of pH on the rate of activity of alcohol dehydrogenase.
Figure 1 shows a graph of his results.

Figure 1

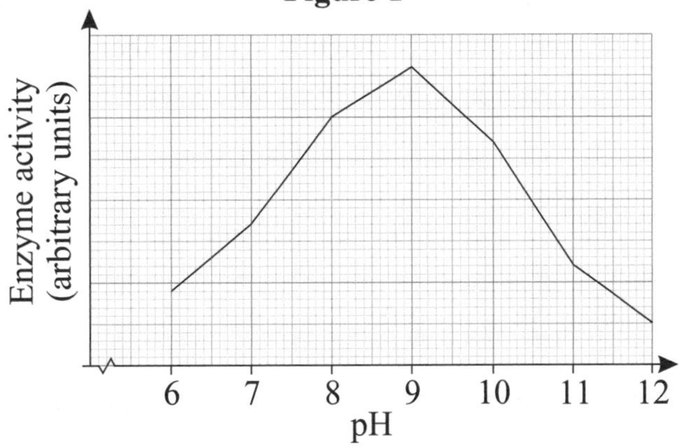

1.3   What is the optimum pH for the enzyme?

....

[1]

1.4   Suggest and explain the effect an acid with a pH of 1 would have on the enzyme.

....

....

....

[3]

1.5   Which of the following statements about alcohol is **not true**? Tick **one** box.

☐ Too much alcohol can cause liver disease.

☐ Alcohol is a risk factor for lung cancer.

☐ Alcohol can cause brain damage.

☐ Alcohol can affect unborn babies.

[1]

[Total 7 marks]

2   A group of students were investigating the effect of air flow on the
     rate of transpiration. They set up their apparatus as shown in **Figure 2**.

Figure 2

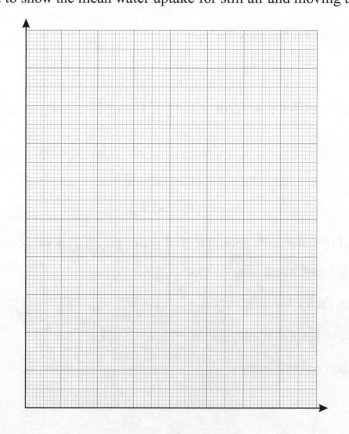

fan

plant cutting

cork seal

layer of oil

graduated pipette

tubing

2.1 The tubing and graduated pipette were filled with water.
     Suggest why a layer of oil was added to the surface of the water in the pipette.

....

[1]

The students recorded the change in the volume of water in the pipette over 30 minutes,
in normal conditions. They repeated this five times. They then carried out these steps with
the fan turned on to simulate windy conditions. **Table 1** shows their results.

Table 1

	Repeat	1	2	3	4	5	Mean
Water uptake in 30 minutes (cm³)	Still Air	1.2	1.2	1.0	0.8	1.1	1.1
	Moving Air	2.0	1.8	2.3	1.9	1.7	1.9

2.2 Draw a bar chart to show the mean water uptake for still air and moving air.

[2]

2.3 Describe the relationship between air flow around the plant and transpiration rate.

....
[1]

2.4 Explain the effect of air flow on the rate of transpiration.

....

....

....
[2]

2.5 Calculate the range of the results for still air.

Range = ... cm^3
[1]

2.6 The rate of transpiration can be calculated using the formula:

$$\text{rate of transpiration} = \frac{\text{mean volume of water uptake}}{\text{time taken}}$$

Calculate the rate of transpiration for the plant in moving air.
Give your answer in cm^3/hour.

.... cm^3/hour
[2]
[Total 9 marks]

3   Aerobic respiration transfers energy from glucose.   (Grade 6-7)

3.1 Name the subcellular structures where aerobic respiration takes place.

....
[1]

3.2 Complete the word equation for aerobic respiration.

.... + ... → .... + ...
[2]

3.3 Outline the role that glucose plays in the production of proteins in the body.

....

....

....

....
[3]
[Total 6 marks]

4 The endocrine system uses hormones to produce effects within the body. **(Grade 6-7)**

4.1 Outline how a hormone travels from a gland to its target organ in the body.

....

....

[2]

The menstrual cycle is controlled by hormones.

Figure 3 shows the change in the levels of these hormones during one menstrual cycle. It also shows the change in the lining of the uterus.

Figure 3

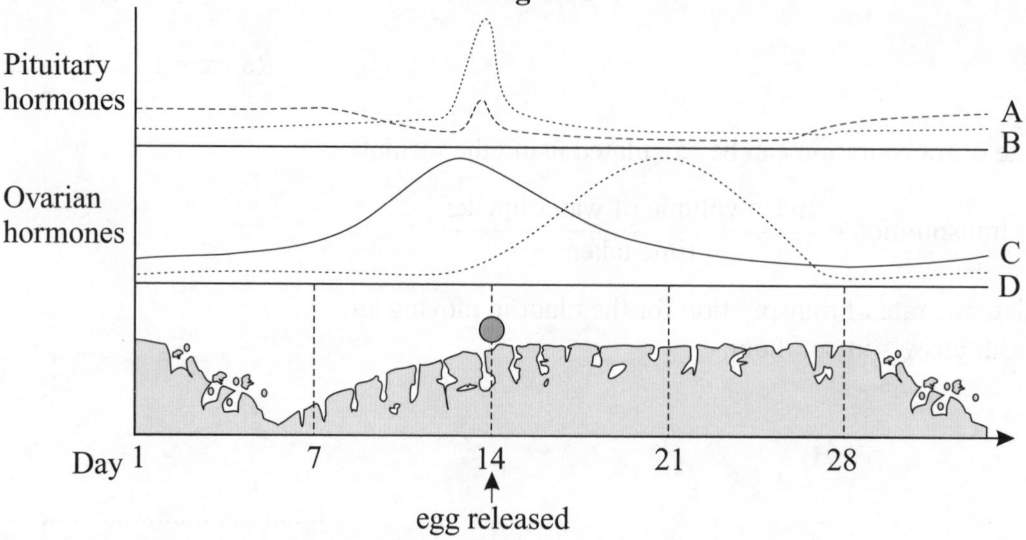

4.2 Which line in **Figure 3** represents oestrogen? Tick **one** box.

☐ A   ☐ B   ☐ C   ☐ D

[1]

4.3 Which line in **Figure 3** represents luteinising hormone? Tick **one** box.

☐ A   ☐ B   ☐ C   ☐ D

[1]

4.4 What is the function of luteinising hormone?

....

[1]

4.5 Where in the body is progesterone produced?

....

[1]

4.6 Taking the combined pill keeps the level of oestrogen in the body constantly high. Explain how this reduces fertility.

....

....

[2]

[Total 8 marks]

Biology Mixed Questions

5   A student was investigating the effect of limiting factors on the rate of photosynthesis by green algae.

The student set up two boiling tubes as shown in **Figure 4**. She also set up a third tube that did not contain any algae. The colour of the indicator solution changes as follows:

Figure 4

- At atmospheric CO_2 concentration, the indicator is red.
- At low CO_2 concentrations, the indicator is purple.
- At high CO_2 concentrations, the indicator is yellow.

The student covered one of the boiling tubes containing algae with foil. All three tubes were left for several hours at room temperature with a constant light source. The colour of the indicator solution was then recorded. The results are shown in **Table 2**.

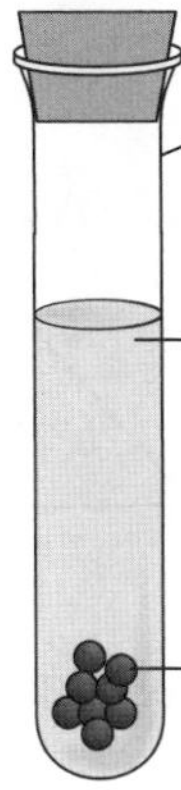

Table 2

	Algae?	Foil?	Indicator colour at start	Indicator colour at end
Tube 1	yes	yes	red	yellow
Tube 2	yes	no	red	purple
Tube 3	no	no	red	red

5.1 Name the waste product of photosynthesis.

....

[1]

5.2 Name the limiting factor of photosynthesis that is being investigated in this experiment.

....

[1]

5.3 At the end of the experiment, which tube has the highest carbon dioxide concentration? Tick **one** box.

☐ Tube 1   ☐ Tube 2   ☐ Tube 3

[1]

5.4 Explain the results of Tube 1 and Tube 2.

....

....

....

....

....

[4]

5.5 Give **two** variables that needed to be controlled in this experiment.

....

....

[2]

Biology Mixed Questions

A scientist investigating the effect of limiting factors on photosynthesis sketched the graph shown in **Figure 5**.

Figure 5

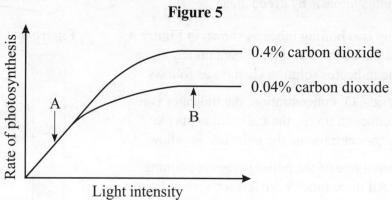

5.6 What is the limiting factor at point **A**? Explain your answer.

....

....

[2]

5.7 Name the limiting factor at point **B**.

....

[1]

[Total 12 marks]

6 In pea plants, seed shape is controlled by a single gene. (Grade 7-9)

The allele for round seed shape is R and the allele for wrinkled seed shape is r.
R is a dominant allele and r is recessive.

6.1 What is the genotype of a pea plant that is homozygous dominant for seed shape?

....

[1]

6.2 What is the phenotype of a pea plant that is heterozygous for seed shape?

....

[1]

6.3 Two pea plants were crossed. All of the offspring produced had the genotype **Rr**.
Construct a Punnett square to find the genotypes of the parent plants.

Genotypes: .... and ....

[3]

[Total 5 marks]

Chemistry Mixed Questions

1 A substance can be classified as an element, a compound or a mixture. [Grade 4-6]

1.1 Draw a line to connect each type of substance with an example of it.

compound		bromine water
element		helium
mixture		iron oxide

[2]

1.2 Formulations are a special type of mixture. Explain what is meant by the term 'formulation'.

....

....

[2]

[Total 4 marks]

2 Salt is the common name for sodium chloride. Salt can be obtained by mining rock salt, which also contains sand and insoluble bits of rock. [Grade 4-6]

2.1 How could the sand and bits of rock be separated from the salt? Tick **one** box.

Dissolve the rock salt in water and distil the water. ☐

Dissolve the rock salt in water and crystallise the sodium chloride. ☐

Dissolve the rock salt in water and filter. ☐

Dissolve the rock salt in water and carry out chromatography. ☐

[1]

2.2 Explain why sodium chloride is classified as a compound.

....

....

[2]

2.3 The structure of sodium chloride is shown in **Figure 1**.

State the type of bonding in sodium chloride.

....

[1]

[Total 4 marks]

Figure 1

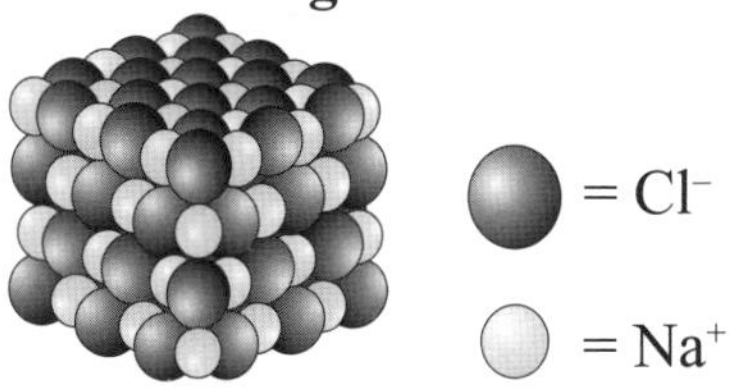

● = Cl^-

○ = Na^+

Exam Tip

Pay close attention to the wording of the questions. For 'state' questions, you just need to give a simple answer.
If the question asks you to explain your answer, you will need to give a bit of extra detail in addition to your answer.

280

3 Oxygen atoms have the electronic structure 2,6. **Grade 4-6**

3.1 State which group of the periodic table oxygen is in.
Explain your answer with reference to the electronic structure of oxygen.

Group: ....

Explanation: ....

....
[2]

3.2 Oxygen can react to form oxide ions. Predict, with reasoning the charge on an oxide ion.

....

....
[2]

3.3 When magnesium reacts with oxygen, it forms magnesium oxide. What type of reaction does magnesium undergo? Tick **one** box.

Displacement ☐   Oxidation ☐

Electrolysis ☐   Reduction ☐
[1]

[Total 5 marks]

4 Chlorine is a Group 7 element that exists as molecules of Cl_2. **Grade 4-6**

4.1 Complete the dot-and-cross diagram below to show the bonding in Cl_2.
You only need to show the outer electron shells.

Cl   Cl
[2]

4.2 Chlorine has two main isotopes — ^{35}Cl and ^{37}Cl. Explain the term 'isotope'.

....

....
[2]

4.3 Describe a test you could carry out for chlorine. **PRACTICAL**
Include any observations you would expect.

....

....
[2]

4.4 Predict what happens if you mix chlorine water and sodium iodide solution. Explain your answer.

....

....
[2]

[Total 8 marks]

Chemistry Mixed Questions

5 When sodium hydrogencarbonate reacts with ethanoic acid, the temperature of the surroundings decreases. *(Grade 4-6)*

5.1 Is this reaction endothermic or exothermic?

....
[1]

5.2 Will the energy of the products be higher or lower than the energy of the reactants?

....
[1]

5.3 Explain the temperature change of this reaction in terms of the energy required to break the bonds in the reactants and the energy released when bonds are formed in the products.

....

....
[2]

5.4 Suggest one practical use of this reaction.

....
[1]

[Total 5 marks]

6 Pentane, C_5H_{12}, and decane, $C_{10}H_{22}$, are both hydrocarbons in the same homologous series. *(Grade 6-7)*

6.1 What homologous series do pentane and decane belong to?

....
[1]

6.2 Name a process that could be used to separate pentane from decane.

....
[1]

6.3 Name a process that could be used to produce pentane from decane.

....
[1]

6.4 Predict, with reasoning, whether pentane or decane will have a higher boiling point.

....

....

....
[3]

6.5 Write a balanced symbol equation for the complete combustion of pentane in oxygen to form carbon dioxide and water.

....
[2]

[Total 8 marks]

Exam Tip
You should be familiar with the practical uses of certain key reactions, as well as the chemistry that makes them work.

7 Iron and silver are both metals. Iron has a melting point of 1538 °C, whilst silver has a melting point of 962 °C. Iron boils at 2862 °C and silver boils at 2162 °C.

Grade 6-7

7.1 Describe the bonding in metals, like iron and silver, when they are solid.

....

....

....

[3]

7.2 What states would iron and silver be in if they were both at a temperature of 1000 °C?

Iron: ....   Silver: ....

[2]

7.3 Use the information above to predict which metal has the strongest bonds. Explain your answer.

....

....

[3]

[Total 8 marks]

8 Copper is a metal found in a number of everyday mixtures and compounds.

Grade 6-7

8.1 State, with reasoning, how you would extract copper from copper oxide.

....

....

[2]

8.2 Describe how bioleaching can be used to extract copper from low grade ores.

....

....

....

[3]

8.3 Copper can be drawn out into thin wires which are used in electrical cables.
Explain **two** ways in which the bonding and structure of copper make it suitable for this.

....

....

[2]

8.4 Statues can be made from bronze, an alloy of copper that contains tin. Explain how the structure of bronze makes it more suitable than pure copper for this use.

....

....

....

[3]

[Total 10 marks]

9 Models of the structure of the atom went through a lot of development in the early 1900s. *(Grade 6-7)*

9.1 Ernest Rutherford set up an experiment which involved firing alpha particles at a piece of gold foil. The results of the experiment did not match the prediction of what should have happened if the plum pudding model had been correct. Describe the model that Rutherford developed to replace the plum pudding model.

....

....

[2]

9.2 Describe the model of the atom used today, with reference to protons, neutrons and electrons.

....

....

....

[3]

[Total 5 marks]

PRACTICAL

10 When the following reaction is carried out in an unsealed reaction flask, the mass changes over the course of the reaction: $2HCl_{(aq)} + Na_2CO_{3(aq)} \rightarrow 2NaCl_{(aq)} + H_2O_{(l)} + CO_{2(g)}$ *(Grade 6-7)*

10.1 Explain, in terms of the particle model, why the mass of the reaction flask changes in the reaction.

....

....

....

[3]

10.2 The volume of gas produced by the reaction mixture can be used to investigate how the concentration of acid affects the rate of the reaction. Write a method the student could use to carry out this experiment.

....

....

....

....

....

[6]

10.3 At the start of an experiment, the gas syringe was empty. After 30 s, it contained 12.0 cm³ of gas. Calculate the mean rate of reaction during this time.

Mean rate = ... cm³/s

[2]

[Total 11 marks]

Chemistry Mixed Questions

11 Carbon dioxide is a greenhouse gas found naturally in Earth's atmosphere. (Grade 6-7)

11.1 Millions of years ago, the amount of carbon dioxide in the atmosphere was much higher than it is today. State **two** ways in which carbon dioxide was removed from the atmosphere.

....

....

[2]

11.2 Human activities are increasing the amount of carbon dioxide in the atmosphere. Name **one** other greenhouse gas that is increasing due to human activity. Give an activity causing this increase.

....

....

[2]

11.3*Give examples of pollutant gases, other than carbon dioxide and the one mentioned in your answer to 11.2, that are produced by human activity. Explain how these gases form and how they impact on the environment and human health.

....

....

....

....

....

....

[6]

[Total 10 marks]

12 A student reacts lithium in an excess of water to produce lithium hydroxide and hydrogen gas. The equation for this reaction is: $2Li + 2H_2O \rightarrow 2LiOH + H_2$ (Grade 6-7)
Atomic masses, A_r: Li = 7, O = 16, H = 1

12.1 Calculate the relative formula mass of lithium hydroxide.

Relative formula mass = ...
[1]

12.2 A student performed this reaction using 1.75 g of lithium. How many moles is this?

Number of moles = ... mol
[2]

12.3 Use the symbol equation to calculate the mass, in g, of lithium hydroxide that would be produced using 0.50 mol lithium and an excess of water.

Mass = ... g
[3]

[Total 6 marks]

13 When zinc sulfate solution is electrolysed, the reaction at the cathode is: $2H^+_{(aq)} + 2e^- \rightarrow H_{2(g)}$ (Grade 7-9)

13.1 Explain why it is easier to discharge hydrogen rather than zinc, and what this tells you about the relative abilities of hydrogen and zinc to form positive ions.

....

....

[2]

13.2 What type of reaction takes place at the cathode? Explain your answer.

....

....

[2]

13.3 Write a balanced half equation for the reaction that occurs at the anode.

....

[2]

[Total 6 marks]

14 Some of the properties and reactions of different Group 1 metals are shown in **Table 1**. (Grade 7-9)

Table 1

Metal	Melting point (°C)	Typical ion that forms in reactions	Reaction with acid
Lithium	181	+1	vigorous
Sodium		+1	very vigorous, ignites
Potassium	63	+1	extremely vigorous, ignites

14.1*Describe the similarities and differences in how lithium and sodium react, as shown in **Table 1**. Give reasons for them, based on the electronic structures of the atoms.

....

....

....

....

....

....

[6]

14.2 Using the data in the table, predict the melting point of sodium.

melting point = ... °C

[1]

[Total 7 marks]

Exam Tip

It's really easy to accidentally hit the wrong key on your calculator when you're under exam conditions, which could cause you to lose a mark or two. Always double-check that your answers make sense and keep an eye out for any mistakes.

Physics Mixed Questions

1   A student uses a compass to investigate magnetic field patterns.   *(Grade 4-6)*

1.1   The compass contains a permanent bar magnet.
Describe the difference between a permanent magnet and an induced magnet.

....

.... **[2]**

1.2   The student moves the compass around the current-carrying solenoid shown in **Figure 1**.
The student uses the compass to plot the magnetic field produced by the solenoid.
Sketch the magnetic field produced by the solenoid on **Figure 1**.

Figure 1

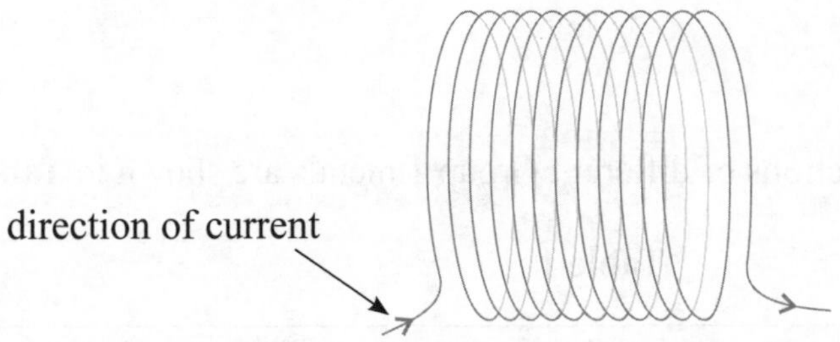

direction of current

[3]

[Total 5 marks]

2   When a nucleus decays, it can emit alpha, beta or gamma radiation.   *(Grade 4-6)*

2.1   Use words from the box below to complete the passage about radioactive decay.
You can only use a word once and you do not need to use all of the words.

can	stable	cannot	unstable	forced	random

Radioactive decay is where a nucleus releases radiation to become more ....

It is a .... process, which means you .... predict

which individual nucleus in a sample will decay next.

[2]

2.2   The term 'activity' can be used when describing a radioactive source.
Define activity and state the unit it is measured in.

....

[2]

2.3   The term 'half-life' can also be used when describing a source of radiation.
Define half-life in terms of activity.

....

[1]

[Total 5 marks]

3   **Figure 2** shows an electric fan.

Figure 2

3.1 The fan is connected to the mains with a cable that contains three wires.
     What is the name of this type of cable? Tick **one** box.

☐ three-colour cable   ☐ two-core cable   ☐ three-core cable   ☐ triple cable

[1]

3.2 Complete **Table 1** to show the properties of each wire in the cable.

Table 1

Name of wire	Colour of insulation	Potential difference (V)
Live	....	....
....	blue	....
....	....	0

[3]

3.3 The fan works by transferring energy. Use phrases from the box below to complete the passage.
     You can only use a phrase once and you do not need to use all of the phrases.

| electrically   thermal   by heating   kinetic   mechanically   elastic potential |

Energy is transferred .... from the mains supply to the

.... energy store of the fan's blades.

[2]

3.4 The fan has a power of 30 W. Calculate the energy transferred by the fan in 30 minutes.

Energy transferred = ... J

[2]

[Total 8 marks]

Physics Mixed Questions

4 A student tests the relationship between potential difference and current for a filament bulb.

4.1 **Figure 3** shows four *I-V* characteristics.
Tick the box under the *I-V* characteristic for a filament bulb.

Figure 3

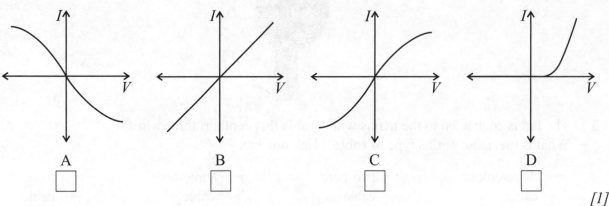

A ☐   B ☐   C ☐   D ☐

[1]

At a potential difference of 240 V the current through the bulb is 1.2 A.

4.2 Write down the equation that links potential difference, current and resistance.

....

[1]

4.3 Calculate the resistance of the bulb.

Resistance = ... Ω
[2]

[Total 4 marks]

5 Waves on a string are an example of a transverse wave.

5.1 Which of the following are examples of transverse waves? Tick **two** boxes.

☐ sound waves   ☐ water ripples   ☐ ultrasound waves   ☐ gamma rays

[1]

A wave on a string has a wavelength of 60 cm and a frequency of 40 Hz.

5.2 Calculate the period of the wave. Give your answer in milliseconds.

Period = ... ms
[3]

5.3 Write down the equation that links wave speed, frequency and wavelength.

....

[1]

5.4 Calculate the speed of the wave.

Speed = ... m/s
[2]

[Total 7 marks]

6   A child is playing with a remote-controlled toy car.

Figure 4

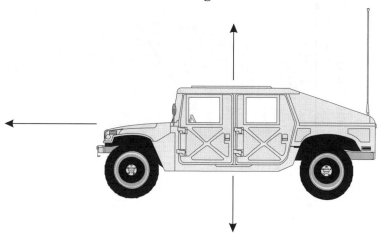

6.1 **Figure 4** shows an incomplete force diagram for the toy. Complete the force diagram to show the resultant resistive force acting on the car as it travels at a steady speed.

[2]

6.2 Write down the equation that links distance travelled, speed and time.

....

[1]

6.3 Calculate the distance the car travels in 30 seconds at a steady speed of 5.0 m/s.

Distance travelled = ... m

[2]

6.4 The car has a mass of 0.50 kg.
Calculate the energy in the kinetic energy store of the car as it travels at 5.0 m/s.

Energy = ... J

[2]

The car is powered by an electric motor. The efficiency of the motor is 65%.
During a short journey, 1200 J of energy was transferred to the motor.

6.5 Write down the equation that links efficiency, the useful output energy transfer and the useful input energy transfer.

....

[1]

6.6 Calculate the useful output energy transferred by the motor during the journey.

Output energy = ... J

[2]

[Total 11 marks]

7   A man goes for a bike ride. **Figure 5** shows a velocity-time graph for the man's journey.

Figure 5

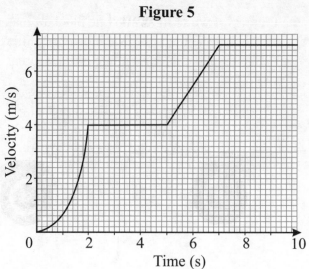

7.1 Describe the motion of the man:

During the first two seconds of the journey: ....

At four seconds from the start of the journey: ....

Between 5-7 s from the start of the journey: ....
[3]

7.2 Calculate the acceleration of the cyclist 6 seconds from the start of his bike ride.

Acceleration = ... m/s^2
[3]

7.3 Ten seconds after the beginning of the cyclist's bike ride, a car turns out of a junction 12 m
in front of him. The cyclist is alert and quickly applies the bike's brakes, which provide a constant
braking force of 440 N. The combined mass of the man and the bicycle is 83 kg.
Calculate the deceleration of the bicycle.

Deceleration = ... m/s^2
[3]

7.4 Use your answer from 7.3 to determine whether or not the cyclist will hit the car.
Write down any assumptions you make about the cyclist's reaction time.

....
[5]

[Total 14 marks]

8 A student is investigating the properties of visible light. She uses the set-up in **Figure 6** to test how different materials refract light.

She begins by shining a thin ray of white light into one block of material and marking where the light ray emerges from the block. She then places a block of a different material next to the first block, leaving no air gap. She repeats this for a range of transparent and translucent materials.

Figure 6

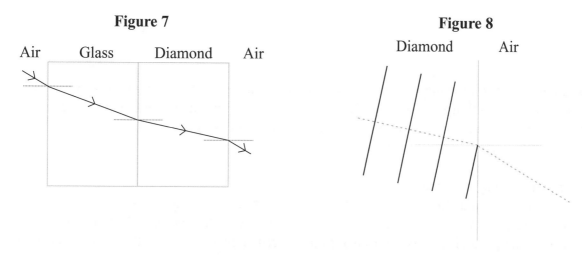

8.1 Complete the wave front diagram in **Figure 8** for the light ray crossing the boundary between diamond and air.

[2]

8.2* Explain why the light ray refracts when it crosses the boundary between diamond and air. Your answer should refer to the wave fronts drawn in **Figure 8**.

....

....

....

....

....

....

....

....

....

[6]

[Total 8 marks]

Physics Mixed Questions

9 A student is designing a basic electronic toy. He wants the toy to be able to light up and spin around. He creates a basic circuit of a battery connected to a motor. He connects two filament bulbs and a fixed resistor in parallel to the motor. The two bulbs and the resistor are all in series with each other. The bulbs and the motor can be switched on and off separately.

9.1 Draw the circuit diagram for the circuit created by the student.

[5]

9.2 The student turns on the motor alone. The potential difference across the motor is 6.0 V and a current of 70.0 mA flows through the motor. After 15 minutes, the student switches off the motor and measures the temperature of the motor's casing.
He finds that it has increased by 7.0 °C.

The motor's casing has a mass of 25.0 g.
The material it is made from has a specific heat capacity of 120 J/kg °C.
Calculate the amount of energy that is usefully transferred by the motor in 15 minutes.
You can assume that all energy not transferred to thermal energy store of the motor's casing is usefully transferred.

Energy usefully transferred = ... J

[5]

9.3 Explain **one** modification that the student could make to the toy to make it more efficient.

....

....

....

[2]

[Total 12 marks]

Answers

Topic B1 — Cell Biology

Pages 1-2 — Cells

Warm up

many, plant/animal, animal/plant, single, smaller/simpler, simpler/smaller

1.1

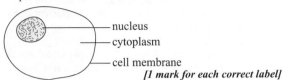

— nucleus
— cytoplasm
— cell membrane

[1 mark for each correct label]

1.2 Cell membrane — controls what substances go in and out of the cell *[1 mark]*.
Cytoplasm — where most of the chemical reactions take place *[1 mark]*.
Nucleus — controls the activities of the cell / contains genetic material *[1 mark]*.

1.3 E.g. mitochondria *[1 mark]* where aerobic respiration takes place *[1 mark]*, ribosomes *[1 mark]* where protein synthesis occurs *[1 mark]*.

1.4 There is no cell wall/vacuole. / There are no chloroplasts. *[1 mark]*

2.1 bacterium *[1 mark]*

2.2 X – chromosome/DNA/genetic material *[1 mark]*
Y – cell wall *[1 mark]*
Z – plasmid *[1 mark]*

2.3 It contains genetic material *[1 mark]*.

2.4 10 times larger / 1 order of magnitude larger *[1 mark]*

2.5 1 mm × 1000 = 1000 µm
1000 µm ÷ 1 µm = **1000 cells** *[2 marks for the correct answer, otherwise 1 mark for correct working.]*

2.6 E.g. eukaryotic cells have a nucleus, prokaryotic cells do not. / DNA is found inside the nucleus of eukaryotic cells, but is not enclosed in prokaryotic cells. / Prokaryotic cells contain plasmids, eukaryotic cells do not. / Eukaryotic cells have mitochondria, prokaryotic cells do not. *[1 mark]*

Page 3 — Microscopy

1 length of cell A in image = 24 mm
24 / 0.012 = × **2000** *[2 marks for the correct answer, otherwise 1 mark for correct working.]*

2.1 size of real object = size of image ÷ magnification
actual length = 10 mm ÷ 1000 = **0.01 mm** *[2 marks for correct answer, otherwise 1 mark for correct working.]*

2.2 1 mm = 1000 µm
0.01 mm × 1000 = **10 µm** *[1 mark]*

2.3 Electron microscopes have a higher magnification *[1 mark]* and a higher resolution than light microscopes *[1 mark]*.

2.4 E.g. more cell structures can be seen under an electron microscope *[1 mark]* and they can be seen with greater detail *[1 mark]*.

Page 4 — More on Microscopy

1.1 When the specimen is colourless *[1 mark]*.

1.2 × 4 *[1 mark]*

Remember, you should always start with the lowest-powered objective lens — this makes it easier to get your specimen into view.

1.3 They bring the sample into focus by moving the stage up and down *[1 mark]*.

1.4 She should select the × 40 or × 10 objective lens *[1 mark]* and use the adjustment knobs to bring the sample back into focus *[1 mark]*.

1.5 Any two from: e.g. she should use a pencil with a sharp point. / She should make sure her drawing takes up at least half of the space available. / She should not colour or shade her diagram. / She should ensure that the subcellular structures are drawn in proportion. / She should include a title. / She should write down the magnification that it was observed under. / She should label the important features of her drawing using straight, uncrossed lines. *[2 marks]*

Page 5 — Cell Differentiation and Specialisation

Warm up

root hair cell — Long finger-like projection increases surface area for absorption of water.
xylem — Cells that are hollow in the centre and have no end cell walls form a continuous tube for transporting water from roots to leaves.
phloem — Very few subcellular structures and holes in the end cell walls allow dissolved sugars to move from one cell to the next.

1 differentiation *[1 mark]*

2.1 To fertilise an egg. / To carry the male DNA to the female DNA (in the egg). *[1 mark]*

2.2 E.g. it has a tail to enable it to swim to the egg *[1 mark]*.
It has lots of mitochondria to give it energy *[1 mark]*.
It has a streamlined head to aid swimming *[1 mark]*.
The head contains enzymes to help the sperm penetrate the egg *[1 mark]*.

Page 6 — Chromosomes and Mitosis

1.1

— chromosomes

[1 mark]

1.2 DNA *[1 mark]*

1.3 The number of subcellular structures is increasing *[1 mark]*.
The chromosomes are doubling *[1 mark]*.

1.4 The cytoplasm is dividing *[1 mark]*.
The cell membrane is dividing *[1 mark]*.

1.5 They are genetically identical *[1 mark]*.

Pages 7-8 — Stem Cells

1.1 meristems *[1 mark]*

1.2 E.g. plants can be produced quickly and cheaply *[1 mark]*.
Rare species can be cloned to protect them from extinction *[1 mark]*. Large numbers of identical crop plants with desirable features, e.g. disease resistance, can be grown for farmers *[1 mark]*.

2.1 Stem cells can differentiate into many types of body cell *[1 mark]*.

2.2 To increase the number of cells (available for use) *[1 mark]*.

2.3 E.g. because body cells that are already differentiated are not capable of changing into any other types of cell *[1 mark]*.

2.4 E.g. human embryos *[1 mark]*

2.5 E.g. diabetes / paralysis *[1 mark]*

2.6 E.g. the cells in the culture medium may become infected with a virus that may then be transferred to the patient *[1 mark]*.

3.1 The production of an embryo with the same genes as a patient *[1 mark]*

3.2 The stem cells produced by therapeutic cloning won't be rejected by the patient's body *[1 mark]* because they contain the same genes as the patient *[1 mark]*.

3.3   How to grade your answer:

Level 0: There is no relevant information. *[No marks]*

Level 1: One or two ethical issues surrounding the use of embryonic stem cells are briefly described, but only one point of view is given.
[1 to 2 marks]

Level 2: A detailed discussion of issues surrounding the use of embryonic stem cells is given, including an account of both points of view.
[3 to 4 marks]

Here are some points your answer may include:

Some people feel that embryonic stem cells from human embryos shouldn't be used for experiments since each embryo is a potential human life.

Some people may argue that there are other sources of stem cells that scientists could use, so using embryos to create stem cells is unjustified.

Some people think that using embryonic stem cells to cure patients who already exist and who are suffering is more important than the rights of embryos.

Some people argue that many embryonic stem cells are sourced from unwanted embryos from fertility clinics, which would probably be destroyed anyway.

Page 9 — Diffusion

Warm up

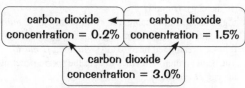

1   protein *[1 mark]*

2.1   The spreading out of particles of a gas *[1 mark]*, resulting in net movement *[1 mark]* from an area of higher concentration to an area of lower concentration *[1 mark]*.

2.2   Increasing the concentration of ammonia increases the rate of diffusion *[1 mark]*.

2.3   Any two from: e.g. the surface area of the cell. / The temperature. / The distance for diffusion. / The permeability of the membrane. *[2 marks]*

2.4   By repeating the experiment and calculating a mean *[1 mark]*.

Pages 10-11 — Osmosis

1.1   The movement of water molecules *[1 mark]* across a partially permeable membrane *[1 mark]* from a region of higher water concentration (a dilute solution) to a region of lower water concentration (a more concentrated solution) *[1 mark]*.

1.2   A plant is absorbing water from the soil *[1 mark]*.

2.1   So that all the pieces of potato have the same water concentration. / Because different potatoes will have different water concentrations. *[1 mark]*

2.2 $\dfrac{(6.58 - 5.73)}{5.73} \times 100$

= **14.8 %** (3 s.f.) *[2 marks for the correct answer, otherwise 1 mark for correct working.]*

2.3   E.g. 4% *[1 mark. Accept a percentage between 2% and 5%.]*

3.1   Any two from: e.g. the volume of sucrose solution the student puts in the Visking tubing. / The volume of sucrose solution the student puts in the beaker. / The temperature the beaker is kept at. / The size of the Visking tubing bag *[2 marks]*.

3.2   It will stay the same *[1 mark]*. The water concentration of the solution in the tubing is the same as the water concentration of the solution in the beaker, so there will be no net movement of water molecules *[1 mark]*.

3.3   E.g. at first, the level of the solution in the beaker will gradually increase *[1 mark]*. The water concentration of the solution in the tubing is greater than the water concentration of the solution in the beaker, so there will be a net movement of water molecules out of the tubing *[1 mark]*. Later, the level of the solution in the beaker will stop changing *[1 mark]*. The water concentration of the solutions in the tubing and the beaker will have become the same, so there will be no net movement of water molecules *[1 mark]*.

Page 12 — Active Transport

1.1   The movement of a substance from a more dilute solution to a more concentrated solution (against a concentration gradient) *[1 mark]*.

1.2   For energy/respiration *[1 mark]*.

1.3   It needs energy from respiration *[1 mark]*.

2.1   For growth *[1 mark]*.

2.2   The concentration of minerals is higher inside the plant cells than in the soil (outside the plant cells) *[1 mark]* so the minerals would move out of the plant cells by diffusion *[1 mark]*.

2.3   Active transport occurs against a concentration gradient but diffusion occurs down a concentration gradient *[1 mark]*. Active transport needs energy from respiration but diffusion doesn't *[1 mark]*.

2.4   The function of root hair cells is to take up substances from the soil *[1 mark]*. Root hair cells have elongated 'hairs' that stick out into the soil *[1 mark]*. These 'hairs' give the root a large surface area for absorbing substances *[1 mark]*.

Page 13 — Exchange Surfaces

Warm up

1   1 — blue whale, 2 — tiger, 3 — domestic cat, 4 — bacterium

1   A large surface area. / A thin membrane. / An efficient blood supply. / Being ventilated. *[4 marks]*

2.1   X = (3 × 3) × 6 = **54 cm²** *[1 mark]*
Y = 3 × 3 × 3 = **27 cm³** *[1 mark]*

2.2   Z = 150 ÷ 125 = **1.2** *[1 mark]*

2.3   5 × 5 × 5, because it has the smallest surface area to volume ratio / it has the most volume for the least surface area / it has the longest diffusion distance to the centre *[1 mark]*.

Page 14 — Exchanging Substances

1.1   A = carbon dioxide *[1 mark]*
B = oxygen *[1 mark]*

1.2   diffusion *[1 mark]*

1.3   short diffusion pathway — the walls of the alveoli are thin /one cell thick *[1 mark]*
large surface area — lots of alveoli *[1 mark]*

2   As the walls of the alveoli are broken down, the surface area in the lungs is reduced *[1 mark]*, so the amount of oxygen that can diffuse into the blood (from the air in the alveoli) at any one time is reduced *[1 mark]*. This means that their body cells are not getting enough oxygen for respiration during exercise, which results in lower energy levels *[1 mark]*.

3   The small intestine is covered in villi *[1 mark]* which increases the surface area for absorption *[1 mark]*.
There is a good blood supply *[1 mark]* which maintains the concentration gradient so absorption can happen quickly *[1 mark]*. The villi have a single layer of surface cells *[1 mark]* which give a short diffusion pathway *[1 mark]*.

Page 15 — More on Exchanging Substances

1.1   stomata *[1 mark]*

1.2   Carbon dioxide diffuses into the leaf *[1 mark]*.
Water vapour diffuses out of the leaf *[1 mark]*.
Oxygen diffuses out of the leaf *[1 mark]*.

1.3   They increase the surface area for carbon dioxide to diffuse into the cells *[1 mark]*.

2.1   They increase the surface area *[1 mark]*.

2.2   To (further) increase the surface area of the gills *[1 mark]*.

2.3   A good blood supply *[1 mark]*.

2.4   A fast-moving fish has more, longer gill filaments than a slow-moving fish. / A slow-moving fish has fewer, shorter gill filaments fast-moving fish. *[1 mark]*

2.5   Fast-moving fish are more active than slow-moving fish / Fast-moving fish do more respiration than slow-moving fish *[1 mark]* so they require more oxygen *[1 mark]*.

Topic B2 — Organisation

Page 16 — Cell Organisation

Warm-up

        Organ system – 4, Tissue – 2, Cell – 1, Organ – 3

1.1   X = Liver *[1 mark]*
        Y = Large intestine *[1 mark]*
        Z = Small intestine *[1 mark]*

1.2   A group of organs working together to perform a particular function *[1 mark]*.

1.3   A group of similar cells that work together to carry out a particular function *[1 mark]*.

1.4   It breaks down and absorbs food *[1 mark]*.

1.5   A group of different tissues that work together to perform a certain function *[1 mark]*.

Page 17 — Enzymes

1.1   active site *[1 mark]*

1.2   Part X/the active site is where the substrate involved in the reaction fits *[1 mark]*.

2.1   Line 2 *[1 mark]*

2.2   Line 2 shows an enzyme with a higher optimum temperature than the enzyme shown by Line 1 *[1 mark]* and it doesn't denature until a higher temperature *[1 mark]*. This suggests that the enzyme is adapted to working at the higher temperatures of a thermal vent than the enzyme represented by Line 1 *[1 mark]*.

2.3   The enzyme has been denatured *[1 mark]*, which has changed the shape of its active site *[1 mark]*. This means that the substrate will no longer fit the active site *[1 mark]*, so the enzyme will no longer catalyse the reaction *[1 mark]*.

Don't panic in the exam if you get a question about a context you've not met before. Just stop and think about what you know about enzymes, and it'll all become clear.

Page 18 — Investigating Enzymatic Reactions

1.1   pH 6 as this was the pH at which the iodine solution stopped turning blue-black first *[1 mark]*, meaning the starch had been broken down the fastest *[1 mark]*.

1.2   E.g. the amylase was denatured by the high pH, so the starch was not broken down *[1 mark]*.

1.3   By putting the test tubes in a water bath *[1 mark]*.

1.4   Any two from: e.g. the concentration of starch solution / the concentration of amylase / the volume of starch and amylase solution added to the iodine / the volume of iodine solution in the wells *[2 marks]*

1.5   E.g. test the solutions more frequently (e.g. every 10 seconds) *[1 mark]*.

Pages 19-20 — Enzymes and Digestion

Warm-up

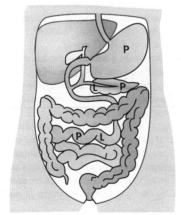

1.1   Carbohydrases *[1 mark]*

1.2   Sugars *[1 mark]*

2.1   They break down big molecules from food into smaller, soluble molecules that can pass easily through the walls of the digestive system *[1 mark]*, allowing them to be absorbed into the bloodstream *[1 mark]*.

2.2   Any two from: to make new carbohydrates. / To make new proteins. / To make new lipids. / Some glucose is used in respiration *[2 marks]*.

3.1   Produced: liver *[1 mark]*
        Stored: gall bladder *[1 mark]*

3.2   It neutralises the acid from the stomach in the small intestine and makes the conditions in the small intestine alkaline *[1 mark]*. This is important because the enzymes in the small intestine work best in these conditions *[1 mark]*. It emulsifies fat *[1 mark]*, which increases the surface area of fat for the enzyme lipase to work on, which makes its digestion faster *[1 mark]*.

4   How to grade your answer:

      Level 0:   There is no relevant information. *[No marks]*

      Level 1:   There is a brief description which includes the names of one or more of the relevant enzymes or where in the body they are produced. *[1 to 2 marks]*

      Level 2:   There is some description of how one or more of carbohydrates, proteins or lipids are digested, including where in the body the relevant enzymes are produced. *[3 to 4 marks]*

      Level 3:   There is a clear and detailed description of how carbohydrates, proteins and lipids are digested, including reference to where in the body the relevant enzymes are produced and to the end products of the reactions. *[5 to 6 marks]*

Here are some points your answer may include:

Carbohydrate digestion begins in the mouth, where amylase is produced by the salivary glands.

Carbohydrate digestion also occurs in the small intestine, which produces its own supply of amylase and also contains amylase produced by the pancreas.

Amylase converts the carbohydrates into sugars.

Protein is digested in the stomach, where proteases are produced.

Protein digestion also occurs in the small intestine, which produces proteases and also contains proteases produced by the pancreas.

Proteases convert protein into amino acids.

Lipids are digested in the small intestine, which produces lipases and also contains lipases produced by the pancreas.

Lipases convert lipids to fatty acids and glycerol.

The products of the digestive enzymes are absorbed into the bloodstream.

Page 21 — Food Tests

Warm-up

        Biuret test — Proteins, Benedict's test — Reducing sugars, Sudan III test — Lipids, Iodine test — Starch

1   How to grade your answer:

      Level 0:   There is no relevant information. *[No marks]*

      Level 1:   There is a brief description of how to carry out the investigation. *[1 to 2 marks]*

      Level 2:   There is some description of how to carry out the investigation but some details are missing. *[3 to 4 marks]*

      Level 3:   There is a clear and detailed description of how to carry out the investigation. *[5 to 6 marks]*

Here are some points your answer may include:

Grind up a sample of the egg white using a pestle and mortar.

Put the sample into a beaker and add some distilled water.

Stir well with a glass rod to allow some of the food to dissolve in the water.

Filter the mixture through a funnel lined with filter paper.

Transfer 2 cm^3 of the filtered solution into a clean test tube.

Add 2 cm^3 of Biuret solution and gently shake the test tube.

If the food sample contains protein, the solution will change from blue to pink or purple.

If no protein is present, the solution will stay bright blue.

2.1 He should add some Benedict's solution to each test tube using a pipette *[1 mark]*. He should then place the test tubes in a water bath set at 75 °C and leave them for 5 minutes *[1 mark]*. He should look out for a colour change and note which of a range of colours the solutions become *[1 mark]*.

Glucose is a reducing sugar so the Benedict's test can be used to determine the relative concentrations of glucose in the test tubes.

2.2

	Tube 1	Tube 2	Tube 3	Tube 4
substance observed	yellow precipitate	blue solution	red precipitate	green precipitate
glucose concentration (M)	**0.1**	**0**	**1**	**0.02**

[1 mark]

The higher the concentration of glucose in the solution, the further the colour change goes along the following scale: blue — green — yellow — brick red. If no precipitate forms then there are no reducing sugars in the solution.

Page 22 — The Lungs

Warm-up

bronchi, alveoli, oxygenates, carbon dioxide

1.1 A = trachea *[1 mark]*
B = bronchus *[1 mark]*
C = alveolus/alveoli *[1 mark]*

1.2 capillary *[1 mark]*

1.3 The capillary carries blood that is returning from the rest of the body and contains a higher concentration of carbon dioxide than in the lungs *[1 mark]*. The carbon dioxide diffuses into the alveoli, where there is a lower concentration, to be breathed out *[1 mark]*. The capillary also picks up oxygen from the alveoli, which contain a higher concentration of oxygen than in the blood *[1 mark]*. Oxygen diffuses from the alveoli into the blood, where there is a lower concentration, to be carried to the body cells *[1 mark]*.

Page 23 — Circulatory System — The Heart

1.1 X = aorta
Y = pulmonary vein
Z = (right) ventricle

1.2

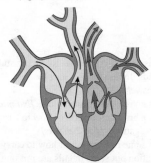

[1 mark for arrow(s) showing blood flow from the vena cava, through the right atrium and ventricle, then up through the pulmonary artery.]

1.3 Because it consists of two circuits joined together *[1 mark]*. The first one pumps deoxygenated blood to the lungs to take in oxygen and returns oxygenated blood to the heart *[1 mark]*. The second one pumps oxygenated blood around all the other organs of the body and returns deoxygenated blood to the heart *[1 mark]*.

2.1 The heartbeat is controlled by a group of cells in the right atrium wall *[1 mark]* that act as a pacemaker *[1 mark]*.

2.2 An artificial pacemaker could be fitted *[1 mark]*. This produces an electric current to keep the heart beating regularly *[1 mark]*.

Pages 24-25 — Circulatory System — Blood Vessels

1.1 A *[1 mark]*

1.2 The walls of arteries contain thick layers of muscle to make them strong *[1 mark]* and elastic fibres to allow them to stretch and spring back *[1 mark]*.

1.3 veins *[1 mark]*

1.4 To prevent the blood flowing backwards / to keep the blood flowing in the right direction *[1 mark]*.

1.5 Capillaries carry blood close to cells to exchange substances with them *[1 mark]*. Having thin walls increases the rate at which substances can diffuse across them by decreasing the distance over which diffusion occurs *[1 mark]*.

2.1 E.g. the graph shows that as an increasing amount of mass was added and then removed from the ring of artery, the percentage change in the ring's length remained at 0 *[1 mark]*, so the ring returned to its original length each time the mass was removed *[1 mark]*. As the amount of mass added and then removed from the ring of vein increased, the percentage change in the ring's length increased *[1 mark]*, so the ring did not return to its original length once the mass was removed and the greater the mass, the further it was from its original length *[1 mark]*.

2.2 Any sensible precaution, e.g. wear safety goggles / wear gloves / disinfect the workstation after the experiment / wash hands after the experiment *[1 mark]*.

Page 26 — Circulatory System — Blood

1.1 Because white blood cells defend against infection *[1 mark]*.

1.2 Some white blood cells can change shape to engulf microorganisms in a process called phagocytosis *[1 mark]*. Others produce antibodies to fight microorganisms *[1 mark]* or antitoxins to neutralise any toxins produced by the microorganisms *[1 mark]*.

1.3 They have a biconcave disc shape to give a large surface area for absorbing oxygen *[1 mark]*. They don't have a nucleus, which allows more room to carry oxygen *[1 mark]*. They contain haemoglobin, which binds to oxygen and transports it to cells in the body tissues *[1 mark]*.

1.4 plasma *[1 mark]*

1.5 Platelets are small fragments of cells with no nucleus *[1 mark]*. They help the blood to clot at a wound *[1 mark]*.

Pages 27-28 — Cardiovascular Disease

Warm-up

blood vessels, coronary heart disease, coronary arteries, fatty material

1.1 Because it restricts the blood flow to the heart muscle *[1 mark]*, leading to a lack of oxygen reaching it *[1 mark]*.

1.2 The doctor might recommend a stent *[1 mark]*. Stents are tubes that are inserted inside arteries to keep them open to make sure that blood can pass through to the heart muscle *[1 mark]*.

2.1 They reduce the amount of 'bad' cholesterol present in the bloodstream *[1 mark]*. This slows down the rate of fatty deposits forming in the coronary arteries *[1 mark]*.

2.2 E.g. he is worried about side effects the statins might cause *[1 mark]*.

3.1 It would allow the blood to flow in both directions in part of the heart *[1 mark]*, meaning that blood doesn't circulate around the body as effectively as normal *[1 mark]*.

3.2 It might not open fully *[1 mark]*.

3.3 A valve taken from a human or another mammal *[1 mark]*.

3.4 A man-made/artificial valve *[1 mark]*.

3.5 To keep a patient alive while waiting for a donor heart to be found *[1 mark]* or to help a person recover by allowing their heart to rest and heal *[1 mark]*.

3.6 Advantage — e.g. natural donor hearts don't have any mechanical parts like electric motors that could wear out. / Blood flows more smoothly through natural hearts *[1 mark]*. Disadvantage — e.g. natural donor hearts aren't always available straight away. / Natural donor hearts are more likely to be rejected by the body's immune system *[1 mark]*.

Page 29 — Health and Disease

1.1 A disease that can spread from person to person or between animals and people *[1 mark]*.

1.2 Any two from: whether you have a good, balanced diet. / The stress you are under. / Your life situation *[2 marks]*.

2.1

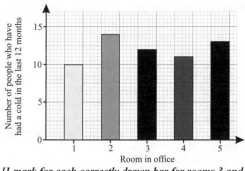

[1 mark for each correctly drawn bar for rooms 3 and 5.]

Room 1	Room 2	Room 3	Room 4	Room 5	**Total**
10	**14**	12	11	**13**	60

[1 mark for each number filled in correctly.]

You're given the total number of people who have had colds in the table (60). So to work out the figure for Room 5, you'd take the total for Rooms 1–4 away from 60.

2.2   It would increase the chance of the person getting a communicable disease *[1 mark]* because their body is less likely to be able to defend itself against the pathogen that causes the disease *[1 mark]*.

Pages 30-31 — Risk Factors for Non-Communicable Diseases

1.1   Something that is linked to an increase in the likelihood that a person will develop a certain disease during their lifetime *[1 mark]*.

1.2   Aspects of a person's lifestyle *[1 mark]*. Substances in the body *[1 mark]*.

1.3   E.g. type 2 diabetes *[1 mark]*

2.1   Any two from: e.g. a high fat diet / a lack of exercise / smoking *[2 marks]*

2.2   Any two from: e.g. the cost of researching and treating non-communicable diseases is huge. / Families may have to move or adapt their home to help a family member with a non-communicable disease, which can be costly. / If someone has to give up work/dies because of a non-communicable disease, family income will reduce. / A reduction in the people able to work may affect a country's economy *[2 marks]*.

3.1   The number of people with diabetes increased between 2012 and 2018 *[1 mark]*.

3.2   How to grade your answer:
     Level 0:   There is no relevant information. *[No marks]*
     Level 1:   One or two comments about the student's statements are made but only points in support of or against the student's statement are given.
          [1 to 2 marks]
     Level 2:   A detailed discussion of the student's statement is given, including points both in support and against.
          [3 to 4 marks]

Here are some points your answer may include:
<u>In support of the student's statement:</u>
Both graphs show an overall positive correlation. / Both the rate of obesity and the rate of diabetes increase overall between 2012 and 2018.
It is generally accepted that obesity is a risk factor for Type 2 diabetes.
<u>Against the student's statement:</u>
A correlation between the number of people with diabetes and the prevalence of obesity doesn't show that diabetes is caused by obesity — there may be another factor that affects both.
Figure 1 shows that the percentage of people with obesity fell between 2015 and 2016, while the number of people with diabetes increased in the same year, which contradicts the student's statement.
The student is only comparing data for seven years — it may be that the trend is not present over a longer period of time.

Page 32 — Cancer

Warm-up

Malignant Tumours — Are cancerous
Benign Tumours — Are not cancerous
— Can invade neighbouring tissues

1.1   Uncontrolled cell division *[1 mark]*
1.2   genetic risk factors *[1 mark]*
2.1   malignant *[1 mark]*
2.2   Cells break off a tumour and spread to other parts of the body by travelling in the bloodstream *[1 mark]*. The malignant cells then invade healthy tissues elsewhere in the body and form secondary tumours *[1 mark]*.

Page 33 — Plant Cell Organisation

1.1   An organ system *[1 mark]*
1.2   Water *[1 mark]*, mineral ions *[1 mark]*
2.1   Growing tips of roots *[1 mark]*
     Growing tips of shoots *[1 mark]*
2.2   It can differentiate into lots of different types of plant cells *[1 mark]*.
3.1   A: palisade mesophyll tissue *[1 mark]*
     B: spongy mesophyll tissue *[1 mark]*
3.2   It contains lots of chloroplasts, which are the structures where photosynthesis takes place *[1 mark]* and is located near the top of the leaf so that the chloroplasts can get the most light *[1 mark]*.
3.3   They increase the rate of diffusion of gases *[1 mark]*.

Page 34 — Transpiration and Translocation

Warm-up

transpiration, evaporation, leaves, translocation, sugars, phloem

1   How to grade your answer:
     Level 0:   There is no relevant information. *[No marks]*
     Level 1:   There is a brief description of either the structure or the function of one or both of the plant tissues. *[1 to 2 marks]*
     Level 2:   There is some description of both the structure and the function of both plant tissues. *[3 to 4 marks]*
     Level 3:   There is detailed description of both the structure and the function of both plant tissues. *[5 to 6 marks]*

Here are some points your answer may include:
Xylem is made of dead cells joined together end to end.
The walls are strengthened with lignin.
The dead cells have no end walls between them, so there is a hole down the middle of the tissue.
Water and mineral ions travel through the xylem tubes from the roots to the stem and leaves.
This is called the transpiration stream.
Phloem is made of columns of elongated living cells.
The cells have small pores in the end walls to allow cell sap to flow through.
This means that dissolved sugars made in the leaves can travel to the rest of the plant.
Phloem can transport dissolved sugars in both directions in the tissue.
Transport of dissolved sugars in phloem is called translocation.

Page 35-36 — Transpiration and Stomata

1.1   X = stomata *[1 mark]*
     Y = guard cells *[1 mark]*
1.2   They are responsible for opening and closing the stomata *[1 mark]* in order to control gas exchange and water loss from a leaf *[1 mark]*.
2.1   Mean width of stomata in leaf A =
     (25.2 + 20.1 + 18.7 + 17.9 + 19.1 + 19.3 + 22.0 + 23.1 + 21.8 + 20.3) ÷ 10 = **20.8 μm** *[1 mark]*

     Mean width of stomata in leaf B =
     (14.7 + 12.8 + 14.1 + 13.2 + 12.9 + 11.9 + 12.1 + 13.4 + 10.9 + 11.7) ÷ 10 = **12.8 μm** *[1 mark]*
2.2   Leaf B *[1 mark]*

2.3 Because stomata begin to close when it gets darker / Less carbon dioxide is needed for photosynthesis at lower light intensities *[1 mark]* and so the leaf with the lower mean will have had the measurements taken in a lower light intensity *[1 mark]*.

3.1

[1 mark for using a sensible scale for the y-axis, 1 mark for labelling the y-axis, 1 mark for accurately plotting the points, 1 mark for connecting the points with straight lines through the centre of each point.]

It might sound a bit obvious, but make sure you always use a sharp pencil to draw graphs like this. Your graph might turn out inaccurate if your pencil is blunt, which could lose you marks.

3.2 5.0 cm³/hour *[1 mark]*
3.3 5.1 cm³/hour *[1 mark]*
3.4 Any two from: e.g. light intensity increased. / Temperature increased. / Air flow around the leaf improved. / Humidity decreased *[2 marks]*.

Topic B3 — Infection and Response

Page 37 — Communicable Disease

1.1 Both bacteria and viruses can reproduce quickly in the body *[1 mark]*.
1.2 It can cause the cells to burst *[1 mark]*.
2 How to grade your answer:

Level 0: There is no relevant information. *[No marks]*
Level 1: There is a brief description of either how the housefly picks up pathogens or how it spreads them to humans. *[1 to 2 marks]*
Level 2: There is some description of how the housefly picks up pathogens and how it spreads them to humans. *[3 to 4 marks]*
Level 3: There is a detailed description of how the housefly picks up pathogens and how it spreads them to humans. *[5 to 6 marks]*

Here are some points your answer may include:
Picking up pathogens:
The housefly uses its wings to fly to a dirty place, e.g. animal faeces, dustbin, rubbish dump, etc.
Pathogens stick to the fly's body.
Pathogens stick to the hairs on the fly's legs.
Pathogens are picked up on the fly's wings.
Pathogens are eaten by the fly.
Transfer to humans:
The fly uses its wings to travel to a human food source.
The fly secretes saliva on a human food source along with pathogens that the fly ate.
The housefly transfers pathogens onto a human food source from its body/leg hairs/wings.
The housefly deposits faeces onto a human food source.
Humans then eat the contaminated food source and take in the pathogens.

Pages 38-39 — Viral, Fungal and Protist Diseases

Warm-up
protist, vectors, fever, breeding

1.1 virus *[1 mark]*
1.2 The infected person coughs/sneezes *[1 mark]*. The virus is carried in the air in droplets *[1 mark]*. Other people on the train breathe in/inhale the droplets *[1 mark]*.

Remember, pathogens can be spread by water, through the air, by vectors, or by direct contact.

1.3 The person can be vaccinated against the pathogen *[1 mark]*.
2.1 antiretroviral drugs *[1 mark]*
2.2 the immune system *[1 mark]*
2.3 sexual contact *[1 mark]*, exchange of blood when people share needles *[1 mark]*
3.1 E.g. tomato plant *[1 mark]*
3.2 The leaves have a mosaic pattern (where parts of the leaves become discoloured) *[1 mark]*.
3.3 The discolouration of the leaves means that the plant can't carry out photosynthesis as well, so growth is affected *[1 mark]*.
3.4 E.g. the diameter of the fruit from the infected plant is smaller than the healthy plant *[1 mark]*. The fruit from the infected plant has a lower/smaller mass than the healthy plant *[1 mark]*.
4.1 Purple or black spots develop on the leaves *[1 mark]*. These leaves can then turn yellow *[1 mark]* and drop off *[1 mark]*.
4.2 Because the disease can spread to other plants in water or by the wind *[1 mark]*.
4.3 If any leaves are left, the fungus could spread to other living rose plants *[1 mark]*.

By destroying the fungus, there won't be any left to spread to other plants.

Page 40 — Bacterial Diseases and Preventing Disease

1.1 Any two from: e.g. fever / stomach cramps / vomiting / diarrhoea *[2 marks]*.
1.2 toxins *[1 mark]*
1.3 The vaccination helps to prevent the spread of the disease in poultry *[1 mark]*. This means that the poultry that humans eat will be less likely to be contaminated with the *Salmonella* bacteria *[1 mark]*.
1.4 E.g. by washing hands thoroughly after using the toilet. / By avoiding preparing food. / By the infected person being isolated from other individuals *[1 mark]*.

There's more than one right answer here — just think of any sensible way of preventing the bacteria from being transferred from person to person.

2.1 Through sexual contact *[1 mark]*.
2.2 E.g. pain when urinating *[1 mark]*. A thick yellow or green discharge from the vagina *[1 mark]*.
2.3 penicillin *[1 mark]*
2.4 condoms *[1 mark]*

Page 41 — Fighting Disease

1.1 It acts as a barrier to stop pathogens getting inside the body *[1 mark]*. It secretes antimicrobial substances, which kill pathogens *[1 mark]*.
1.2 It has hairs and mucus, which trap particles that could contain pathogens *[1 mark]*.
2 How to grade your answer:

Level 0: There is no relevant information. *[No marks]*
Level 1: There is a brief description of either the body's defences or the role of the immune system. *[1 to 2 marks]*
Level 2: There is at least one correct description of the body's defences and at least one correct description of the role of the immune system. *[3 to 4 marks]*
Level 3: There is more than one correct description of the body's defences and more than one correct description of the role of the immune system. *[5 to 6 marks]*

Here are some points your answer may include:
The body's defences:
The trachea and bronchi secrete mucus to trap pathogens that have entered the body.
The trachea and bronchi are lined with cilia.
Cilia are hair-like structures which waft mucus up to the back of the throat where it can be swallowed.
The stomach produces hydrochloric acid, which kills pathogens that have been swallowed.
The role of the immune system:
The immune system contains white blood cells, which travel round the body in the blood.
White blood cells can engulf pathogens and digest them — this is called phagocytosis.
White blood cells can produce antibodies that can kill pathogens.
White blood cells can produce antitoxins that counteract toxins produced by invading bacteria.

You wouldn't get marks for talking about the skin or about the hairs in the nose — they're there to stop pathogens getting inside your body in the first place. This question is asking you to describe that defences that the body has for pathogens that have managed to make it inside your body.

Page 42 — Fighting Disease — Vaccination

1.1 small amounts of dead/inactive pathogens *[1 mark]*
1.2 White blood cells are stimulated to produce antibodies *[1 mark]*.
2.1 Because the body should be able to rapidly mass-produce antibodies to kill off the mumps pathogens *[1 mark]*.
2.2 The large proportion of the population who have been vaccinated against the pathogen are unlikely to catch the disease *[1 mark]*. This means that the people who aren't vaccinated are unlikely to catch the disease because there are fewer people able to pass it on *[1 mark]*.
3.1 The traveller is less likely to become ill with cholera whilst they are visiting the country *[1 mark]* and then bring it back to their own country *[1 mark]*.
3.2 It can help to prevent anyone from bringing certain diseases into the country *[1 mark]*.

Page 43 — Fighting Disease — Drugs

1.1 Viruses reproduce using your body cells *[1 mark]*, which makes it very difficult to develop drugs that destroy just the virus without killing the body's cells *[1 mark]*.
1.2 E.g. painkiller / cold remedy *[1 mark]*
1.3 Because the drug is unable to kill pathogens *[1 mark]*.
2.1 Bacteria that can't be killed by an antibiotic *[1 mark]*.
2.2 The number of antibiotic-resistant infections increased between 2013 and 2015 *[1 mark]*.
2.3 153 − 84 = 69
(69 ÷ 84) × 100 = 82.14 = **82%** *[2 marks for correct answer, otherwise 1 mark for correct working.]*

Page 44 — Developing Drugs

1.1 E.g. toxicity, efficacy and dosage *[3 marks]*
1.2 cells, tissues and live animals *[1 mark]*
It'd be no use testing on dead animals, as their cells and tissues won't respond in the same way as living tissues. You also wouldn't want to test on humans or patients at this stage, just in case the drug proves to be dangerous.
2.1 In case the drug has any harmful effects *[1 mark]*.
2.2 In double blind trials, patients would be randomly split into two groups *[1 mark]*. One group would be given a placebo and the other group would be given the drug *[1 mark]*. Neither the patients nor the doctors would know who was in which group until after the results had been gathered *[1 mark]*.
2.3 It allows for the placebo effect. / It prevents the patient expecting the treatment to work and therefore feeling better, even though the treatment isn't doing anything. / It prevents the doctors who are analysing the results from being subconsciously influenced by their knowledge. *[1 mark]*
2.4 E.g. it helps to check that the work is valid. / It helps to prevent false claims *[1 mark]*.
2.5 E.g. to prevent them showing bias *[1 mark]* in their analysis of the results, and giving support to the results when in fact they weren't valid *[1 mark]*.

Topic B4 — Bioenergetics

Page 45 — Photosynthesis and Limiting Factors

1.1 the Sun / the environment *[1 mark]*
1.2 **carbon dioxide** *[1 mark]* + water → glucose + **oxygen** *[1 mark]*
1.3 cellulose *[1 mark]*
1.4 Any two from: e.g. for respiration. / For making amino acids (which are used to make proteins) by combining the glucose with nitrate ions. / It is converted to lipids (fats and oils) for storage. / It is turned into starch for storage *[2 marks]*.
2.1 An endothermic reaction is where energy is transferred from the environment during the process *[1 mark]*.
2.2 nitrate concentration *[1 mark]*
2.3 The rate of photosynthesis would decrease *[1 mark]* because the chloroplasts wouldn't be able to absorb as much light *[1 mark]*.

Pages 46-48 — The Rate of Photosynthesis

Warm-up
low, slowly, high, damaged

1.1 Any two from: e.g. adding a heater — to increase the temperature, which will increase the rate of photosynthesis. / Supplying artificial light — to increase the light intensity, which will increase the rate of photosynthesis. / Adding a paraffin heater — to increase the carbon dioxide concentration, which will increase the rate of photosynthesis. *[1 mark for each correct improvement and 1 mark for each correct explanation, up to 4 marks.]*
1.2 Because the farmer will get a better yield *[1 mark]*, which means they will also make more money/profit *[1 mark]*.
2.1 At first, as the carbon dioxide concentration increases, the rate of photosynthesis increases as well *[1 mark]*. Then, at 0.10 arbitrary units of carbon dioxide, the graph flattens out — as the carbon dioxide concentration increases, the rate of photosynthesis no longer increases *[1 mark]*.
2.2 E.g. temperature *[1 mark]*, light intensity *[1 mark]*
2.3

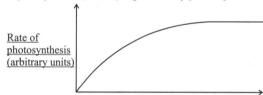

Rate of photosynthesis (arbitrary units)

Light intensity (arbitrary units)

[1 mark for correctly labelled axes, 1 mark for correctly sketched line.]
3.1 It will increase *[1 mark]*.
3.2 distance = 20 cm, so 20^2 = 400 *[1 mark]*
1 ÷ 400 = **0.0025 arbitrary units** *[1 mark]*
3.3 How to grade your answer:
Level 0: There is no relevant information. *[No marks]*
Level 1: There is a brief description of a method used to investigate the effect of temperature on the rate of photosynthesis, with no control variables mentioned. *[1 to 2 marks]*
Level 2: There is some description of a method used to investigate the effect of temperature on the rate of photosynthesis, including an example of a variable to control. *[3 to 4 marks]*
Level 3: There is detailed description of a method used to investigate the effect of temperature on the rate of photosynthesis, including more than one example of variables to control. *[5 to 6 marks]*
Here are some points your answer may include:
A test tube is clamped in place in a water bath at a particular temperature, e.g. 10 °C.
Once the water in the test tube has reached the correct temperature, the pondweed is added to the test tube and the test tube is sealed.
A capillary tube and syringe are attached to the test tube.
The pondweed is left to photosynthesise for a set amount of time.
At the end of the experiment, the syringe is used to draw the gas bubble in the capillary tube up alongside a ruler and the length of the gas bubble that has formed is measured. This is proportional to the volume of oxygen produced.

The experiment is repeated twice at this starting temperature. Then the whole experiment is repeated at different temperatures, e.g. 15 °C, 20 °C, 25 °C.
The variables that should be controlled in this experiment include light intensity and the concentration of carbon dioxide.

Pages 49-50 — Respiration and Metabolism

1.1   exothermic (reaction) *[1 mark]*

1.2   E.g. to build up larger molecules from smaller ones *[1 mark]*. To allow the gull's muscles to contract *[1 mark]*. To keep the gull's body temperature steady in cooler surroundings *[1 mark]*.

2.1   Plants, e.g: cellulose / starch / proteins *[1 mark]*
    Animals, e.g: glycogen / proteins *[1 mark]*

2.2   A lipid is made from one molecule of glycerol *[1 mark]* and three fatty acids *[1 mark]*.

2.3   Glucose is combined with nitrate ions *[1 mark]* to make amino acids, which are then made into proteins *[1 mark]*.

2.4   urea *[1 mark]*

3.1   Any two from, e.g. the mass of the peas or glass beads in the flask / the size of the flask / the type of peas / the temperature outside of the flasks / the temperature of the peas at the start of the experiment *[2 marks]*.

3.2   E.g. she could repeat her experiment and calculate a mean temperature increase for each flask *[1 mark]*.

3.3   The boiled peas will not germinate, so flask 2 is included to show that the increase in temperature in flask 1 is due to the peas germinating *[1 mark]*. Flask 3 is included to show that the temperature change is due to the presence of the peas and no other factor *[1 mark]*.

The temperature in flask 3 should remain constant — if it changed, this would suggest there was an error in the experiment.

3.4   E.g. she could include another flask that contained disinfected boiled peas. / She could disinfect the peas (and the glass beads) with an antiseptic before starting the experiment *[1 mark]*

If there was no temperature change in a flask containing disinfected boiled peas, the student could conclude that the temperature increase in the flask of boiled peas in her first experiment was due to the presence of microorganisms.

Pages 51-52 — Aerobic and Anaerobic Respiration

Warm-up
    Aerobic respiration — Respiration using oxygen.
    Anaerobic respiration — Respiration without oxygen.
    Fermentation — Respiration without oxygen.

1.1   E.g. the snail must have enough oxygen for two hours / the snail must not dry out *[1 mark]*.

1.2   The percentage of carbon dioxide in the air has increased over the two hours because the snail gives out carbon dioxide as it respires *[1 mark]*.

1.3   The percentage of carbon dioxide in the air has stayed the same over the two hours because the glass beads were not respiring *[1 mark]*.

1.4   It will have decreased *[1 mark]* because the snail will have used up oxygen as it respired *[1 mark]*.

1.5   To show that it's the snail producing carbon dioxide (and not just the presence of something in the beaker) *[1 mark]*.

2.1   glucose *[1 mark]*

2.2   Ethanol — to make alcoholic drinks *[1 mark]*.
    Carbon dioxide — to make bread rise *[1 mark]*.

3   Aerobic respiration in muscle cells uses oxygen, whereas anaerobic respiration doesn't *[1 mark]*. Aerobic respiration in muscle cells forms carbon dioxide and water, whereas anaerobic respiration forms lactic acid *[1 mark]*. Aerobic respiration in muscles cells transfers a lot of energy, whereas anaerobic respiration in muscle cells transfers a small amount of energy *[1 mark]*.

Pages 53-54 — Exercise

Warm-up
    muscles, oxygen debt, oxygen, lactic acid

1.1 $(12 + 11 + 12) \div 3 = 11.6... = $ **12** breaths per minute *[1 mark]*

1.2   During exercise the breathing rate increased *[1 mark]* to get more oxygen into the blood *[1 mark]*, which was needed for increased respiration in the muscles *[1 mark]*.

1.3   The breathing rate remained high one minute after exercise *[1 mark]* because there were still high levels of lactic acid and carbon dioxide in the blood *[1 mark]*. The high breathing rate helps remove these from the body *[1 mark]*. The breathing rate had returned to normal by five minutes after exercise *[1 mark]* because the oxygen debt had been paid off *[1 mark]*.

1.4   breath volume *[1 mark]*, heart rate *[1 mark]*

2.1 $80 - 20 = 60$
    $(60 \div 20) \times 100 = $ **300%** *[2 marks for correct answer, otherwise 1 mark for correct working.]*

2.2   The muscles started to respire anaerobically *[1 mark]*, which formed lactic acid *[1 mark]* as a result of the incomplete oxidation of glucose *[1 mark]*.

2.3   They become fatigued *[1 mark]* and stop contracting efficiently *[1 mark]*.

2.4   Blood transports the lactic acid to the liver *[1 mark]*, where it is converted back to glucose *[1 mark]*.

Topic B5 — Homeostasis and Response

Page 55 — Homeostasis

1.1   The regulation of the conditions inside the body/cells to maintain a stable internal environment *[1 mark]* in response to changes in internal and external conditions *[1 mark]*.

1.2   They maintain the right conditions for cells to function properly. / They maintain the right conditions for enzyme action. *[1 mark]*

1.3   receptor *[1 mark]*

1.4   The receptors detect that the blood pressure is too high and send a signal to the coordination centre *[1 mark]*. The coordination centre processes the information and organises a response / stimulates an effector *[1 mark]*. The effector produces a response to decrease the blood pressure (back to its optimum level) *[1 mark]*.

You don't need to know all about the regulation of blood pressure to answer this question — you just need to know the sequence of events in a negative feedback response, from receptors to effectors.

2.1   15 minutes *[1 mark]*

2.2 $30 - 20 = 10$ min
    $35.0 - 34.5 = 0.5$ °C
    $0.5 \div 10 = $ **0.05 °C/min** *[2 marks for correct answer, otherwise 1 mark for correct working.]*

Pages 56-57 — The Nervous System

1.1   X — brain *[1 mark]*
    Y— spinal cord *[1 mark]*

1.2   central nervous system/CNS *[1 mark]*

1.3   It receives information from receptors and coordinates a response (which is carried out by effectors) *[1 mark]*.

2.1   It allows organisms to react to their surroundings *[1 mark]* and coordinate their behaviour *[1 mark]*.

2.2   Spinal cord — coordinator *[1 mark]*
    Bright light — stimulus *[1 mark]*
    Blinking — response *[1 mark]*

2.3   Sensory neurones *[1 mark]* and motor neurones *[1 mark]*.

2.4   Muscles — contract *[1 mark]*
    Glands — secrete hormones *[1 mark]*

3.1   E.g. it will reduce the effect of random errors on their results *[1 mark]*.

3.2   uncertainty = range ÷ 2 = $(25 - 15) \div 2 = 10 \div 2$
    $= \pm$ **5 mm** *[2 marks for correct answer, otherwise 1 mark for correct working.]*

3.3   E.g. move the toothpicks together at smaller intervals (e.g. 1 mm) around the point where the person can only feel one toothpick *[1 mark]*.

3.4   Repeat the experiment on the forearm more times to see if it still doesn't fit in with the rest of the results *[1 mark]*.

3.5   The students have only tested three parts of the body / they haven't tested all parts of the body *[1 mark]*, so they can only conclude that the palm is the most sensitive out of the parts tested *[1 mark]*.

Page 58 — Synapses and Reflexes

Warm-up

Dropping a hot plate. The pupil widening in dim light.
Reflex reactions are rapid and automatic. *[1 mark]*

2.1 X — sensory neurone *[1 mark]*
Y — relay neurone *[1 mark]*
Z — motor neurone *[1 mark]*

2.2 stimulus — flame/fire *[1 mark]*
coordinator — spinal cord / relay neurone *[1 mark]*
effector — muscle *[1 mark]*

2.3 synapse *[1 mark]*

2.4 Chemicals diffuse across the gap and transfer the nerve signal *[1 mark]*.

Page 59 — Investigating Reaction Time

1.1 Student 2 = (0.16 + 0.13 + 0.15) ÷ 3 = 0.1466...
= **0.15 s** *[1 mark]*
Student 3 = (0.20 + 0.22 + 0.19) ÷ 3 = 0.2033...
= **0.20 s** *[1 mark]*

1.2 Student 1, Test 3 (0.43 s) *[1 mark]*

1.3 The students' reaction times without caffeine would act as a control for each student *[1 mark]*. The results from each student's tests could then be compared to the control to see if caffeine actually had an effect on reaction time *[1 mark]*.

1.4 E.g. the reaction times of student 1, 2 and 3 will be affected to different extents by caffeine due to natural variation between them *[1 mark]*, so the investigation isn't a fair test *[1 mark]*. / Two variables (the caffeinated drink and the student) are being changed *[1 mark]*, so the investigation isn't a fair test *[1 mark]*.

1.5 Any three from: e.g. the hand that the student used to catch the ruler. / The height from which the ruler was dropped. / The ruler used. / The person dropping the ruler. / The way that the student was positioned to catch the ruler. / The time between the consumption of caffeine and the test.
[3 marks — 1 mark for each correct answer.]

You wouldn't get a mark for saying that the amount of caffeine given to each student should be the same each time — this was said in the question.

Page 60 — The Endocrine System

1.1 Glands secrete hormones directly into the blood. *[1 mark]*

1.2 Hormones are chemical molecules. *[1 mark]*

1.3 E.g. the effects of the endocrine system are slower *[1 mark]*. The effects of the endocrine system are longer lasting *[1 mark]*.

2.1 A — pituitary gland *[1 mark]*
B — thyroid *[1 mark]*
C — adrenal gland *[1 mark]*
D — pancreas *[1 mark]*
E — ovary *[1 mark]*

2.2 pituitary gland *[1 mark]*

2.3 They act on other glands *[1 mark]* to direct them to release other hormones that bring about change *[1 mark]*.

Page 61-62 — Controlling Blood Glucose

1.1 pancreas *[1 mark]*

1.2 insulin *[1 mark]*

1.3 It moves into liver and muscle cells *[1 mark]* and is converted to glycogen for storage *[1 mark]*.

2.1 The pancreas produces little or no insulin *[1 mark]*.

2.2 Uncontrolled high blood glucose level *[1 mark]*.

2.3 E.g. the person's diet. / How active the person is. *[1 mark]*

2.4 The body cells no longer respond to the insulin produced by the pancreas *[1 mark]*.

2.5 Eat a carbohydrate-controlled diet *[1 mark]* and get regular exercise *[1 mark]*.

2.6 being overweight / obesity *[1 mark]*

3.1 The blood glucose concentration starts increasing as glucose from the drink is absorbed into the blood *[1 mark]*.
The pancreas detects a high blood glucose concentration and secretes insulin *[1 mark]*. Insulin causes the blood glucose concentration to fall back down *[1 mark]*.

3.2 glucagon *[1 mark]*

3.3 It increases the concentration of glucose in the blood *[1 mark]*.

3.4 Glucagon causes glycogen to be converted into glucose and be released into the blood *[1 mark]*.

3.5 E.g. after drinking the glucose drink, the blood glucose concentration would carry on increasing / stay high / not start to fall / fall more slowly *[1 mark]*.

Page 63 — Puberty and the Menstrual Cycle

1.1 oestrogen *[1 mark]*
1.2 ovulation *[1 mark]*
1.3 Every 28 days *[1 mark]*
1.4 luteinising hormone *[1 mark]*
1.5 testosterone *[1 mark]*
1.6 testes *[1 mark]*
2.1 oestrogen *[1 mark]*, progesterone *[1 mark]*
2.2 pituitary gland *[1 mark]*
2.3 It causes an egg to mature in one of the ovaries *[1 mark]* and stimulates the ovaries to produce hormones/oestrogen *[1 mark]*.
2.4 oestrogen *[1 mark]*

Pages 64-65 — Controlling Fertility

Warm-up

Hormonal	Non-hormonal
contraceptive injection plastic intrauterine device contraceptive patch	abstinence condom diaphragm sterilisation

1.1 As a tablet taken by mouth. *[1 mark]*
1.2 The hormones inhibit FSH production *[1 mark]*.
1.3 progesterone *[1 mark]*
1.4 It stops the maturation/release of eggs. / It makes it hard for sperm to swim to the egg. / It stops any fertilised egg implanting in the uterus. *[1 mark]*
2.1 condom *[1 mark]*
2.2 female condom / diaphragm *[1 mark]*
2.3 They prevent the sperm reaching an egg *[1 mark]*.
2.4 spermicidal agents / spermicides *[1 mark]*
2.5 Avoiding intercourse when the woman is at the most fertile point in her menstrual cycle *[1 mark]*.
2.6 sterilisation *[1 mark]*
2.7 condom *[1 mark]*
3.1 E.g. the woman does not have to remember to take the contraceptive every day *[1 mark]*.
3.2 E.g. the injection lasts for several months, so if she has any side effects they may last for a long time *[1 mark]*.
3.3 E.g. barrier methods do not have the possible side effects associated with taking hormones *[1 mark]*.

Page 66 — More on Controlling Fertility

1.1 FSH is needed to stimulate eggs to mature. / No eggs would be released so the woman would not be able to become pregnant. *[1 mark]*
1.2 Luteinising hormone / LH *[1 mark]* because it stimulates the release of an egg *[1 mark]*.
1.3 Advantage: e.g. the woman may become pregnant naturally / without needing IVF *[1 mark]*.
Disadvantage: e.g. some women need several treatments so it can be expensive. / Too many eggs may be stimulated resulting in unexpected multiple pregnancies. *[1 mark]*
2.1 The mother is given FSH and LH *[1 mark]* to stimulate the maturation of several eggs *[1 mark]*. Several eggs are collected from the mother and fertilised by sperm from the father in a laboratory *[1 mark]*. The fertilised eggs are grown into embryos in the laboratory *[1 mark]*. At the stage when they are tiny balls of cells, one or two embryos are inserted into the mother's uterus *[1 mark]*.
2.2 Any two from: e.g. the treatment may not work so repeated attempts are needed, which could be upsetting/stressful for the couple. / It can result in multiple births which can be a risk to the mother's health. / The mother may have a strong reaction to the hormones (e.g. pain, vomiting). *[2 marks]*

Page 67 — Adrenaline and Thyroxine

Warm-up

Clockwise from top left: high, inhibited, normal, stimulated, low.

1.1 Thyroxine regulates basal metabolic rate *[1 mark]*.
1.2 thyroid gland *[1 mark]*
2.1 adrenal glands *[1 mark]*
2.2 E.g. it increases heart rate *[1 mark]*, which boosts the delivery of oxygen to the brain and muscles *[1 mark]* and also boosts the delivery of glucose to the brain and muscles *[1 mark]*.
2.3 flight or fight *[1 mark]*

Topic B6 — Inheritance, Variation and Evolution

Page 68 — DNA

1.1 DNA is located in the nucleus of animal and plant cells *[1 mark]*.
1.2 The structures that contain DNA *[1 mark]*.
2.1 Genes code for particular sequences of amino acids *[1 mark]*, which are put together to make specific proteins *[1 mark]*.
2.2 The entire set of genetic material in an organism *[1 mark]*.
2.3 E.g. it allows scientists to identify genes that are linked to different types of diseases *[1 mark]*. Knowing which genes are linked to inherited diseases could help us to develop effective treatments for them *[1 mark]*.

Page 69 — Reproduction

1.1 sperm *[1 mark]*
1.2 egg (cell) *[1 mark]*
1.3 meiosis *[1 mark]*
1.4 clones *[1 mark]*
1.5 mitosis *[1 mark]*
2.1 Because gametes only have half the number of chromosomes of a normal cell *[1 mark]*, so when two gametes fuse together the fertilised egg cell has the full number of chromosomes *[1 mark]*.
2.2 Any four from: e.g. asexual reproduction only involves one parent, whereas sexual reproduction involves two. / Unlike in sexual reproduction, there is no fusion of gametes in asexual reproduction. / Unlike in sexual reproduction, there is no mixing of chromosomes in asexual reproduction. / Unlike sexual reproduction, asexual reproduction doesn't give rise to genetic variation (as the offspring are genetically identical to the parent). / Asexual reproduction doesn't involve meiosis, whereas sexual reproduction does. *[4 marks — 1 mark for each correct answer.]*

Page 70 — Meiosis

1.1 In the reproductive organs / ovaries and testes *[1 mark]*.
1.2 It is duplicated *[1 mark]*.
1.3 two *[1 mark]*
1.4 Four gametes are produced *[1 mark]*, each with only a single set of chromosomes *[1 mark]*. Each of the gametes is genetically different from the others *[1 mark]*.
2.1 two *[1 mark]*
2.2 mitosis *[1 mark]*
2.3 They differentiate into different types of specialised cell *[1 mark]*.

Page 71 — X and Y Chromosomes

1.1 23 pairs of chromosomes *[1 mark]*
1.2

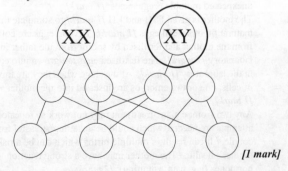

[1 mark]

1.3

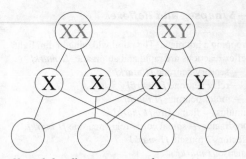

[1 mark for all gametes correct]

1.4

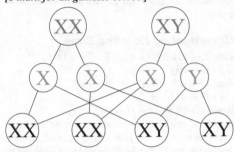

[1 mark if all the offspring genotypes are correct]

1.5 50:50 / 1:1 *[1 mark]*
1.6 E.g.

	X	X
X	XX	XX
Y	XY	XY

[1 mark for correct gametes of parents, 1 mark for correct genotypes of offspring.]

Pages 72-73 — Genetic Diagrams

Warm-up

alleles, recessive, homozygous, heterozygous, a single gene, multiple genes

1.1 Because there are carriers who don't have the disease *[1 mark]*.
1.2

	D	d
D	DD	Dd
d	Dd	dd

probability = **25%**

[1 mark for correct genotypes of parents, 1 mark if all gametes are correct, 1 mark if all offspring genotypes are correct, 1 mark for correct probability.]

2.1 3:1 *[1 mark]*
2.2

number of long-haired puppies = **8**
[1 mark for correct gametes, 1 mark for correct offspring genotypes, 1 mark for correct number of long-haired puppies.]

2.3 E.g.

	H	h
h	Hh	hh
h	Hh	hh

ratio = **1:1**

[1 mark if all gametes are correct, 1 mark if all offspring genotypes are correct, 1 mark for correct probability.]

Page 74 — Inherited Disorders

1.1 Being born with extra fingers or toes *[1 mark]*.
1.2 That the allele for polydactyly is dominant *[1 mark]*.
1.3 Because the allele for cystic fibrosis is recessive *[1 mark]*, so the offspring must have two copies of the allele to have the disorder *[1 mark]*. There is only a 1 in 4 chance of this occurring when each parent has one copy of the allele *[1 mark]*.
2.1 E.g. it implies that people with genetic problems are undesirable, which could increase prejudice *[1 mark]*. Screening is expensive *[1 mark]*. There could become a point where everyone wants to screen their embryo in IVF to pick the most desirable one *[1 mark]*.
2.2 E.g. it will help to stop people suffering from genetic disorders *[1 mark]*. Treating disorders costs the government and taxpayer a lot of money. Screening to reduce the number of people with disorders could save money *[1 mark]*. Parents cannot use it to select desirable characteristics for their baby, as there are laws to stop screening going too far *[1 mark]*.

Page 75 — Variation

1.1 genetic *[1 mark]*
1.2 environmental *[1 mark]*
2 The mutation could lead to a new phenotype *[1 mark]*. If the environment changes, the new phenotype could make the individual more suited to the new environment *[1 mark]*. It could then become common throughout the species relatively quickly by natural selection *[1 mark]*.

Page 76— Evolution

1 The environment changes too quickly *[1 mark]*. A new predator kills them all *[1 mark]*. A new disease kills them all *[1 mark]*. They can't compete with another new species for food *[1 mark]*. A catastrophic event occurs that kills them all *[1 mark]*.
2 Species show a wide variation in their characteristics because of differences in their alleles/genes *[1 mark]*. In this case, hares with smaller ears have more suitable characteristics for a cold environment because they will lose less heat *[1 mark]*, so are more likely to survive and successfully reproduce *[1 mark]* and pass on the genes controlling smaller ears to the next generation/ their offspring *[1 mark]*. Over time, these genes will have become more common in the species, causing the hares to evolve *[1 mark]*.

Page 77 — Selective Breeding

1.1 Artificial selection *[1 mark]*
1.2 The breeding of organisms so that the genes for particular useful or attractive characteristics stay in the population *[1 mark]*.
1.3 To produce cows that produce lots of milk/have a high milk yield *[1 mark]*.
2.1 How to grade your answer:
Level 0: There is no relevant information. *[No marks]*
Level 1: There are some relevant points describing selective breeding but the answer is missing some detail. *[1 to 2 marks]*
Level 2: There is a clear, detailed description of selective breeding that explains how dogs can be selectively bred for good, gentle temperament. *[3 to 4 marks]*
Here are some points your answer may include:
He could have selected two individuals from the population with the best temperaments.
These two individuals would have been bred together.
He would then have selected the individuals from the offspring with the best temperaments and bred them together.
He would have repeated this process over several generations.
This would make the good temperament trait become stronger over time.
Eventually all the puppies would have the good, gentle temperament trait.
2.2 Because selective breeding leads to there being a reduced number of different alleles in the population / a reduced gene pool *[1 mark]*, so there's more chance of the puppies inheriting a genetic defect if it's present in the population *[1 mark]*.

2.3 There is less variation in a selectively bred population *[1 mark]*, so there's less chance of there being any alleles in the population that would give the puppies resistance to the disease *[1 mark]*, so if one individual gets the disease, the others are also likely to succumb to it *[1 mark]*.

Pages 78-79 — Genetic Engineering

Warm-up
False, False, True, True
1.1 The transfer of a gene responsible for a desirable characteristic *[1 mark]* from one organism's genome into another organism's genome *[1 mark]*.
1.2 Enzyme are used to isolate/cut the desired gene from the organism's genome *[1 mark]*.
1.3 The gene is first inserted into a vector *[1 mark]*. The vector is then introduced to the target organism *[1 mark]* and this inserts the gene into the organism's cells so that the organism develops with the desired characteristic *[1 mark]*.
1.4 Any two from: e.g. bacteria have been genetically engineered to produce human insulin that can be used to treat diabetes. / Sheep have been genetically engineered to produce drugs in their milk that can treat human diseases. / Scientists are researching genetic modification treatments (gene therapy) for inherited diseases caused by faulty genes *[2 marks — 1 mark for each correct answer.]*.
2.1 genetically modified *[1 mark]*
2.2 Any two from: e.g. to make them resistant to herbicides. / To make them resistant to disease. / To make them resistant to insects. *[2 marks — 1 mark for each correct answer.]*.
2.3 Mean fruit circumference of Plant 1 =
$(16.4 + 16.8 + 15.9 + 16.2 + 15.7 + 16.4 + 16.3 + 16.0 + 15.9 + 16.0) \div 10 =$ **16.2 cm (3 s.f.)** *[1 mark]*
Mean fruit circumference of Plant 2 =
$(20.2 + 20.4 + 19.8 + 19.6 + 20.4 + 20.6 + 20.2 + 19.9 + 20.1 + 20.0) \div 10 =$ **20.1 cm (3 s.f.)** *[1 mark]*
2.4 $20.1 - 16.2 = 3.9$ cm
$(3.9 \div 16.2) \times 100 =$ **24.1% (3 s.f.)**
[1 mark for correct working, 1 mark for correct answer.]
To calculate percentage change, you first need to work out the difference between the two figures. You then need calculate what percentage that difference is of the first figure.
2.5 Any one from: e.g. some people say that growing GM crops will affect the number of wild flowers, and so the population of insects, that live in and around the crops — reducing farmland biodiversity. / Some people are concerned that we might not fully understand the effects of eating GM crops on human health. / People are concerned that transplanted genes might get out into the natural environment. *[1 mark]*

Page 80 — Fossils

Warm-up
False, True, True
1.1 Because decay microbes can't survive in the sap or amber *[1 mark]* as there isn't any oxygen or moisture *[1 mark]*.
1.2 From gradual replacement of parts of an organism by minerals *[1 mark]*. From the preserved casts and impressions of things like burrows/footprints/rootlet traces in a soft material (like clay) *[1 mark]*.
1.3 Many early life-forms were soft bodied and decayed completely, without forming fossils *[1 mark]*. Fossils that did form may have been destroyed by geological activity *[1 mark]*. This means that the fossil record is incomplete *[1 mark]*.

Pages 81-82 — Antibiotic-Resistant Bacteria

1.1 E.g when they are prescribed for viral infections *[1 mark]* or non-serious conditions *[1 mark]*.
1.2 Because this ensures that all bacteria are destroyed *[1 mark]*, so there are none left to mutate *[1 mark]* and develop into antibiotic-resistant strains *[1 mark]*.
2.1 Because the rate of development of new antibiotics is slow *[1 mark]* and it is a costly process *[1 mark]*.

2.2 Bacteria develop random mutations in their DNA *[1 mark]*, some of which lead to the bacteria becoming less affected by antibiotics *[1 mark]*. These bacteria are better able to survive and reproduce in hosts undergoing antibiotic treatment *[1 mark]*, meaning that the gene becomes more common in the population, forming antibiotic-resistant strains *[1 mark]*. As there is no effective treatment for these strains, they can spread very easily between individuals *[1 mark]*.

3.1 How to grade your answer:
Level 0: There is no relevant information. *[No marks]*
Level 1: There is a brief description of a method that could be used to carry out the investigation. Very little detail is included and some steps may be in the wrong order. *[1 to 2 marks]*
Level 2: There is a good description of a method that could be used to carry out the investigation. Some detail is missing, but all of the steps are in a sensible order. *[3 to 4 marks]*
Level 3: There is a clear and detailed description of a method that could be used to carry out the investigation. All of the steps are in a sensible order. *[5 to 6 marks]*

Here are some points your answer may include:
Use a sterile pipette to measure out equal volumes of sterile nutrient broth solution into four sterile glass bottles.
Use another sterile pipette to add equal volumes of ampicillin solution to two of the glass bottles.
Use another sterile pipette to transfer some of strain A to one bottle with ampicillin in it and one bottle without ampicillin.
Use another sterile pipette to transfer some of strain B to one bottle with ampicillin and one bottle without ampicillin.
Set up a control experiment without bacteria / just broth solution and the antibiotic.
Put lids on all of the bottles. Store them all at the same temperature for a few days.
Observe each bottle to see if the nutrient broth solution has gone cloudy.

3.2 E.g. if strain B is resistant to ampicillin, it may cause bacterial infections that are difficult to treat if it is released into the general population, so it must be disposed of properly. / The bacteria used may pose a health risk to humans if not disposed of properly. / If the antibiotic used is not disposed of properly it may be released into the environment, where other bacteria may develop resistance to it *[1 mark]*.

Page 83 — Classification

1.1 E.g. current classification data *[1 mark]* and information from the fossil record *[1 mark]*.
1.2 B *[1 mark]*
1.3 G and H *[1 mark]*
2.1 kingdom, phylum, class, order, family, genus, species *[1 mark]*
2.2 (Carl) Woese *[1 mark]*
2.3 plants *[1 mark]*, animals *[1 mark]*, protists *[1 mark]*

Topic B7 — Ecology

Page 84 — Competition

1.1 the soil *[1 mark]*
1.2 light *[1 mark]* and space *[1 mark]*
1.3 Any three from: space/territory / food / water / mates *[3 marks]*
2.1 interdependence *[1 mark]*
2.2 E.g. the number of blue tits might decrease *[1 mark]* because there would be no caterpillars for them to eat *[1 mark]*. The numbers of plants might increase *[1 mark]* because there would be no caterpillars to eat them *[1 mark]*.
2.3 A stable community is one where all the species and environmental factors are in balance *[1 mark]* so that the population sizes remain fairly constant *[1 mark]*.

Pages 85-86 — Abiotic and Biotic Factors

1.1 Light intensity, temperature and carbon dioxide level are all examples of abiotic factors. *[1 mark]*
The other answers are incorrect because they mix up examples of biotic and abiotic factors. Remember, abiotic factors are non-living factors and biotic factors are living factors.
1.2 E.g. oxygen level *[1 mark]*
1.3 Any two from: e.g. moisture level / soil pH / soil mineral content / carbon dioxide level *[2 marks]*
2 E.g. because the grey and red squirrels were in competition *[1 mark]* for the same resources such as food and shelter *[1 mark]*. The grey squirrels out-competed the red squirrels *[1 mark]*.
3 The birds would not be feeding on the insects *[1 mark]*, so insects would breed and increase in numbers *[1 mark]*. More insects would eat more grass so the grass plant numbers might decrease *[1 mark]*.
4.1 Both populations increase then decrease sharply, then increase again over the ten years *[1 mark]*. The heron population starts to decrease and increase slightly later than the perch population *[1 mark]*.
4.2 The average pH of the lake fell between years 4 and 5 *[1 mark]*. Possibly not all of the perch could survive in the more acidic water *[1 mark]*. The data cannot confirm the reason because there might have been another abiotic or biotic factor that affected the perch population *[1 mark]*.
You still get the second mark here if you came up with any other sensible reason why the fall in the pH of the water might have caused the perch population to decrease.
4.3 E.g. there might be other fish/prey in the lake, which aren't affected by the disease, that the herons can eat *[1 mark]*. The other fish/prey might have more food if the perch population falls, so their populations will increase *[1 mark]*. So the herons might still have as much food as before *[1 mark]*.

Pages 87-88 — Adaptations

1.1 extremophiles *[1 mark]*
1.2 bacteria *[1 mark]*
1.3 high pressure *[1 mark]*
2.1 Long eyelashes stop sand getting into the eyes *[1 mark]*. Large feet stop the camel sinking into the sand / make it easier for the camel to walk in sand *[1 mark]*.
2.2 It reduces water loss *[1 mark]*.
2.3 A swollen stem stores water *[1 mark]*.
2.4 Shallow, wide-spreading roots allow water to be absorbed over a larger area *[1 mark]* while long, deep roots allow the plant to absorb water from deep below the surface *[1 mark]*.
3.1 E.g. they would seek shade *[1 mark]*.
3.2 dark coloured skin *[1 mark]*
3.3 functional adaptation *[1 mark]*

Page 89 — Food Chains

Warm-up
producer — seaweed, secondary consumer — shark
1.1 primary consumer *[1 mark]*
1.2 They produce glucose *[1 mark]* by carrying out photosynthesis *[1 mark]*. They then use this glucose to make biological molecules that make up the plant's biomass *[1 mark]*.
2.1 The number of lynx increases *[1 mark]* because the number of snowshoe hares is increasing and so they have lots of food *[1 mark]*.
2.2 An increase in the number of lynx, which mean more hares are eaten *[1 mark]*.

Page 90 — Using Quadrats

1.1 It avoids the data being biased *[1 mark]*.
1.2 13 buttercups *[1 mark]*
1.3 15.5 buttercups *[1 mark]*
1.4 $(15 + 13 + 16 + 23 + 26 + 23 + 13 + 12 + 16 + 13) \div 10 = 170 \div 10 = $ **17 buttercups per 0.5 m^2** *[1 mark]*

1.5   Mean number of buttercups per m² = 17 × 2 = 34
Estimated population size = mean number of buttercups
per m² × total area of the field in m²
Estimated population size = 34 × 1750
= **59 500 buttercups** *[3 marks for correct answer, otherwise
1 mark for '34 buttercups per m²' and 1 mark for
'34 × 1750'.]*

Pages 91-92 — Using Transects

1.1   Zones B and C. *[1 mark]*
1.2   long grass *[1 mark]*
1.3   Zone A is closest to the pond where the soil has more moisture *[1 mark]*. Zone A also has a higher light intensity *[1 mark]*.
1.4   Zone B *[1 mark]* because only short grass grows in zone B *[1 mark]*
1.5   The light levels may be too low. / The moisture level may be too low. *[1 mark]*
1.6   Record the number of times each of the four species touch the transect line. / Count the number of species/measure the percentage cover of each species using a quadrat placed along the transect. *[1 mark]*
2.1   E.g. the ground might be slippery / there might be large waves from the sea / the tide might come in *[1 mark]*.

Any sensible suggestion of a hazard you might find at a beach would get you the mark for this question.

2.2   Advantage: e.g. you can cover a larger distance in the same amount of time / it takes less time to collect data from along the transect *[1 mark]*.
Disadvantage: e.g. the results might not be as accurate / some species might get missed *[1 mark]*.
2.3   The percentage cover of bladderwrack increases between 2 m and 18 m from the low tide point / the further the distance from the low tide point, the higher the percentage cover of bladderwrack, up to 18 m *[1 mark]*. The percentage cover then falls between 18 m and 20 m *[1 mark]*.
2.4   E.g. they could measure the salt concentration of the water around the bladderwrack at each interval *[1 mark]*.

Page 93 — The Water Cycle

Warm-up
   evaporate, water vapour, cools, precipitation
1.1   evaporation *[1 mark]*
1.2   Precipitation is water that falls from the clouds *[1 mark]*.
1.3   It provides fresh water for plants and animals *[1 mark]*.

Page 94 — The Carbon Cycle

1.1   photosynthesis *[1 mark]*
1.2   (green) plants *[1 mark]*
1.3   burning *[1 mark]*
1.4   Any one from: e.g. leather / wool. *[1 mark]*
1.5   Carbon dioxide is returned back to the atmosphere *[1 mark]* when the microorganisms involved in decay respire *[1 mark]*.

Pages 95-96 — Biodiversity and Waste Management

1.1   The variety of different species of organisms on Earth, or within an ecosystem. *[1 mark]*
1.2   E.g. deforestation / waste production *[1 mark]*
2.1   The human population is growing *[1 mark]* and the standard of living is increasing *[1 mark]*.
2.2   Any two from: e.g. sewage / toxic chemicals / fertilisers / pesticides / herbicides *[2 marks]*
2.3   E.g. smoke *[1 mark]* and acidic gases *[1 mark]*.
3.1   It reduces the variety of plants on the land (by killing the weeds) *[1 mark]* and it may kill plants and animals if it is washed into nearby water / it pollutes nearby water *[1 mark]*.
3.2   Because all the different species in the ecosystem depend on each other (e.g. for shelter and food) *[1 mark]*. Different species can also help to maintain the right physical environment for each other *[1 mark]*.

4.1   River 2 has a higher level of water pollution than River 1 *[1 mark]*. River 2 contains more rat-tailed maggots than River 1, and these are found in highly polluted water *[1 mark]*. River 2 also contains fewer freshwater shrimp and water lice than River 1, and these are found in water with a medium or low level of pollution *[1 mark]*.

You'd also get the marks here for explaining this the other way round — for describing how you can tell that River 1 has a lower level of pollution than River 2.

4.2   The student would need to survey one area that is just downstream of the discharge site, which will be affected by the waste water *[1 mark]*, and one area that is just upstream of the discharge site, where no waste water is present *[1 mark]*. Then the student can compare the populations of the indicator species present at both sites to assess the water pollution levels *[1 mark]*.

Page 97 — Global Warming

Warm-up
   the Sun, space, gases, increases
1.1   carbon dioxide and methane *[1 mark]*
1.2   Higher temperatures could cause seawater to expand / ice to melt *[1 mark]*, which could cause the sea level to rise above low-lying land *[1 mark]*.
1.3   Any two from: e.g. changes in the distribution of species where temperature/rainfall has changed. / Changes to the migration pattern of some animals. / Reduction in biodiversity as some species become extinct.
[2 marks — 1 mark for each correct answer.]

Page 98 — Deforestation and Land Use

1   Any two from: e.g. building / farming / quarrying / dumping waste *[2 marks — 1 mark for each correct answer]*.
2.1   E.g. to use the land as farmland. / To use the peat as compost. *[1 mark]*
2.2   Carbon dioxide is released *[1 mark]*, which contributes to global warming *[1 mark]*.
2.3   It reduces biodiversity *[1 mark]* because it destroys habitats / reduces the area of habitats *[1 mark]*.
3.1   To clear land to grow the crops needed to produce biofuels *[1 mark]*.
3.2   E.g. to provide land for cattle (to raise for food) *[1 mark]*.
To provide land to grow crops, e.g. rice (to provide more food) *[1 mark]*.
4   Any two from: e.g. it increases the amount of carbon dioxide in the atmosphere *[1 mark]* because carbon dioxide is released by burning wood and the decomposing of wood by microorganisms *[1 mark]*. / It reduces the rate at which carbon dioxide is removed from the atmosphere *[1 mark]* because there are fewer trees taking it up for photosynthesis *[1 mark]*. / It leads to a reduction in biodiversity in the area *[1 mark]* because trees/habitats are destroyed *[1 mark]*.

Page 99 — Maintaining Ecosystems and Biodiversity

1.1   Burning fewer fossil fuels. *[1 mark]*
1.2   E.g. this could reduce the amount of land taken over for landfill *[1 mark]*, leaving ecosystems in place *[1 mark]*.
2.1   It decreases biodiversity *[1 mark]*, because the habitat wouldn't be able to support a wide range of organisms *[1 mark]*.
2.2   The strips of grassland and hedgerows increase the biodiversity by providing more habitats / food sources *[1 mark]*.
3   E.g. it costs money to protect biodiversity (and make sure that the programmes are being followed) and some people may feel that the money should be spent on other things *[1 mark]*. Protecting biodiversity may have a negative impact on local people's livelihood (e.g. if they're employed in tree-felling), which could affect the local economy *[1 mark]*. Some people (e.g. farmers) may want to kill organisms that are regarded as pests to protect crops and livestock *[1 mark]*. Some people may want to use land for new housing or agricultural land *[1 mark]*.

Topic C1 — Atomic Structure and the Periodic Table

Page 100 — Atoms

Warm-up

The radius of an atom is approximately **0.1** nanometres. The radius of the nucleus is around 1×10^{-14} metres. That's about **1/10 000** of the radius of an atom. An atom doesn't have an overall **charge** as it has equal numbers of **protons/electrons** and **electrons/protons**.

1.1   nucleus *[1 mark]*

1.2   −1 *[1 mark]*

1.3   neutron: 0 charge *[1 mark]*
proton: +1 charge *[1 mark]*

2.1   mass number = 39 *[1 mark]*

2.2   atomic number = 19 *[1 mark]*

2.3   protons = 19 *[1 mark]*
neutrons = mass number – atomic number
      = 39 – 19 = **20** *[1 mark]*
electrons = 19 *[1 mark]*

Page 101 — Elements

1.1   Atoms are the smallest part of an element that can exist *[1 mark]*.

1.2   They have the same number of protons / 17 protons *[1 mark]* but a different number of neutrons / $^{35}_{17}$Cl has 2 less neutrons than $^{37}_{17}$Cl *[1 mark]*.

2.1

Isotope	No. of Protons	No. of Neutrons	No. of Electrons
^{32}S	16	16	16
^{33}S	16	17	16
^{34}S	16	18	16
^{36}S	16	20	16

[3 marks — 1 mark for each correct column]

2.2   Relative atomic mass = [(94.99 × 32) + (0.75 × 33) + (4.25 × 34) + (0.01 × 36)] ÷ (94.99 + 0.75 + 4.25 + 0.01) = 3209.29 ÷ 100 = 32.0929 = **32.1** *[2 marks for correct answer, otherwise one mark for using correct equation]*

2.3   X and Z are isotopes *[1 mark]*. They have the same atomic number / same number of protons *[1 mark]* but different mass numbers / number of neutrons *[1 mark]*.

Page 102 — Compounds

1.1   It contains two elements chemically combined *[1 mark]*.

1.2   4 *[1 mark]*
A molecule of ammonia contains 1 nitrogen atom and 3 hydrogen atoms making a total of 4 atoms altogether.

2.1   sodium chloride *[1 mark]*

2.2   Any one of: **B.** NaCl / **C.** C_2H_4 / **E.** H_2O *[1 mark]*
It contains two or more elements chemically combined (in fixed proportions) *[1 mark]*.

2.3   6 *[1 mark]*
C_2H_4 contains 2 carbon atoms and 4 hydrogen atoms.

2.4   Yes, a new compound has been made as the atoms in C_2H_6 are in different proportions to the atoms in C or F / there are a different number of hydrogen atoms in the molecule *[1 mark]*.

Page 103 — Chemical Equations

Warm-up

1   True

2   False

3   True

4   True

1.1   sodium + chlorine → sodium chloride *[1 mark]*

1.2 $2Na + Cl_2 \rightarrow 2NaCl$ *[1 mark]*

2.1 $4NH_3 + 5O_2 \rightarrow 4NO + 6H_2O$ /
$2NH_3 + 2.5O_2 \rightarrow 2NO + 3H_2O$ *[1 mark]*

2.2   E.g. there are 7 oxygen atoms on the left hand side of the equation and only 6 on the right hand side *[1 mark]*.

Page 104 — Mixtures and Chromatography

1.1   Mixture *[1 mark]*. Air consists of two or more elements or compounds *[1 mark]* that aren't chemically combined together *[1 mark]*.

1.2   No *[1 mark]*, as argon is an element in a mixture. Chemical properties are not affected by being in a mixture *[1 mark]*.

2   How to grade your answer:
Level 0:   Nothing written worthy of credit *[No marks]*.
Level 1:   Some explanation or description given but little detail and key information missing *[1–2 marks]*.
Level 2:   Clear description of method and some explanation of results but some detail missing *[3–4 marks]*.
Level 3:   A clear and detailed description of method and a full explanation of results *[5–6 marks]*.
Here are some points your answer may include:
<u>Setting up the experiment</u>
Draw a line in pencil near the bottom of a piece of chromatography paper.
Place a small sample of each ink on the pencil line.
Pour a shallow layer of water / solvent into a beaker.
Place the chromatography paper in the container.
The water should be below the pencil line and the ink spots.
Place a lid on the container and wait for the solvent to rise to near the top of the paper.
Remove the paper from the container when the solvent has risen close to the top of the paper.
<u>Explanation of results</u>
A shows one spot, so only contains one dye.
B shows two spots that have separated, so contains two dyes.
C shows three spots that have separated, so contains three dyes.
B and C are mixtures as they contain more than one element or compound not chemically combined together.
B and C contain at least one of the same dyes

Page 105 — More Separation Techniques

1.1   Add water to the mixture to dissolve the potassium chloride *[1 mark]*. Filter the mixture. The chalk will stay on the filter paper, *[1 mark]* the dissolved potassium chloride will pass through *[1 mark]*.

1.2   E.g. evaporate the potassium chloride solution to a much smaller volume and then leave it to cool *[1 mark]*.

2.1   Add the mixture to methylbenzene. The sulfur will dissolve (the iron will not dissolve) *[1 mark]*. Filter the solution to obtain the insoluble iron *[1 mark]*. Evaporate the methylbenzene to obtain crystals of sulfur *[1 mark]*.

2.2   No, the student is incorrect *[1 mark]*. The iron and sulfur are chemically combined in iron(II) sulfide / iron(II) sulfide is a compound *[1 mark]* so chemical methods would be needed to separate them out *[1 mark]*.

Pages 106-107 — Distillation

1   Simple distillation *[1 mark]*

2.1   Place a stopper / stopper with a thermometer in the top of the distillation flask *[1 mark]*.

2.2   The solution is heated/boiled and the octane evaporates first as it has a lower boiling point than the impurity *[1 mark]*. There is cold water flowing through the (Liebig) condenser *[1 mark]*. This condenses the gaseous octane back into a liquid which is then collected *[1 mark]*.

2.3   The octane has a boiling point greater than 100 °C / greater than the boiling point of water *[1 mark]*. So it would not evaporate *[1 mark]*.

3.1 In the first step, the temperature that the student heated the solution to was too high *[1 mark]*. Heating the mixture to 120 °C will cause both the ethanol and the water to evaporate, leaving a mixture of both salts in the flask *[1 mark]*.

3.2 The student should heat the mixture to a temperature of 78 °C. This will cause the ethanol in the mixture to evaporate, but not the water *[1 mark]*.

3.3 Ethanol is a flammable solvent so the mixture could catch fire if there is a lot left in the solution *[1 mark]*.

3.4 Gently heat the solution in an evaporating dish until some of the liquid has evaporated, according to the student's method. When crystals start to form, remove the dish from the heat and leave to cool *[1 mark]*. Filter the crystals out of the solution and leave to dry in a warm place *[1 mark]*.

Pages 108-109 — The History of The Atom

Warm-up

New experimental evidence can disprove models — **True**
Scientific models can be based on existing theories and new experimental evidence — **True**
Older scientific theories must be ignored when new ones are adopted — **False**

1.1 Tiny solid spheres that can't be divided *[1 mark]*.

1.2 Plum pudding model — A positively charged 'ball' with negatively charged electrons in it *[1 mark]*.
Bohr's model — Electrons in fixed orbits surrounding a small positively charged nucleus *[1 mark]*.
Rutherford's nuclear model — A small positively charged nucleus surrounded by a 'cloud' of negative electrons *[1 mark]*.

1.3 neutron *[1 mark]*

2.1 Most of the atom is "empty" space *[1 mark]*.

2.2 Niels Bohr *[1 mark]*

3.1 Atoms are neutral / have no overall charge *[1 mark]*.
Therefore there must have been positive charge to balance the negative charge of the electrons *[1 mark]*.

3.2 How to grade your answer:
Level 0: Nothing written worthy of credit *[No marks]*.
Level 1: A brief description of either the nuclear or the 'plum pudding' model is given *[1 to 2 marks]*.
Level 2: A description of both the nuclear model and the plum pudding model is given and some comparisons made *[3 to 4 marks]*.
Level 3: A full comparison of the models is given and similarities and differences are clearly explained *[5 to 6 marks]*.
Here are some points your answer may include:
Similarities
They both have areas of positive charge.
They both have electrons.
They are both neutral overall.
Differences
Positive charge isn't divided into protons in plum pudding model.
Plum pudding model does not have a nucleus but has a 'ball' of positive charge instead.
Plum pudding model does not have neutrons or protons, it only has electrons surrounded by a positive charge.
Plum pudding model does not have shells of electrons (surrounding nucleus), the electrons are arranged randomly within a sphere of positive charge.
Modern nuclear model has most of the mass concentrated in the nucleus but the plum pudding model has the mass spread evenly throughout the entire atom.

Page 110 — Electronic Structure

1.1 2,8,8,2 *[1 mark]*

1.2 The electrons in an atom occupy the lowest energy levels/ innermost shell first *[1 mark]*. The innermost shell/lowest energy level can hold 2 electrons *[1 mark]*.

2.1 Chlorine: 2,8,7 *[1 mark]*

2.2

[1 mark for correct number of electrons, 1 mark for correct arrangement]
You don't have to have the electrons paired up on the diagram. As long as there is the same number of electrons on the same shells you get the marks.

2.3 Phosphorus/P *[1 mark]*

Page 111 — Development of The Periodic Table

1.1 He left gaps so that elements with similar properties were in the same group / for elements that had not yet been discovered *[1 mark]*.

1.2 **D.** Between 2.4 and 7.2 g/cm³ *[1 mark]*. **E.** EkO_2 *[1 mark]*
F. $EkCl_4$ *[1 mark]* **G.** Very slow *[1 mark]*.

2.1 Protons (neutrons and electrons) had not been discovered / atomic numbers weren't known *[1 mark]*.

2.2 Ar and K / Te and I *[1 mark]*.

2.3 Isotopes of an element have different numbers of neutrons/ different atomic masses *[1 mark]*, but the same chemical properties *[1 mark]*.

Page 112 — The Modern Periodic Table

1.1 By atomic number / proton number *[1 mark]*.

1.2 Similar properties occur at regular intervals / there are repeating patterns in the properties of the elements *[1 mark]*.

1.3 They have the same number of outer shell electrons *[1 mark]*.

2.1 Group 2 *[1 mark]*. The atom has 2 outer shell electrons. *[1 mark]*.

2.2 Period 3 *[1 mark]*. The atom has 3 shells of electrons *[1 mark]*.

2.3 Magnesium/Mg *[1 mark]*

2.4 Choose one from: beryllium / calcium / strontium / barium / radium *[1 mark]*

Page 113 — Metals and Non-Metals

1.1 A^{2+}: metal X^{2-}: non-metal *[1 mark if both correct.]*

1.2 Any three from, e.g.: dull / brittle / poor conductor of electricity / low density / lower melting point/boiling point than metals
[1 mark for each].

2.1 Metals: Towards the left and bottom.
Non-metals: Towards the right and top *[1 mark]*.

2.2 Elements that react to form positive ions are metals *[1 mark]*.

2.3 Any one from: e.g. good electrical conductor / good thermal conductor / strong / high boiling point / high melting point / malleable *[1 mark]*.

2.4 Both are metals that lose their (2 or 3) outer shell electrons *[1 mark]* to form positive ions *[1 mark]*.

Page 114 — Group 1 Elements

1.1 **Y** *[1 mark]*. As element **Y** has a higher melting point, it must be higher up the group than **X** *[1 mark]*.
The higher up the group an element is, the lower its atomic number.

1.2 $2X_{(s)} + 2H_2O_{(l)} \rightarrow 2XOH_{(aq)} + H_{2(g)}$
[1 mark for correct reactants and products and 1 mark for balanced equation. Half the ratio is acceptable]

1.3 Anything between 8-14 *[1 mark]*.

2.1

	Boiling Point / °C	Radius of atom / pm
K	758.8	227
Rb	687.8	248
Cs	**Accept lower than 687.8**	**Accept greater than 248**

[1 mark for each correct answer]

2.2 Caesium would be more reactive than rubidium *[1 mark]*. As you go further down the group the outer electron is further away from the nucleus *[1 mark]*, so the attraction between the nucleus and the electron decreases and the electron is more easily lost *[1 mark]*.

2.3 Formula: Cs_3P *[1 mark]*
Equation: $12Cs + P_4 \rightarrow 4Cs_3P$ *[1 mark for correct reactants and products, 1 mark for correctly balancing the equation]*

Pages 115-116 — Group 7 Elements

Warm-up
Fluorine
Chlorine
Bromine
Iodine

1.1 They are non-metals that exist as molecules of two atoms *[1 mark]*.

1.2 Chlorine is more reactive than bromine *[1 mark]*. This is because chlorine's outer shell is closer to the nucleus *[1 mark]* so it's easier for chlorine to gain an electron when it reacts *[1 mark]*.
Because of the increasing distance between the nucleus and the outer shell, reactivity decreases down the group. Bromine is further down the group than chlorine, it's outer shell is further away from the nucleus and therefore it's less reactive than chlorine.

1.3 P *[1 mark]*

2.1 $2Fe + 3Br_2 \rightarrow 2FeBr_3$ *[1 mark for Br₂ and 1 mark for balanced equation. Half the ratio is acceptable]*

2.2 −1 *[1 mark]*
All halide ions form ions with a −1 charge.

3.1 chlorine + potassium bromide → **potassium chloride** + bromine *[1 mark]*

3.2 The solution will turn orange *[1 mark]*.

3.3 displacement *[1 mark]*

3.4 No *[1 mark]*, as chlorine is less reactive than fluorine *[1 mark]*.

4.1 The halogens have seven electrons in their outer shell *[1 mark]*. As you go further down the group additional shells are added so the outer electron is further away from the nucleus *[1 mark]*.

4.2 Astatine will react more slowly than fluorine *[1 mark]* since reactivity decreases down the group *[1 mark]*. Both astatine and fluorine have 7 outer shell electrons so react in a similar way *[1 mark]*. So astatine will react with hydrogen to form hydrogen astatide/HAt *[1 mark]*. $H_2 + At_2 \rightarrow 2HAt$ *[1 mark]*

Page 117 — Group 0 Elements

1.1 Rn Boiling Point: Above −108 °C *[1 mark]*, Xe Density: Between 0.0037 and 0.0097 *[1 mark]*, Ar Atomic Radius: Less than 109 pm *[1 mark]*.

1.2 Krypton is unreactive *[1 mark]*. It has a stable electron arrangement / full outer shell / 8 electrons in its outer shell *[1 mark]*.

1.3 Helium only has 2 electrons in its outer shell. The rest of the noble gases have 8 *[1 mark]*.

2.1 Noble gases are unreactive / they have stable electron arrangements / full outer shells / 8 electrons in their outer shell *[1 mark]*.

2.2 Iodine is much less reactive than fluorine *[1 mark]*.

2.3 Neon solidified at −249 °C and xenon at −112 °C *[1 mark]*. Boiling points increase down the group *[1 mark]* and xenon is further down the group than neon so will have the higher boiling point *[1 mark]*.

Topic C2 — Bonding, Structure and Properties of Matter

Page 118 — Formation of Ions

1.1 Metal atoms usually lose electrons to become positive ions *[1 mark]*.

1.2
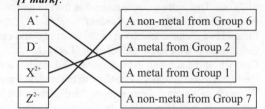

[2 marks if all four correct, otherwise 1 mark if two correct]

2.1 2− *[1 mark]*

2.2 2,8,8 *[1 mark]*. Sulfur gains two electrons *[1 mark]* to achieve a noble gas electronic structure/a full outer shell *[1 mark]*.

2.3 Argon/Ar *[1 mark]*

Pages 119-120 — Ionic Bonding

Warm-up

Dot and cross diagram	Ionic formula
$\left[Na\right]^+ \left[Cl\right]^-$	NaCl
$\left[Na\right]^+ \left[O\right]^{2-} \left[Na\right]^+$	Na_2O
$\left[Cl\right]^- \left[Mg\right]^{2+} \left[Cl\right]^-$	$MgCl_2$

1.1 calcium chloride *[1 mark]* and potassium oxide *[1 mark]*
Compounds that contain ionic bonding have to be made up of a metal and a non-metal. All the other options only contain non-metals, so can't be held together by ionic bonds.

1.2
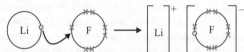

[1 mark for arrow showing electron transfer from Li to F, 1 mark for correct electronic structure of fluoride ion, with seven crosses and one dot, 1 mark for correct charges on the ions]

1.3 electrostatic attraction / electrostatic force *[1 mark]*

1.4 E.g. the particles in the compound are oppositely charged ions / have opposite charges / the bond is formed by electrons being transferred from one atom to another *[1 mark]*.

2.1

[1 mark for no electrons in outer shell, 1 mark for correct charge]
If you showed the second electron shell of magnesium containing eight electrons as dots, you also get the mark.

$\left[O\right]^{2-}$

[1 mark for eight electrons in the outer shell, with two dots and six crosses, 1 mark for correct charge]

2.2 E.g. the magnesium atom transfers two electrons to the oxygen atom *[1 mark]*. A magnesium ion with a 2+ charge forms *[1 mark]*, and an oxide ion with a 2− charge forms *[1 mark]*. The oppositely charged ions are attracted to each other by electrostatic attraction *[1 mark]*.

3.1 Element X: Group 7 *[1 mark]*
Reason: Any one of, e.g. it has formed an ion by gaining 1 electron / it forms 1– ions / the uncharged element would have seven electrons in its outer shell *[1 mark]*.
Element Z: Group 2 *[1 mark]*
Reason: Any one of, e.g. it has formed an ion by losing 2 electrons / it forms 2+ ions / the uncharged element would have two electrons in its outer shell *[1 mark]*.

3.2 How to grade your answer:
Level 0: There is no relevant information *[No marks]*.
Level 1: The discussion is limited and doesn't mention both the uses and limitations of dot and cross diagrams *[1 to 2 marks]*.
Level 2: There is some discussion of dot and cross diagrams, with at least one use and one limitation covered *[3 to 4 marks]*.
Level 3: The discussion is comprehensive in evaluating both the uses and limitations of dot and cross diagrams *[5 to 6 marks]*.
Here are some points your answer may include:
<u>Dot and cross diagrams show:</u>
Charge of the ions.
The arrangement of electrons in an atom or ion.
Which atoms the electrons in an ion originally come from.
Empirical formula (correct ratio of ions).
<u>Dot and cross diagrams do not:</u>
Show the structure of the compound.
Correctly represent the sizes of ions.

Pages 121-122 — Ionic Compounds

Warm-up

In an ionic compound, the particles are held together by **strong** forces of attraction. These forces act **in all directions** which results in the particles bonding together to form **giant lattices**.

1.1 conduct electricity in the solid state *[1 mark]*
1.2 giant ionic lattice *[1 mark]*
2.1 Sodium chloride contains positive sodium ions (Na^+) *[1 mark]* and negative chloride ions (Cl^-) *[1 mark]* that are arranged in a regular lattice/giant ionic lattice *[1 mark]*. The oppositely charged ions are held together by electrostatic forces acting in all directions *[1 mark]*.
2.2 To melt sodium chloride, you have to overcome the very strong electrostatic forces/ionic bonds between the particles *[1 mark]*, which requires lots of energy *[1 mark]*.
3.1 E.g.

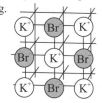

[1 mark for K⁺ ions, 1 mark for Br⁻ ions, 1 mark for correct structure, with alternating ions]

You'd also get the marks if you labelled all the white circles as Br⁻ and all the grey circles as K⁺.

3.2 Advantage: Any one of, e.g. the diagram shows the 3D arrangement of the ions / it suggests the structure is extended / it shows the regular (repeating) pattern of the ions *[1 mark]*.
Disadvantage: Any one of, e.g. the diagram doesn't correctly represent the sizes of ions / it shows gaps between the ions *[1 mark]*.
3.3 KBr *[1 mark]*

Remember that the overall charge of the ionic compound must be neutral. So you can work out the empirical formula by seeing that you only need one bromide ion to balance the charge on a potassium ion.

3.4 Boiling point: Potassium bromide has a giant structure with strong ionic bonds *[1 mark]*. In order to boil, these bonds need to be broken, which takes a lot of energy *[1 mark]*.
Electrical conductivity of solid: The ions are in fixed positions in the lattice *[1 mark]* and so are not able to move and carry a charge through the solid *[1 mark]*.
Electrical conductivity of solution: In solution, the ions are free to move *[1 mark]* and can carry a charge from place to place *[1 mark]*.

Pages 123-124 — Covalent Bonding

1.1 They share a pair of electrons *[1 mark]*.
1.2 Non-metals *[1 mark]*
1.3 BH_3 *[1 mark]*
Find the molecular formula by counting up how many atoms of each element there are in the diagram.
2

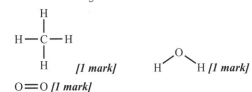

$O\!=\!O$ *[1 mark]*
Each line represents one covalent bond. Oxygen has a double bond, so you need to draw two lines between the oxygen atoms to show this.
3.1 E.g. it contains only non-metals *[1 mark]* and Figure 1 shows shared electrons *[1 mark]*.
3.2 Any two from, e.g. they don't show how the atoms are arranged in space / they don't show the relative sizes of the atoms *[2 marks — 1 mark for each correct answer]*.
3.3 One electron from hydrogen and one from carbon form a shared pair *[1 mark]* that are attracted to the nuclei of the carbon and hydrogen atoms *[1 mark]* by electrostatic attraction *[1 mark]*.
4.1 Displayed formula: e.g. it shows how all the atoms in a molecule are connected in a simple way *[1 mark]*, but it doesn't show the 3D structure of the molecule / it doesn't show which atom the electrons in the bond originally come from *[1 mark]*.
Dot and cross diagram: e.g. it shows where the electrons in each covalent bond originally came from *[1 mark]* but it doesn't show the 3D structure of the molecule / they can become very complicated if the molecule is large *[1 mark]*.
3D model: e.g. it shows how all the atoms are arranged in space in relation to each other / it shows the correct bond angles in the molecule *[1 mark]* but it quickly becomes complicated for large molecules / you can't tell which atom in the bonds the electrons originally came from *[1 mark]*.
4.2 The displayed formula *[1 mark]* would be the best as it is easy to see how the atoms in a large molecule are connected without the diagram becoming too complicated *[1 mark]*.

Pages 125-126 — Simple Molecular Substances

1.1 The bonds between the atoms are strong *[1 mark]*, but the forces between the molecules are weak *[1 mark]*.
1.2 The weak forces between the molecules / the intermolecular forces *[1 mark]*.
2.1

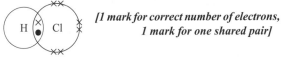

[1 mark for correct number of electrons, 1 mark for one shared pair]

2.2

[1 mark for correct number of electrons, 1 mark for three shared pairs]

2.3 E.g. N_2 has a triple covalent bond, whilst HCl has a single covalent bond *[1 mark]*.

3.1 Simple molecular substances have weak forces between molecules *[1 mark]* so not much energy is needed to overcome them/they normally have low melting points *[1 mark]*

3.2 Iodine won't conduct electricity *[1 mark]* because the I_2 molecules aren't charged / the electrons aren't free to move so can't carry a charge *[1 mark]*.

4.1 When methane boils, the forces between the molecules are overcome *[1 mark]* and it turns from a liquid into a gas *[1 mark]*. Methane is a smaller molecule then butane *[1 mark]* so the forces between the molecules are weaker *[1 mark]* and less energy is needed to overcome them *[1 mark]*.

4.2 Carbon needs four more electrons to get a full outer shell, and does this by forming four covalent bonds *[1 mark]*. Hydrogen only needs one more electron to complete its outer shell, so can only form one covalent bond *[1 mark]*.

Remember that the outer electron shell in hydrogen only needs two electrons to be filled, not eight like other electron shells.

4.3 Four *[1 mark]*. Silicon has four outer electrons so needs four more to get a full outer shell / silicon has the same number of outer shell electrons as carbon so will form the same number of bonds *[1 mark]*.

Page 127 — Polymers and Giant Covalent Substances
Warm-up

1.1 Ammonia *[1 mark]*

Ammonia has a simple covalent structure — it forms small molecules.

1.2 The covalent bonds are very strong *[1 mark]*, so a lot of energy is needed to break them *[1 mark]*.

2.1 $(C_2H_4)_n$ *[1 mark]*

2.2 Solid *[1 mark]*. The molecule is very large and so the intermolecular forces are strong *[1 mark]* and need lots of energy to be broken *[1 mark]*.

2.3 covalent bonds *[1 mark]*

Page 128 — Allotropes of Carbon
1.1

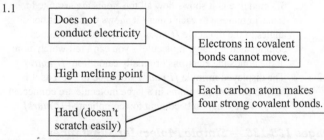

[2 marks if all three correct, otherwise 1 mark if one correct]

1.2 A: graphene *[1 mark]*
B: buckminster fullerene *[1 mark]*
C: carbon nanotube / fullerene *[1 mark]*

1.3 Any one of, e.g. to strengthen materials / to deliver drugs into the body / as a catalyst / as a lubricant / in electronics *[1 mark]*

2.1 Graphite is made up of sheets of carbon atoms arranged in hexagons *[1 mark]*, with weak forces between the sheets *[1 mark]*. Each carbon atom forms three covalent bonds *[1 mark]*, and has one delocalised electron *[1 mark]*.

2.2 Graphite has delocalised electrons *[1 mark]* which are free to move through the substance and carry an electric charge *[1 mark]*.

Page 129 — Metallic Bonding
1.1 E.g.

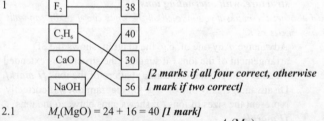
— Metal ions in a regular pattern
— Delocalised electrons

[1 mark for regular arrangement of metal ions, 1 mark for delocalised electron, 1 mark for correct labels]

1.2 There is a strong electrostatic attraction *[1 mark]* between the delocalised electrons and the positive metal ions *[1 mark]*.

1.3 High *[1 mark]* because the bonding is strong so requires lots of energy to break *[1 mark]*.

1.4 Good *[1 mark]* because the electrons are free to move throughout the structure and carry an electrical charge *[1 mark]*.

2.1 Metallic structures have layers of atoms *[1 mark]* that are able to slide over one another *[1 mark]*.

2.2 Atoms of different elements are different sizes *[1 mark]*. Adding atoms of a different size to a pure metal distorts the layers *[1 mark]* making it harder for them to slide over one another *[1 mark]*.

Page 130 — States of Matter
1.1 solid, liquid, gas *[1 mark]*
1.2 $NaCl_{(s)}$: solid *[1 mark]*
$O_{2(g)}$: gas *[1 mark]*
$Hg_{(l)}$: liquid *[1 mark]*
2.1 solid spheres *[1 mark]*
2.2 liquid *[1 mark]*
2.3 Any two from: melting / boiling / condensing / freezing *[1 mark for each]*
2.4 Any two from: e.g. the model says nothing about forces between particles / particles aren't really spheres / particles are mostly empty space, not solid *[1 mark for each]*.

Page 131 — Changing State
1.1 melting *[1 mark]*
1.2 boiling point *[1 mark]*
1.3 The bonds are strong *[1 mark]*.
2.1 sodium chloride *[1 mark]*

At 900 °C, water would be a gas and copper would be a solid.

2.2 Sodium chloride *[1 mark]* and water *[1 mark]*.

At 1500 °C, copper would be a liquid.

2.3 Boiling sodium chloride *[1 mark]*.
2.4 No *[1 mark]*. When copper boils, the metallic bonds are broken *[1 mark]*, but when water boils only the intermolecular forces are broken *[1 mark]*, so you can't tell anything about the strength of the covalent bonds *[1 mark]*.

Topic C3 — Quantitative Chemistry

Page 132 — Relative Formula Mass
1

F_2	38
C_2H_6	40
CaO	30
NaOH	56

[2 marks if all four correct, otherwise 1 mark if two correct]

2.1 $M_r(MgO) = 24 + 16 = 40$ *[1 mark]*

percentage by mass of magnesium $= \dfrac{A_r(Mg)}{M_r(MgO)} \times 100$

$= \dfrac{24}{40} \times 100 = $ **60%** *[1 mark]*

2.2 Mass of magnesium ions $= 200 \times \dfrac{15}{100} = $ **30 g** *[1 mark]*

2.3   Mass of magnesium oxide containing 30 g of
magnesium ions = 30 ÷ (60 ÷ 100) = **50 g** *[1 mark]*

If you used the percentage mass of magnesium ions as 40% and the mass of magnesium ions in the mixture as 20 g, your answer will also be 50 g.

Page 133 — The Mole

Warm-up

    6.02×10^{23}

1.1 M_r of carbon dioxide = 12 + (16 × 2) = **44** *[1 mark]*

1.2   Moles of carbon dioxide = 110 ÷ 44 = **2.5 mol** *[1 mark]*

1.3   1 mole of carbon dioxide would weigh more *[1 mark]*.
It has a higher relative formula mass *[1 mark]*.

2.1   2 mol sulfur = 2 × 32 g = **64 g** *[1 mark]*

2.2 M_r of iron sulfide = 56 + 32 = 88
Moles of iron sulfide = 44 ÷ 88 = **0.50 mol** *[2 marks for correct answer, otherwise 1 mark for correct working]*

2.3   The number of atoms in 3 moles of sulfur is greater than the number of molecules in 2 moles of iron sulfide *[1 mark]*.
There's the same number of atoms in 1 mole of sulfur as there are molecules in 1 mole of iron sulfide so in 3 moles of sulfur there will be more atoms than there are molecules in 2 moles of iron sulfide *[1 mark]*.

Pages 134-136 — Conservation of Mass

1.1 $2Mg + O_2 \rightarrow 2MgO$ *[1 mark]*

1.2   Mass of oxygen = 20 g of MgO − 12 g of Mg = **8 g** *[2 marks for correct answer, otherwise 1 mark for correct working]*

2.1   The mass of reactants equals the mass of products in a chemical reaction *[1 mark]*. Atoms are not made or destroyed during a chemical reaction *[1 mark]*. So, there must be the same number of each type of atom in the products as in the reactants *[1 mark]*.

2.2   The mass of the powder would increase *[1 mark]*.
Oxygen gas was not included as part of the original measurement *[1 mark]*. Particles of oxygen are added to the zinc to form zinc oxide powder *[1 mark]*.

3.1   The measurement is correct *[1 mark]*. Carbon dioxide (a gas) is produced and released into the atmosphere *[1 mark]*. So, the student only measured the mass of the solid product, not both products *[1 mark]*.

3.2 M_r of sodium oxide = 106 − 44 = **62** *[1 mark]*

3.3   Moles of Na_2CO_3 = 53 ÷ 106 = 0.50
For every mole of Na_2CO_3 that reacts, 1 mole of CO_2 is produced. Only 0.50 moles of Na_2CO_3 react so 0.50 moles of CO_2 are produced.
Mass of carbon dioxide = 0.50 × 44 = **22 g** *[3 marks for correct answer, otherwise 1 mark for 0.50 moles of Na_2CO_3 and 1 mark for a 1:1 molar ratio]*

To work out a molar ratio, you need to use the balanced symbol equation for the reaction. The numbers in front of the chemical formulas show the number of moles of a substance that react or are produced in the reaction. In this question, for every 1 mole Na_2CO_3 heated, 1 mole of carbon dioxide is produced — a 1:1 molar ratio.

3.4   Mass of sodium oxide = 53 g − 22 g = **31 g** *[1 mark]*

4.1   E.g. the reading of the final mass might have been taken before the reaction completed *[1 mark]*.

4.2   Table 1: Range = 1.42 − 1.31 = 0.11 g
uncertainty = range ÷ 2 = 0.11 ÷ 2 = ±0.055 g *[1 mark]*
percentage uncertainty = (0.055 ÷ 1.37) × 100%
                       = 4.0% (to 2 s.f.) *[1 mark]*
Table 2: Range = 2.75 − 2.66 = 0.09 g
uncertainty = range ÷ 2 = 0.09 ÷ 2 = ±0.045 g *[1 mark]*
percentage uncertainty = (0.045 ÷ 2.71) × 100%
                       = 1.7% (to 2 s.f.) *[1 mark]*

4.3   The size of the uncertainty is similar in both sets of results, but the percentage uncertainty is greater in table 1 *[1 mark]*. This suggests that the size of the random errors in the measurement of the final mass was similar in both sets of experiments *[1 mark]*, but the effect of these errors is smaller in table 2 because the experiments in table 2 used a larger initial mass of the compound *[1 mark]*.

Pages 137-138 — The Mole and Equations

Warm-up

    3

1   $H_2SO_4 + 2NaOH \rightarrow Na_2SO_4 + 2H_2O$ *[1 mark]*

2.1   Moles of sodium = 9.2 ÷ 23 = **0.4 mol** *[1 mark]*

2.2 M_r of water = (1 × 2) + 16 = 18
Moles of water = 7.2 g ÷ 18 = **0.4 mol** *[2 marks for correct answer, otherwise 1 mark for correct working]*

2.3   Divide the number of moles of each substance by the lowest of these number of moles (0.2 mol) to give the molar ratios.
Na = 0.4 ÷ 0.2 = 2 mol
H_2O = 0.4 ÷ 0.2 = 2 mol
NaOH = 0.4 ÷ 0.2 = 2 mol
H_2 = 0.2 ÷ 0.2 = 1 mol
$2Na + 2H_2O \rightarrow 2NaOH + H_2$ *[3 marks for correct answer, otherwise 1 mark for correct method and 1 mark for at least 2 correct numbers in the equation]*

3.1   Moles of methane = 8 g ÷ 16 = 0.5 mol
Moles of oxygen = 32 g ÷ 32 = 1 mol
Moles of carbon dioxide = 22 g ÷ 44 = 0.5 mol
Moles of water = 18 g ÷ 18 = 1 mol *[1 mark]*
Divide by the lowest of these numbers which is 0.5:
Methane = 0.5 ÷ 0.5 = 1 mol
Oxygen = 1 ÷ 0.5 = 2 mol
Carbon dioxide = 0.5 ÷ 0.5 = 1 mol
Water = 1 ÷ 0.5 = 2 mol *[1 mark]*
$CH_4 + 2O_2 \rightarrow CO_2 + 2H_2O$ *[1 mark]*

3.2   Moles of oxygen = 48 g ÷ 32 = 1.5 mol
Molar ratio of oxygen : carbon dioxide = 2:1
Moles of carbon dioxide = 1.5 mol ÷ 2 = **0.75 mol** *[3 marks for correct answer, otherwise 1 mark for 1.5 mol of oxygen and 1 mark for molar ratio of 2:1]*

3.3   Molar ratio of CH_4 : H_2O = 1:2
4 mol of methane will produce **8 mol** of water *[1 mark]*.

3.4   Mass of water = 18 × 8 = **144 g** *[1 mark]*

If you got the equation wrong in 3.1 but used all the right working in parts 3.2, 3.3 and 3.4, you still get the marks, even if you got a different answer to the one here.

Page 139 — Limiting Reactants

1.1   To make sure that all the hydrochloric acid was used up in the reaction *[1 mark]*.

1.2   The limiting reactant is completely used up during a reaction *[1 mark]* and so its quantity limits the amount of product that can be formed *[1 mark]*.

2.1   Molar ratio of copper oxide : copper sulfate = 1:1
Therefore, 0.50 mol of copper sulfate is produced.
M_r of copper sulfate = 63.5 + 32 + (16 × 4) = 159.5
Mass of copper sulfate = 0.50 × 159.5 = **80 g** *[3 marks for correct answer, otherwise 1 mark for 0.50 moles of copper sulfate and 1 mark for M_r of 159.5]*

2.2   The amount of product formed is directly proportional to the amount of limiting reactant *[1 mark]*. So doubling the quantity of the sulfuric acid will double the mass of the copper sulfate *[1 mark]*.

2.3   If only 0.4 mol of copper oxide is present, there will not be enough molecules to react with all the sulfuric acid *[1 mark]*. The copper oxide will be the limiting reactant *[1 mark]* and only 0.4 mol of product will be formed *[1 mark]*.

Page 140 — Concentrations of Solutions

1.1   Conc. of calcium chloride = 28 g ÷ 0.4 dm³ = **70 g/dm³** *[1 mark for correct answer and 1 mark for correct units]*

1.2   The concentration of a solution is the amount of a substance in a given volume of a solution *[1 mark]*.

2.1   Volume in dm³ = 500 ÷ 1000 = 0.50 dm³ *[1 mark]*.
Concentration = 40.0 ÷ 0.500 = **80 g/dm³** *[1 mark]*.

2.2   Mass = 60.0 × 0.500 = **30 g** *[1 mark]*.

2.3   Mean = (18.2 + 18.1 + 18.4 + 18.5) ÷ 4 = **18.3 g/dm³** *[1 mark]*

2.4   Range = 18.5 − 18.1 = 0.4
Uncertainty = range ÷ 2 = 0.4 ÷ 2 = **± 0.2 g/dm³** *[2 marks for correct answer, otherwise 1 mark for calculating range]*

Topic C4 — Chemical Changes

Page 141 — Acids and Bases

Warm-up

Universal indicator will turn **red** in strongly acidic solutions and **purple** in strongly alkaline solutions. In a **neutral** solution, Universal indicator will be green. A pH probe attached to a pH meter is **more** accurate than Universal indicator as it displays a numerical value for pH.

1.1 beer *[1 mark]*
1.2 blue / blue-green *[1 mark]*
1.3 H^+ *[1 mark]*
1.4 0 *[1 mark]* – 14 *[1 mark]*
2.1 acid + alkali → salt + water *[1 mark]*
2.2 $H^+_{(aq)} + OH^-_{(aq)} \rightarrow H_2O_{(l)}$ *[1 mark]*

You still get the marks if you didn't include state symbols.

Page 142 — Strong Acids and Weak Acids

1.1 A strong acid completely ionises/dissociates in solution *[1 mark]*. A weak acid only partly ionises in solution *[1 mark]*.
1.2 Nitric acid would have a lower pH than ethanoic acid *[1 mark]* because it is a stronger acid/more dissociated/ionised *[1 mark]*, so the concentration of H^+ would be greater *[1 mark]*.

You would also get the marks for using the reverse argument — ethanoic acid would have a higher pH because it is a weaker acid so the concentration of H^+ ions is lower.

1.3 3 *[1 mark]*

As the concentration of H^+ ions in solution decreases by a factor of 10, the pH rises by 1.

1.4 Adding water to the beaker *[1 mark]*.
Adding ethanoic acid to the beaker at the same concentration as the citric acid *[1 mark]*.
Changing the citric acid to carbonic acid of the same concentration *[1 mark]*.

Pages 143-144 — Reactions of Acids

1.1 Neutralisation *[1 mark]*
1.2 Fizzing — Carbon dioxide is produced *[1 mark]*
2.1 sulfuric acid + lithium hydroxide → lithium sulfate + water *[1 mark]*
2.2 $H_2SO_4 + 2LiOH \rightarrow Li_2SO_4 + 2H_2O$ *[1 mark for correct formula of Li_2SO_4, 1 mark for correct balancing]*
2.3 Both reactions produce lithium sulfate and water *[1 mark]*. The reaction between sulfuric acid and lithium carbonate also produces carbon dioxide *[1 mark]*.
3.1 Add zinc oxide to hydrochloric acid until the reaction stops / the excess metal oxide sinks to the bottom *[1 mark]*. Filter the excess solid from the solution using a filter funnel *[1 mark]*. Heat the zinc chloride solution to evaporate some of the water and then leave to cool *[1 mark]*. Filter and dry the crystals that form *[1 mark]*.
3.2 E.g. zinc carbonate *[1 mark]*.

Any other insoluble zinc base or zinc metal also gets a mark.

4 How to grade your answer:
Level 0: Nothing written worth of credit *[No marks]*.
Level 1: Some suitable tests are named but it is not clear how the results would enable the solutions to be identified. The chemistry of the tests is not clearly described *[1 to 2 marks]*.
Level 2: Tests that enable at least one solution to be identified are clearly described, or tests that would enable all solutions to be identified are named but not clearly described *[3 to 4 marks]*.
Level 3: At least two tests are described together with the expected outcomes. It is clear how these tests would be used to distinguish between all three solutions. The chemistry of the tests is correctly described *[5 to 6 marks]*.

Here are some points your answer may include:
Test the pH of each solution.
The neutral solution/the solution that turns Universal indicator green is the salt.
Add a couple of drops of Universal indicator to the solutions followed by some dilute acid.
The solution containing sodium carbonate will fizz as it reacts with the acid to release carbon dioxide gas as shown by the equation: acid + sodium carbonate → sodium salt + water + carbon dioxide
The solution containing sodium hydroxide will react with acid changing the Universal indicator solution from blue/purple to green, but there won't be any fizzing as no gas is released as shown by the reaction:
acid + sodium hydroxide → sodium salt + water
The solution containing the sodium salt won't react with acid.

Pages 145-146 — The Reactivity Series

1.1 magnesium + hydrochloric acid → magnesium chloride + hydrogen *[1 mark]*
1.2 Positive magnesium ions *[1 mark]*
1.3 It forms positive ions less easily / it's lower down in the reactivity series *[1 mark]*
1.4 Any one of: e.g. potassium / sodium / lithium / calcium *[1 mark]*
2.1 metal + water → metal hydroxide + hydrogen *[1 mark]*
2.2 $Ca_{(s)} + 2H_2O_{(l)} \rightarrow Ca(OH)_{2(aq)} + H_{2(g)}$ *[1 mark for each correct product]*
2.3 Any one from: e.g. lithium / sodium / potassium *[1 mark]* As it is higher in the reactivity series than calcium / loses electrons more easily than calcium / forms positive ions more easily *[1 mark]*.
2.4 potassium, sodium, zinc *[1 mark]*
3.1 When a metal reacts with an acid, the metal forms positive ions *[1 mark]*. The results show that lithium reacts more vigorously with acid than magnesium does *[1 mark]*, so lithium forms positive ions more easily *[1 mark]*.
3.2 A very vigorous fizzing/more vigorous than lithium *[1 mark]*, sodium disappears *[1 mark]*.
3.3 lithium, calcium, copper *[1 mark]*
3.4 It is not possible to tell the difference between magnesium and zinc from these results since both have same reaction with dilute acid *[1 mark]*. E.g. to find which is more reactive, you could find the effect of adding zinc to water *[1 mark]*.

Page 147 — Separating Metals from Metal Oxides

1.1 E.g. gold *[1 mark]*
1.2 Many metals can react with other elements/oxygen to form compounds/oxides *[1 mark]*.
1.3 Reduction is the loss of oxygen *[1 mark]*.
1.4 Magnesium is more reactive than carbon *[1 mark]*.
2.1 $2Fe_2O_3 + 3C \rightarrow 4Fe + 3CO_2$
[1 mark for correct equation, 1 mark for correct balancing]
2.2 Carbon has been oxidised *[1 mark]* as it has gained oxygen during this reaction *[1 mark]*.
2.3 E.g. extracting magnesium would have high energy costs to provide the high temperature and reduced pressure needed *[1 mark]*, but iron extraction doesn't need to be continuously heated *[1 mark]*.

Page 148 — Redox Reactions

1.1   Reduction is the gain of electrons *[1 mark]*.
1.2   zinc chloride + sodium → zinc + sodium chloride *[1 mark]*
1.3   Hydrogen gains electrons *[1 mark]*.
1.4   Chlorine is neither oxidised nor reduced *[1 mark]*.
2.1 $Mg_{(s)} + Fe^{2+}_{(aq)} \rightarrow Mg^{2+}_{(aq)} + Fe_{(s)}$ *[1 mark]*
You still get the marks if you didn't include state symbols.
2.2   No reaction would occur *[1 mark]*. Copper is less reactive than iron so doesn't displace it *[1 mark]*.

Pages 149-151 — Electrolysis

Warm-up

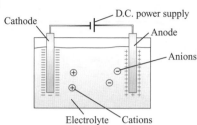

D.C. power supply
Cathode
Anode
Anions
Electrolyte   Cations

1.1   A liquid or solution that can conduct electricity *[1 mark]*.
1.2   lead bromide → lead + bromine *[1 mark]*
1.3   Lead ions have a positive charge *[1 mark]*. This means they are attracted to the negative cathode *[1 mark]*.
1.4 Br^- *[1 mark]*
1.5   oxidation *[1 mark]*
1.6   So the ions can move to the electrodes *[1 mark]*.
2.1   molten aluminium *[1 mark]*
2.2   To lower the melting point of the electrolyte *[1 mark]*.
2.3   Carbon in the electrodes reacts with oxygen to form carbon dioxide *[1 mark]*, so they degrade over time *[1 mark]*.
3.1   Iron ions, chloride ions, hydrogen ions and hydroxide ions
       [1 mark for iron ions and chloride ions, 1 mark for hydrogen ions and hydroxide ions].
3.2   At the cathode: hydrogen is discharged.
       At the anode: chlorine is discharged *[1 mark]*.
3.3   oxygen *[1 mark]*
3.4   Iron can be extracted via reduction with carbon *[1 mark]*, which is less expensive than electrolysis *[1 mark]*.
4.1   E.g.

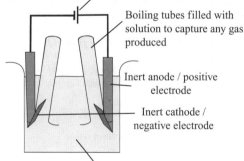

D.C. power supply
Boiling tubes filled with solution to capture any gas produced
Inert anode / positive electrode
Inert cathode / negative electrode
Aqueous solution / electrolyte

[1 mark for power supply, 1 mark for electrodes in solution, 1 mark for boiling tubes over the electrodes, 1 mark for labels]
4.2

Solution	Product at cathode	Product at anode
$CuCl_2$	Cu	Cl_2
KBr	H_2	Br_2
H_2SO_4	H_2	O_2 and H_2O

[1 mark for each correct answer]
4.3   Potassium is more reactive than hydrogen *[1 mark]* so hydrogen is discharged *[1 mark]*. There are no halide ions *[1 mark]* so oxygen and water are discharged *[1 mark]*.
4.4   Cathode: $2H^+ + 2e^- \rightarrow H_2$ *[1 mark]*
       Anode: $4OH^- \rightarrow O_2 + 2H_2O + 4e^-$
              $/ 4OH^- - 4e^- \rightarrow O_2 + 2H_2O$ *[1 mark]*

Topic C5 — Energy Changes

Pages 152-154 — Exothermic and Endothermic Reactions

1   In an endothermic reaction, energy is transferred from the surroundings so the temperature of the surroundings goes down *[1 mark]*.
2.1   endothermic *[1 mark]*
2.2

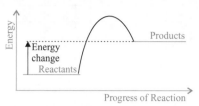

Energy
Products
Energy change
Reactants
Progress of Reaction

[1 mark for correct curve, 1 mark for energy change]
The curve has to go above the energy of the products and then fall back down. If you didn't do this, you don't get the mark.
2.3   From the surroundings *[1 mark]*.
2.4   It stays the same *[1 mark]*.
2.5   E.g. a sports injury pack *[1 mark]*.
3.1   The activation energy is the minimum amount of energy that reactants must have when they collide with each other in order to react *[1 mark]*. It's shown by the difference between the energy of the reactants and the maximum energy reached by the curve on the reaction profile *[1 mark]*.
3.2   Reaction A is the most suitable reaction *[1 mark]*.
       Reaction C is endothermic, so would not give out heat, and couldn't be used to warm your hands *[1 mark]*.
       Reaction A has a lower activation energy than Reaction B / gives out more energy than Reaction B *[1 mark]*.
4.1   Any three from: e.g. thermometer / polystyrene cup (and lid) / mass balance / measuring cylinder / beaker filled with cotton wool / stopwatch *[1 mark for each]*.
4.2   How to grade your answer:
       Level 0:   There is no relevant information *[No marks]*.
       Level 1:   The method is vague, and misses out important details about how the investigation could be carried out *[1 to 2 marks]*.
       Level 2:   The method is clear, but misses out a few key details about how the investigation would be carried out or how the variables could be controlled *[3 to 4 marks]*.
       Level 3:   There is a clear and detailed method that includes ways to reduce energy transfer to the surroundings, and specifies variables that should be controlled throughout the investigation *[5 to 6 marks]*.
       Here are some points your answer may include:
       Measure out an exact volume of the acid solution into the polystyrene cup.
       Record the initial temperature of the acid solution.
       Add one metal powder and stir the mixture.
       Place a lid on the polystyrene cup to reduce the amount of energy transferred to the surroundings.
       Take the temperature of the mixture every 30 seconds and record the highest temperature.
       Repeat the experiment for each different metal.
       Use the same volume and concentration of acid each time you repeat the experiment.
       Make sure the acid starts at the same temperature each time you repeat the experiment.
       Use the same number of moles and the same surface area of metal each time you repeat the experiment.

Answers

5.1 E.g.

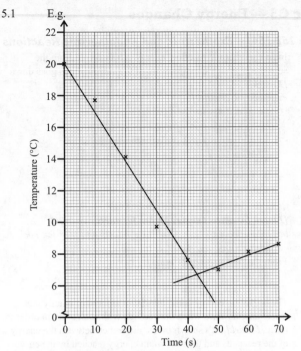

*[2 marks for all points plotted correctly,
otherwise 1 mark for at least six points plotted correctly.
1 mark for two sensible lines of best fit.]*

5.2 Intersection of lines of best fit = 6.7 °C
(allow between 6.2 and 7.2 °C)
Maximum temperature change = 20.0 − 6.7 = **13.3 °C**
(allow between 12.8 and 13.8 °C)
*[2 marks for the correct answer, otherwise 1 mark
for finding the temperature at the intersection]*

Page 155 — Bond Energies

1.1 Energy to break the bonds = (4 × C–H) + Cl–Cl
= (4 × 413) + 243 = 1652 + 243 = 1895 kJ/mol
Energy produced when bonds form = (3 × C–H) + C–Cl + H–Cl
= (3 × 413) + 346 + 432 = 1239 + 346 + 432
= 2017 kJ/mol
Energy change of reaction = Energy to break bonds − Energy
produced when bonds form
= 1895 − 2017 = **−122 kJ/mol** *[3 marks for correct answer,
otherwise 1 mark for 1895 kJ/mol, 1 mark for 2017 kJ/mol,
1 mark for subtracting energy produced when bonds form from
energy needed to break bonds]*

*Three of the C–H bonds are unchanged in this reaction. So you could also
calculate this by working out just the energy needed to break the C–H and
the Cl–Cl bond, and subtracting the energy that's released when the new
C–Cl and H–Cl bonds form.*

1.2 The reaction is exothermic *[1 mark]* because the energy released
when the bonds of the products form is greater than the energy
needed to break the bonds of the reactants *[1 mark]*.

2 Total energy needed to break the bonds in the reactants
= H–H + F–F = 436 + 158 = 594 kJ/mol
Energy change of reaction = Energy needed to break bonds −
Energy released when bonds form
So, energy released when bonds form = Energy needed to break
bonds − Energy change of reaction
= 594 − (−542) = 1136 kJ/mol
Energy released when bonds form = 2 × H–F bond energy
So, H–F bond energy = 1136 ÷ 2 = **568 kJ/mol**
*[3 marks for correct answer, otherwise 1 mark for finding
the energy needed to break the bonds, 1 mark for finding the
energy released by forming bonds]*

Topic C6 — The Rate and Extent of Chemical Change

Pages 156-158 — Rates of Reaction

1.1 Using a larger volume of the solution, but keeping the
concentration the same *[1 mark]*.
1.2 activation energy *[1 mark]*
1.3 A catalyst decreases the activation energy *[1 mark]*.
2 Produced most product: C *[1 mark]*
Finished first: B *[1 mark]*
Started at the slowest rate: A *[1 mark]*
3.1

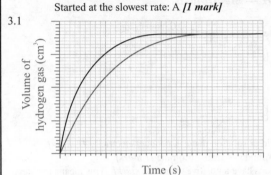

*[1 mark for curve with steeper gradient at the start of the
reaction, 1 mark for curve reaching the final volume earlier,
1 mark for final volume being the same as for the other curve]*

3.2 The frequency of the collisions *[1 mark]* and the energy of the
colliding particles *[1 mark]*.
3.3 There are more particles in a given volume/the particles are
closer together *[1 mark]*, so the collisions between particles are
more frequent *[1 mark]*.
3.4 The rate would increase *[1 mark]*.
3.5 Smaller pieces have a higher surface area to volume ratio
[1 mark]. So for the same volume of solid, the particles around
it will have more area to work on and collisions will be more
frequent *[1 mark]*.
3.6 E.g. changing the temperature / adding a catalyst *[1 mark]*.
4.1 E.g. increasing the volume of the reaction vessel would decrease
the pressure of the reacting gases *[1 mark]*. So the particles
would be more spread out and would collide less frequently
[1 mark], so the reaction rate would decrease *[1 mark]*.
Increasing the temperature would cause the particles to move
faster, so the frequency of collisions would increase *[1 mark]*
and the reaction rate would increase *[1 mark]*.
4.2 It's a catalyst *[1 mark]*.
4.3 The reaction equation won't change *[1 mark]*. Cerium oxide
isn't used up in the reaction, so doesn't appear in the reaction
equation *[1 mark]*.
4.4

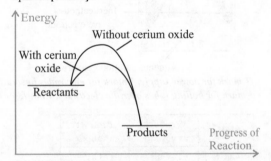

*[1 mark for correct relative energies of products and reactants,
1 mark for start and end energies being the same for reactions
with and without cerium oxide, 1 mark for reaction with cerium
oxide rising to a lower energy than reaction without cerium
oxide]*

Pages 159-161 — Measuring Rates of Reaction

Warm-up

The rate of a reaction can be measured by dividing the amount
of **reactants** used up or the amount of **products** formed by the
time. To find the rate at a particular time from a graph with
a curved line of best fit, you have to find the **gradient** of the
tangent at that time.

1 mass *[1 mark]*, volume of gas *[1 mark]*

2.1   time taken for the solution to go cloudy *[1 mark]*

2.2   temperature *[1 mark]*

2.3   Any one from: e.g. the concentration of the reactants / the volume of the reactants / the depth of the reaction mixture *[1 mark]*.

2.4   It would be more accurate to measure the volume of gas produced *[1 mark]* as this method less subjective *[1 mark]*.

3.1   E.g. a gas syringe / a measuring cylinder inverted in a bowl of water *[1 mark]*.

3.2

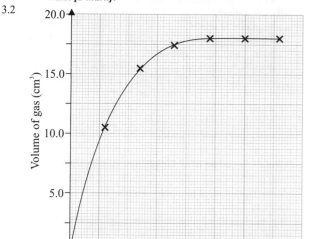

[2 marks for all points plotted correctly, or 1 mark for at least 5 points plotted correctly, 1 mark for line of best fit]

3.3   Any value between 210-240 s *[1 mark]*

When no more gas is produced, the reaction has stopped.

3.4   E.g. Mean rate of reaction = $\dfrac{\text{amount of product formed}}{\text{time for reaction to stop}}$

$$= \dfrac{18.0}{240} = 0.075 \text{ cm}^3\text{/s}$$

[2 marks for correct answer between 0.075-0.086 cm³/s, otherwise 1 mark for correct equation]

If you got the wrong answer in 3.3, but used it correctly here as the change in y, you still get all the marks.

3.5   E.g. repeat the experiment using the same method *[1 mark]* and check that the results are similar *[1 mark]*.

4.1

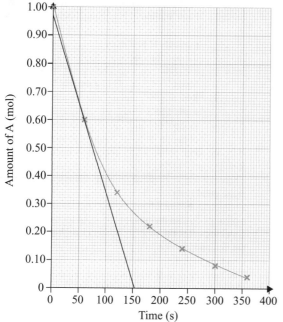

Gradient = $\dfrac{\text{change in } y}{\text{change in } x} = \dfrac{0.97}{153} = $ **0.0063 mol/s**

(allow between 0.0053 mol/s and 0.0073 mol/s)

[4 marks for correct answer, otherwise 1 mark for correctly drawn tangent to curve at 50 s, 1 mark for answer to 2 s.f., 1 mark for correct units]

4.2

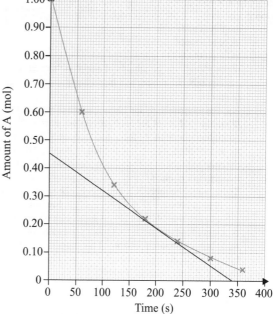

Gradient = $\dfrac{\text{change in } y}{\text{change in } x} = \dfrac{0.45}{340} = $ **0.0013 mol/s**

(allow between 0.0008 mol/s and 0.0018 mol/s)

[4 marks for correct answer, otherwise 1 mark for correctly drawn tangent to curve at 200 s, 1 mark for answer to 2 s.f., 1 mark for correct units]

4.3   The rate decreases *[1 mark]*. This is because, as the amount of reactant A falls, so does its concentration and so the frequency of collisions between the reactant particles decreases *[1 mark]*.

Pages 162-163 — Reversible Reactions

1.1   That the reaction is reversible / can go both ways *[1 mark]*.

1.2   At equilibrium, the rate of the forward reaction is equal to the rate of the backwards reaction *[1 mark]*.

2.1   It will be exothermic *[1 mark]*. The same amount of energy will be released in the reverse reaction as is taken in by the forward reaction *[1 mark]*.

2.2   The system has reached equilibrium *[1 mark]*. This mixture contains both blue copper(II) ions and the yellow copper compound, so the colours mix to form green *[1 mark]*.

2.3   E.g. by changing the temperature / by changing the concentration of one of the reactants *[2 marks — 1 mark for each correct answer]*.

3.1   At time A, some of the methanol was removed from the reaction, lowering the concentration present *[1 mark]*. As the reaction continued, more methanol was produced, increasing the concentration present in the reaction *[1 mark]*.

3.2   The forward reaction must be exothermic *[1 mark]*, as the equilibrium shifts to favour the reverse reaction in order to lower the temperature of the reaction *[1 mark]*.

3.3   At time B, the pressure of the system was increased *[1 mark]*. This shifted the equilibrium in the direction of the side with fewer moles, favouring the forward reaction and therefore decreasing the concentration of the reactants *[1 mark]*.

3.4

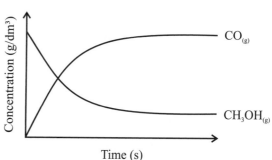

[1 mark for the correct curves, 1 mark for the correct labels]

Pages 164-165 — Le Chatelier's Principle

Warm-up

more reactants
more reactants
more products

1.1 If you change the conditions of a reversible reaction at equilibrium, the system will try to counteract that change *[1 mark]*.

1.2 E.g. the temperature / the concentration of the reactants *[2 marks — 1 mark for each correct answer]*

2.1 At higher temperatures there will be more ICl and less ICl_3 / the equilibrium will shift to the left *[1 mark]*. This is because the reverse reaction is endothermic so opposes the increase in temperature *[1 mark]*.

2.2 There would be more ICl_3 and less ICl *[1 mark]* because the increase in pressure *[1 mark]* causes the equilibrium position to move to the side with the fewest molecules of gas *[1 mark]*.

3.1 At higher temperature there's more product (brown NO_2) in the equilibrium mixture *[1 mark]*. This suggests that the equilibrium has moved to the right/forward direction *[1 mark]*, so the forward reaction is endothermic *[1 mark]*.

From Le Chatelier's principle, you know that increasing the temperature will favour the endothermic reaction as the equilibrium tries to oppose the change. So the forward reaction must be endothermic, as there's more NO_2 in the equilibrium mixture at higher temperatures.

3.2 The mixture would go a darker brown *[1 mark]*, as the decrease in pressure causes the equilibrium to move to the side with the most molecules of gas *[1 mark]*, meaning more NO_2 is formed *[1 mark]*.

4 Observation 1: Increasing amounts of red $FeSCN^{2+}$ are formed, so the solution becomes a darker red *[1 mark]*. When equilibrium is reached, the amount of each substance stops changing, and so does the colour *[1 mark]*.
Observation 2: The concentration of Fe^{3+} initially increases, so the solution becomes more orangey *[1 mark]*. The equilibrium then shifts to make more $FeSCN^{2+}$, so the solution becomes darker red in colour *[1 mark]*.
Observation 3: The concentration of $FeSCN^{2+}$ initially increases, so the solution becomes darker red *[1 mark]*.
The equilibrium then shifts to produce more reactants, so the solution becomes more orangey *[1 mark]*.

Topic C7 — Organic Chemistry

Pages 166-167 — Hydrocarbons

Warm-up

Hydrocarbon	Not a hydrocarbon
propane ethene C_2H_6 C_2H_4	butanoic acid CH_3CH_2Cl hydrochloric acid

1.1 A compound that is formed from hydrogen and carbon atoms only *[1 mark]*.

1.2 butane, propane, ethane, methane *[1 mark]*

1.3 C_nH_{2n+2} *[1 mark]*

1.4 hydrocarbon + oxygen → **carbon dioxide** + **water** *[1 mark]*

1.5 oxidised *[1 mark]*

2.1 **B** *[1 mark]*

2.2 **B, D, and E** *[1 mark]*. They have the general formula C_nH_{2n+2} *[1 mark]*

2.3 **E** *[1 mark]*. Boiling point increases with increasing molecular size/number of carbons *[1 mark]*.

3.1 Diesel will be more viscous than petrol *[1 mark]*. The higher boiling point of diesel means it contains larger molecules/ molecules with longer chains *[1 mark]*.

3.2 Petrol *[1 mark]*. The lower boiling point of petrol means it contains smaller molecules/molecules with shorter chains *[1 mark]*.

3.3 $C_{20}H_{42}$ *[1 mark]*

3.4 $2C_8H_{18} + 25O_2 \rightarrow 16CO_2 + 18H_2O$ *[1 mark for correct formulas of products, 1 mark for balancing]*
Any correct balance of the equation is correct, e.g. $C_8H_{18} + 12\frac{1}{2}O_2 \rightarrow 8CO_2 + 9H_2O$.

Page 168 — Fractional Distillation

1.1 The remains of ancient organisms/plankton *[1 mark]*.

1.2 A resource which is being used quicker than it is being replaced so will run out eventually *[1 mark]*.

1.3 alkanes *[1 mark]*

2.1 boiling point *[1 mark]*

2.2 The fractionating column is hot at the bottom and cool at the top *[1 mark]*. So longer hydrocarbons, which have higher boiling points, will condense and be drained off near the bottom *[1 mark]*. Meanwhile, shorter hydrocarbons, with lower boiling points, will condense and be drained off further up the column *[1 mark]*.

2.3 They contain similar numbers of carbon atoms / they have a similar chain length *[1 mark]*.

Pages 169-171 — Uses and Cracking of Crude Oil

1.1 Any two from: e.g. solvents / lubricants / polymers / detergents *[2 marks — 1 mark for each correct answer]*

1.2 cracking *[1 mark]*

1.3 E.g. shorter chain hydrocarbons are more useful/can be used for more applications *[1 mark]*.

2.1 thermal decomposition / endothermic *[1 mark]*

2.2 Hydrocarbons are vaporised / heated to form gases *[1 mark]*. The vapours are then passed over a hot catalyst / the vapours are mixed with steam and heated to very high temperatures *[1 mark]*.

2.3 E.g. $C_{10}H_{22} \rightarrow C_7H_{16} + C_3H_6$ *[1 mark]*
Cracking equations must always be balanced and have a shorter alkane and an alkene on the right-hand side.

3.1 C_7H_{16} *[1 mark]*

3.2
$$\begin{array}{c} \quad\; H \;\; H \;\; H \;\; H \\ \quad\; | \quad | \quad | \quad | \\ H-C-C-C-C-H \\ \quad\; | \quad | \quad | \quad | \\ \quad\; H \;\; H \;\; H \;\; H \end{array}$$

[1 mark for correct number of carbons, 1 mark for correct displayed formula]

3.3 E.g. to produce polymers / as a starting material for other chemicals *[1 mark]*.

4 How to grade your answer:
Level 0: Nothing written worth of credit *[No marks]*.
Level 1: Basic outline of how some fractions are processed but lacking detail. Some mention of the uses of cracking products *[1 to 2 marks]*.
Level 2: Reason for cracking explained and some detail given about the process. The uses of cracking products are covered in detail *[3 to 4 marks]*.
Level 3: Reasons for cracking and the process of cracking are explained in detail, including an accurate balanced symbol or word equation. Examples given of the uses of the products of cracking *[5 to 6 marks]*.
Here are some points your answer may include:
<u>Reasons for cracking</u>
There is a higher demand for short chain hydrocarbons as these make good fuels.
Long chain hydrocarbons are less useful than short chain hydrocarbons, so there is less demand for them.
Cracking helps the supply of short chain hydrocarbons to meet the demand.
<u>Cracking process</u>
The long chain hydrocarbons are heated and vaporised.
The vapours are passed over a hot catalyst / mixed with steam and heated to a high temperature so that they thermally decompose.
Any relevant word equation: e.g. decane → octane + ethene
Any relevant balanced equation:
e.g. $C_{12}H_{26} \rightarrow C_8H_{18} + 2C_2H_4$
<u>Uses of cracking products</u>
The products of cracking are useful as fuels.
Alkenes are used as a starting material when making lots of other compounds and can be used to make polymers.

5.1 The hydrocarbon is very flammable *[1 mark]*.
The bung prevents hydrocarbon vapour from escaping the boiling tube and igniting *[1 mark]*.

5.2 E.g. they didn't completely fill the test tube with water at the start of the experiment *[1 mark]*.

5.3 E.g. the test tube could be replaced with a measuring cylinder *[1 mark]*.

5.4 If cold water was sucked back into the hot boiling tube, it could cause the boiling tube to crack *[1 mark]*.

5.5 It would not be safe/possible to reach the temperature required to conduct this reaction in a laboratory without a catalyst *[1 mark]*.

Topic C8 — Chemical Analysis

Page 172 — Purity and Formulations

1.1 A single element or compound not mixed with any other substance *[1 mark]*.

1.2 Sample A *[1 mark]*. The purer the substance, the smaller the range of the melting point / purer substances melt at higher temperatures than impure substances *[1 mark]*.

1.3 Sample A *[1 mark]*.

2.1 It is a mixture that has been designed to have a precise purpose *[1 mark]*. Each of the components is present in a measured quantity *[1 mark]* and contributes to the properties of the formulation *[1 mark]*.

2.2 By making sure each component in the mixture is always present in exactly the same quantity *[1 mark]*.

2.3 Any one from: e.g. medicines / cleaning products / fuels / cosmetics / fertilisers / metal alloys *[1 mark]*.

Pages 173-175 — Paper Chromatography

Warm-up

1.1 E: $R_f = \dfrac{\text{distance travelled by substance}}{\text{distance travelled by solvent}} = \dfrac{3.6}{9.5} = \mathbf{0.38}$

[2 marks for correct answer, otherwise 1 mark for using correct equation to calculate R_f]

F: $R_f = \dfrac{\text{distance travelled by substance}}{\text{distance travelled by solvent}} = \dfrac{8.0}{9.5} = \mathbf{0.84}$

[2 marks for correct answer, otherwise 1 mark for using correct equation to calculate R_f]

1.2 E.g. they're distributed differently between the mobile phase and the stationary phase *[1 mark]*.

1.3 They're all pure substances *[1 mark]*.

1.4 **D** and **E** *[1 mark]*.

2.1 E.g. to stop any solvent evaporating *[1 mark]*.

2.2 **A** spends more time in the mobile phase compared to the stationary phase than **B** does *[1 mark]*.

2.3 **B** and **C** *[1 mark]*.

2.4 The student is incorrect *[1 mark]*. Substances have different R_f values in different solvents as the attraction between the substance and solvent changes *[1 mark]*.

2.5 It suggest that there are at least 3 substances in **W** *[1 mark]*.

2.6 There were only two spots in the chromatogram shown because two of the substances in **W** are similarly distributed between the mobile phase/water and stationary phase / they had similar R_f values *[1 mark]*.

3.1 There are at least five compounds in the ink *[1 mark]* because there are 5 spots on the chromatogram *[1 mark]*. There is at least one insoluble compound *[1 mark]*, because there is still a spot on the baseline *[1 mark]*.

The student can't know exactly how many compounds are in the ink, as some compounds may not be soluble in the solvent, and others may have similar R_f values so their spots will overlap.

3.2 The student drew line A from the baseline to the top of the spot *[1 mark]*. They should have drawn the line to the centre of the spot *[1 mark]*. The student drew line B from the baseline to the top of the paper *[1 mark]*. They should have drawn line B from the baseline to the solvent front *[1 mark]*.

Page 176 — Tests for Gases

1.1 litmus paper *[1 mark]*.

1.2 chlorine/Cl_2 *[1 mark]*

2.1 E.g. the gas could be toxic/an irritant *[1 mark]*

2.2 Bubble the gas through limewater *[1 mark]*. If the gas is carbon dioxide, the limewater will turn cloudy *[1 mark]*.

2.3 The gas was not hydrogen *[1 mark]*.

2.4 oxygen *[1 mark]*

Topic C9 — Chemistry of the Atmosphere

Pages 177-178 — The Evolution of the Atmosphere

Warm-up

1 False
2 True
3 True
4 False

1.1 One-fifth oxygen and four-fifths nitrogen *[1 mark]*.

1.2 Any two from: e.g. carbon dioxide / water vapour / named noble gas *[2 marks — 1 mark for each correct answer]*

1.3 By algae and plants photosynthesising *[1 mark]*.

1.4 By volcanic activity *[1 mark]*.

1.5 200 million years *[1 mark]*

2.1 E.g. photosynthesis by plants and algae / carbon dioxide dissolved in the oceans *[1 mark]*.

2.2 From matter that is buried and compressed over millions of years *[1 mark]*.

2.3 Coal: from thick plant deposits *[1 mark]*.
Limestone: from calcium carbonate deposits from the shells and skeletons of marine organisms *[1 mark]*.

3.1 E.g. the long timescale means there's a lack of evidence *[1 mark]*.

3.2 $6CO_2 + 6H_2O \rightarrow C_6H_{12}O_6 + 6O_2$ *[1 mark]*

3.3 Oxygen is produced by photosynthesis *[1 mark]* and there are no plants or algae / there isn't any photosynthesis *[1 mark]* on Mars.

3.4 The fact that the red beds formed about 2 billion years ago suggests that before this time there wasn't enough oxygen in the air for iron oxide to form / from this time there was enough oxygen in the air for iron oxide to form *[1 mark]*.

Pages 179-181 — Greenhouse Gases and Climate Change

1.1 Nitrogen *[1 mark]*

1.2 They help to keep Earth warm *[1 mark]*.

1.3 Any two from: e.g. deforestation / burning fossil fuels / agriculture / producing waste *[2 marks — 1 mark for each correct answer]*

2.1 Greenhouse gases absorb long-wave (thermal) radiation *[1 mark]* reflected from Earth's surface *[1 mark]*. They then reradiate this thermal radiation in all directions, including back towards Earth, helping to warm the atmosphere *[1 mark]*.

2.2 E.g. flooding *[1 mark]* and coastal erosion *[1 mark]*.

2.3 Any one from: e.g. changes in rainfall patterns / the ability of certain regions to produce food might be affected / the frequency/severity of storms might increase / the distribution of wild species might change *[1 mark]*.

Answers

3   How to grade your answer:
     Level 0:   There is no relevant information *[No marks]*.
     Level 1:   Unstructured and no logic. The trends in the
                 variables are described but reasons are not given
                 [1 to 2 marks].
     Level 2:   Some structure and logic but lacking clarity.
                 The trends in the variables are described and
                 there is some explanation of how the increase in
                 carbon dioxide may have come about and how
                 this might be linked to temperature
                 [3 to 4 marks].
     Level 3:   Clear, logical answer. The trends in the variables
                 are described and there is a clear explanation of
                 how the increase in carbon dioxide may have
                 come about and how this may be linked to
                 temperature *[5 to 6 marks]*.
     Here are some points your answer may include:
     The graph shows an increase in carbon dioxide levels in the
     atmosphere between 1960 and 2015.
     The increase in carbon dioxide levels is likely to be due to human
     activities which release carbon dioxide into the atmosphere.
     These activities include increased burning of fossil fuels,
     increased deforestation and increased waste production.
     The graph shows that the increase in carbon dioxide appears to
     correlate with an increase in global temperatures.
     The increase in global temperatures is likely to be due to the
     increase in carbon dioxide in the atmosphere, as carbon dioxide
     is a greenhouse gas so helps to keep Earth warm.

4.1   The global warming potential for methane is significantly
      greater than for carbon dioxide *[1 mark]*.
4.2   It has a very high global warming potential compared to other
      gases *[1 mark]* and stays in the atmosphere for a long time
      [1 mark].
5.1   E.g. the composition of the gases in the bubbles could be
      analysed to find out the concentration of greenhouse gases
      in the atmosphere at different times *[1 mark]*.
5.2   The data does support the scientist's conclusion *[1 mark]*.
      The global temperature anomaly, and therefore the
      global temperature, increases as the concentration
      of carbon dioxide increases *[1 mark]*.
5.3   E.g. increasing carbon dioxide levels in the atmosphere
      cause the global temperature to increase *[1 mark]*.
      Higher temperatures may cause ice caps to melt *[1 mark]*,
      reducing the amount of ice available for scientists to collect
      [1 mark].
5.4   Any one from: e.g. collecting large ice cores is expensive
      / drilling so deep might disturb the local environment /
      scientists may require specialist equipment to collect/store
      large ice cores *[1 mark]*.

Page 182 — Carbon Footprints
1.1   A measure of the amount of carbon dioxide and other
      greenhouse gases *[1 mark]* released over the full life cycle of
      something *[1 mark]*.
1.2   Any two from: e.g. using renewable or nuclear energy sources /
      using more energy efficient appliances *[2 marks — 1 mark for
      each correct answer]*.
1.3   E.g. lack of education / reluctance to change their lifestyle / cost
      of changing lifestyle *[1 mark]*.
2.1   Any two from, e.g: specialist equipment is needed to capture the
      carbon dioxide / it's expensive to capture and store the carbon
      dioxide / it could be difficult to find suitable places to store the
      carbon dioxide *[2 marks — 1 mark for each correct answer]*.
2.2   E.g. governments could tax companies based on the amount
      of greenhouse gases they emit *[1 mark]*. They could also
      put a cap on the emissions produced by a company *[1 mark]*.
      Governments might be reluctant to impose these methods if they
      think it will affect economic growth / could impact on people's
      well-being *[1 mark]*, especially if other countries aren't using
      these methods either / the country is still developing *[1 mark]*.

Page 183 — Air Pollution
1.1   Coal can contain sulfur impurities *[1 mark]*

1.2   Acid rain: sulfur dioxide / nitrogen oxides/nitrogen monoxide/
      nitrogen dioxide/dinitrogen monoxide *[1 mark]*
      Global dimming: e.g. (carbon) particulates *[1 mark]*
1.3   Any two from: e.g. damage to plants / buildings / statues /
      corrodes metals *[2 marks — 1 mark for each correct answer]*.
2.1   The reaction of nitrogen and oxygen from the air *[1 mark]* at the
      high temperatures produced by combustion *[1 mark]*
2.2   Nitrogen oxides cause respiratory problems *[1 mark]* and
      contribute to acid rain *[1 mark]*.
2.3   E.g. they can cause respiratory problems *[1 mark]*.
2.4   Carbon monoxide *[1 mark]*. It is colourless and odourless
      [1 mark].

Topic C10 — Using Resources

Page 184 — Finite and Renewable Resources
1.1   Coal *[1 mark]*. It does not form fast enough to be considered
      replaceable *[1 mark]*.
1.2   A resource that reforms at a similar rate to, or faster, than
      humans can use it *[1 mark]*.
2.1   E.g. the development of fertilisers has meant higher yields of
      crops *[1 mark]*.
2.2   Any one from: e.g. synthetic rubber has replaced natural rubber
      / poly(ester) has replaced cotton in clothes / bricks are used
      instead of timber in construction *[1 mark]*.
3   Any one advantage from: e.g. allows useful products to be made
      / provides jobs / brings money into the area *[1 mark]*.
      Any one disadvantage: e.g. uses large amounts of energy / scars
      the landscape / produces lots of waste / destroys habitats
      [1 mark].

Pages 185-186 — Reuse and Recycling
1.1   An approach to development that takes account of the needs of
      present society *[1 mark]* while not damaging the lives of future
      generations *[1 mark]*.
1.2   E.g. chemists can develop and adapt processes that use less
      resources/do less damage to the environment *[1 mark]*. For
      example, chemists have developed catalysts that reduce the
      amount of energy required for industrial processes *[1 mark]*.
2.1   The raw materials for the jute bag are more sustainable *[1 mark]*
      as plant fibres are a renewable resource, whilst crude oil is a
      finite resource *[1 mark]*.
2.2   The production of the poly(ethene) bag is more sustainable
      [1 mark] as it needs less energy to be produced from its raw
      materials than the jute bag *[1 mark]*.
2.3   The jute bag can be reused and the poly(ethene) bag can be
      recycled, improving both their sustainability *[1 mark]*. However,
      the jute bag is more sustainable if the bags are disposed of in
      landfill *[1 mark]*, as it is biodegradeable, whilst the poly(ethene)
      bag isn't *[1 mark]*.
3.1   Any two from: e.g. often uses less energy / conserves the amount
      of raw materials on Earth / cuts down on waste sent to landfill
      [2 marks — 1 mark for each correct answer].
3.2   Any one from: e.g. glass / metal *[1 mark]*
      E.g. glass is crushed and melted down to form other glass
      products/other purpose / metal is melted and cast into the shape
      of a new product *[1 mark]*.
3.3   reusing *[1 mark]*
4.1   Plants are grown on soil containing copper compounds *[1 mark]*,
      so as they grow, copper builds up in their leaves *[1 mark]*. The
      plants are burned *[1 mark]*. The resulting ash contains the
      copper compounds *[1 mark]*.
4.2   By electrolysis of a solution containing the copper compounds
      [1 mark] or by displacement using scrap iron *[1 mark]*.
4.3   Copper is a finite resource *[1 mark]* and will eventually run out
      [1 mark]. Recycling copper makes it more sustainable *[1 mark]*.

Pages 187-188 — Life Cycle Assessments

Warm-up

Getting the Raw Materials — Coal being mined from the ground.
Manufacturing and Packaging — Books being made from wood pulp.
Using the Product — A car using fuel while driving.
Product Disposal — Plastic bags going on to landfill.

1.1 Any two from: e.g. if a product is disposed of in landfill sites, it will take up space / may pollute land/water / energy is used to transport waste to landfill / pollution can be caused by incineration *[2 marks — 1 mark for each correct answer]*.

1.2 Any one from: e.g. energy / water / some natural resources / certain types of waste *[1 mark]*

1.3 They can be subjective / they are difficult to measure *[1 mark]*.

1.4 No *[1 mark]*. Some elements of the LCA are not objective/ require the assessors to make value judgements/cannot be quantified reliably *[1 mark]*, therefore different people are likely to make a different judgement/estimate *[1 mark]*.

1.5 Selective LCAs could be written so they only show elements that support a company's claims / they could be biased *[1 mark]* in order to give them positive advertising *[1 mark]*.

2.1 E.g. glass bottles can be reused multiple times, but cans are usually only used once *[1 mark]*.

2.2 It will positively affect their life cycle assessment *[1 mark]*. Using recycled aluminium to produce cans requires less energy than producing new cans, which means the manufacturing process will be cheaper *[1 mark]*.

2.3 Glass bottles have to be separated before they can be recycled *[1 mark]*. This will negatively affect the life cycle assessment for the glass bottles because e.g. it makes the recycling process more expensive and time-consuming to complete / some batches might need to be discarded because they are contaminated *[1 mark]*.

2.4 Any one from: e.g. how likely they are to be recycled / how easy/expensive it is to recycle them / the environmental costs of disposal if they are sent to landfill / their biodegradability *[1 mark]*

Pages 189-190 — Potable Water

Warm-up

1 False
2 True
3 False

1.1 pure water *[1 mark]*

1.2 e.g. from the ground / lakes / rivers *[1 mark]*.

1.3 passing water through filter beds — solid waste *[1 mark]*
sterilisation — microbes *[1 mark]*

1.4 E.g. chlorine, ozone, ultraviolet light *[3 marks — 1 mark for each correct answer]*.

2.1 **A**: Bunsen burner *[1 mark]*
B: round bottom flask *[1 mark]*
C: thermometer *[1 mark]*
D: condenser *[1 mark]*

2.2 Pour the salt water into the flask and secure it on top of a tripod *[1 mark]*. Connect the condenser to a supply of cold water *[1 mark]* that goes in at the bottom and out at the top *[1 mark]*. Heat the flask and allow the water to boil *[1 mark]*. Collect the water running out of the condenser in a beaker *[1 mark]*.

2.3 Reverse osmosis / a method which uses membranes *[1 mark]*

2.4 Desalination requires a lot of energy compared to the filtration and sterilisation of fresh water *[1 mark]*. Since the UK has a plentiful supply of fresh water there is no need to use desalination processes *[1 mark]*.

Page 191 — Waste Water Treatment

1.1 organic matter, harmful microbes *[2 marks — 1 mark for each correct answer]*

1.2 It may contain harmful chemicals which need to be removed *[1 mark]*.

2.1 To remove grit *[1 mark]* and large bits of material/twigs/plastic bags *[1 mark]*.

2.2 Substance **A**: sludge *[1 mark]*
Substance **B**: effluent *[1 mark]*

2.3 anaerobic digestion *[1 mark]*

Topic P1 — Energy

Page 192 — Energy Stores and Systems

1.1 An object or a group of objects. *[1 mark]*

1.2 Energy is transferred from: apple's gravitational potential energy store / apple's kinetic energy store *[1 mark]*
Energy is transferred to: apple's kinetic energy store / thermal energy store of the apple and surroundings (as the apple hits the ground) *[1 mark]*

1.3 E.g. work being done by the current in the circuit *[1 mark]*.

2 Level 0: There is no relevant information. *[No marks]*
Level 1: There is a brief explanation of one of the energy transfers, with no mention of the forces doing the work. *[1 to 2 marks]*
Level 2: There is a clear description of the energy transfers that take place, as well as the forces that are doing the work. *[3 to 4 marks]*

Here are some points your answer may include:
Gravitational force does work on the bike.
This causes energy to be transferred from the gravitational potential energy store of the bicycle to its kinetic energy store.
Friction force does work between the brake pads and the wheels.
This causes energy to be transferred from the bicycle's kinetic energy store to the thermal energy store of the brake pads.

Page 193 — Kinetic and Potential Energy Stores

1 $E_e = \frac{1}{2}ke^2 = \frac{1}{2} \times 20 \times 0.01^2$ *[1 mark]* = **0.001 J** *[1 mark]*

2 Energy lost from the g.p.e. store = energy gained in the kinetic energy store *[1 mark]*
$E_p = mgh = 0.1 \times 9.8 \times 0.45 = 0.441$ J *[1 mark]*
$E_k = \frac{1}{2}mv^2$
So $v = \sqrt{(2 \times E) \div m}$
$= \sqrt{(2 \times 0.441) \div 0.1}$ *[1 mark]*
$= 2.969...$ *[1 mark]* = **3 m/s (to 1 s.f.)** *[1 mark]*

3.1 $E_e = \frac{1}{2}ke^2 = \frac{1}{2} \times 144 \times 0.10^2$ *[1 mark]* = 0.72 J
It is assumed that all of the energy stored in the elastic potential energy store of the elastic band is transferred to the kinetic energy store of the ball bearing ($E_e = E_k$)
so energy = **0.72 J** *[1 mark]*

3.2 Speed of child A's ball bearing:
$E_k = \frac{1}{2}mv^2 = 0.72$ J
so $v^2 = (2 \times 0.72) \div 0.0100 = 144$ *[1 mark]*
$v = 12$ m/s so child B's ball bearing speed is:
2×12 m/s = 24 m/s *[1 mark]*
$E_k = \frac{1}{2}mv^2 = \frac{1}{2} \times 0.0100 \times 24^2 = 2.88$ J *[1 mark]*
$E_e = \frac{1}{2}ke^2 = 2.88$ J
so $k = (2 \times 2.88) \div 0.10^2$ *[1 mark]*
$= 576 = $ **580 N/m (to 2 s.f.)** *[1 mark]*

Pages 194-195 — Specific Heat Capacity

Warm-up

The energy needed to raise 1 kg of a substance by 1 °C.

1.1 $\Delta E = mc\Delta\theta$ so $c = \Delta E \div m\Delta\theta$ *[1 mark]*
$= 15\,000 \div (0.3 \times 25)$ *[1 mark]*
Specific heat capacity = **2000** *[1 mark]*

1.2 The current flowing through the immersion heater does work *[1 mark]*, transferring energy electrically *[1 mark]* to the thermal energy store of the immersion heater *[1 mark]*. It is then transferred from the thermal energy store of the immersion heater to the thermal energy store of the liquid *[1 mark]*.

2.2 Material C has the highest specific heat capacity *[1 mark]*.
E.g. The higher the specific heat capacity of a material, the more energy is required to increase the temperature of 1 kg of the material by 1 °C *[1 mark]*. Material C had the smallest increase in temperature when the same amount of energy was transferred to the same mass of each material, so it must have the highest specific heat capacity *[1 mark]*.

You could also have answered this question using the specific heat capacity equation. $Q = mc\Delta T$, so the gradient of the graph is equal to $\frac{1}{mc}$. Since m is the same for all of the materials, this means the line with the shallowest gradient shows the highest specific heat capacity.

320

2.3 Valid results are repeatable and reproducible. To confirm that his results are repeatable, the student should repeat the experiment with the same method, and check that he gets very similar results *[1 mark]*. To confirm his results are reproducible, he should repeat the experiment using different equipment and/or a different experimental method, and check that he gets very similar results *[1 mark]*.

Pages 196-197 — Conservation of Energy and Power
Warm-up
Power is the **rate of** energy transfer or **work done**.
It is measured in **watts**.

1 E.g. energy transferred to a less useful energy store *[1 mark]*
2.1 Energy can be created.
Energy can be destroyed.
[1 mark for both correct answers, otherwise no marks if more than two boxes have been ticked]
2.2 Useful energy store: e.g. kinetic energy store (of razor) *[1 mark]*
Wasted energy store: e.g. thermal energy store (of shaver or surroundings) *[1 mark]*
2.3 E.g. it would reduce the battery life of the battery / it would make the battery go flat quicker / it would mean the battery must be recharged more often *[1 mark]*.
3.1 $P = W \div t$ *[1 mark]*
3.2 $W = Pt = 35 \times 600$ *[1 mark]* = **21 000 J** *[1 mark]*
3.3 $P = E \div t$
so $t = E \div P = 16\,800 \div 35$ *[1 mark]* = **480 s** *[1 mark]*
4.1 It will decrease the time *[1 mark]* because more energy is being transferred to the kinetic energy store of the car per second *[1 mark]* so the car speeds up more quickly *[1 mark]*.
4.2 The same amount of energy is needed to accelerate the car with both engines. The energy transferred by the old engine:
$P = E \div t$, so $E = P \times t = 32\,000 \times 9.0 = 288\,000$ J *[1 mark]*
The time taken for the new engine to transfer the same amount of energy is:
$P = E \div t$, so $t = E \div P = 288\,000 \div 62\,000$
= 4.645... *[1 mark]*
= **4.6 s (to 2 s.f.)** *[1 mark]*

Pages 198-199 — Reducing Unwanted Energy Transfers
1.1 through the roof *[1 mark]*
1.2 E.g. install loft insulation (to reduce convection) *[1 mark]*
1.3 E.g. use draught excluders (to reduce convection) / install double glazing (to reduce conduction) / hang thick curtains (to reduce convection) / reduce the temperature difference between inside and outside the home *[1 mark for each sensible suggestion]*
2 D *[1 mark]*. The lower the rate of energy transfer through the brick, the more energy-efficient the house will be *[1 mark]*. D has a lower thermal conductivity value, so the rate of energy transfer through it will be lower *[1 mark]*. It's also thicker (than brand B), which also reduces the rate of energy transfer through it *[1 mark]*.
3 Doing work against friction causes energy to be dissipated/wasted (usually to thermal energy stores) *[1 mark]*. After lubricating the axle, the frictional forces acting on it were reduced *[1 mark]*. This means that less energy is dissipated as the handle (and axle) is turned and so more energy is transferred to the kinetic energy store of the handle (and axle) and the bucket *[1 mark]*.
4 Best: C   Second best: B   Worst: A *[1 mark]*
The thicker a sample is, the slower the rate of energy transfer through it *[1 mark]* so sample B will be a better insulator than sample A *[1 mark]*. Air has a lower thermal conductivity than glass (so it transfers energy at a slower rate than glass does) *[1 mark]* so even though samples B and C are the same thickness, sample C is a better insulator than sample B *[1 mark]*.

Pages 200-201 — Efficiency
1.1 Efficiency = Useful output energy transfer ÷ Total input energy transfer *[1 mark]*

1.2 Efficiency = 16 000 ÷ 20 000 *[1 mark]*
= **0.8** *[1 mark]*
You'd also get the mark for giving the efficiency as a percentage (80%).
2 Efficiency = 75% = 0.75
Efficiency = Useful power output ÷ Total power input
So Total power input = Useful power output ÷ Efficiency
[1 mark]
= 57 ÷ 0.75 *[1 mark]* = **76 W** *[1 mark]*
3.1 Useful output power of the air blower:
Efficiency = Useful power output ÷ Total power input
so Useful power output = Efficiency × Total power input
= 0.62 × 533 *[1 mark]*
= 330.46 W *[1 mark]*
Useful power output of the turbine:
Efficiency = 13% = 0.13
Total power input = Useful power of air blower
Useful power output = Efficiency × Total power input
= 0.13 × 330.46 *[1 mark]*
= 42.9598
= **43 W (to 2 s.f.)** *[1 mark]*
3.2 E.g. adding more sails (so there is a larger surface area for the air to hit) / increasing the size of the sails (so there is a larger surface area for the air to hit) / adding a lubricant to the moving parts of the turbine (to reduce friction) / changing the angle of the sails so they get hit by more wind *[2 marks — 1 mark for each sensible suggestion]*
4.1 E.g. the student could measure the temperature of the water in the kettle, so that they can be sure they measure the energy transferred to increase the water's temperature to 100 °C (not any more or less) *[1 mark]*.
4.2 The student will record an inaccurate value of energy transferred to the kettle for this reading *[1 mark]*. This is because some of the residual energy in the kettle's thermal energy store from the previous trial will be transferred to the water and begin to increase its temperature, so less energy will need to be transferred from the power supply to boil the water *[1 mark]*.
4.3 The results are not consistent with the prediction.
By calculating the efficiencies at different volumes from the data in Table 1, using efficiency = $\dfrac{\text{useful energy output}}{\text{total energy input}}$ *[1 mark]*, it can be seen that:
E.g. for 660 cm³ of water, efficiency = 0.168 ÷ 0.212
= 0.792... *[1 mark]*,
while for 2000 cm³ of water, efficiency = 0.504 ÷ 0.547
= 0.921... *[1 mark]*.
Therefore, the efficiency of the kettle was greater for a larger volume of water than a smaller volume (the opposite of the student's prediction) *[1 mark]*.
You don't have to have done the exact same calculations we have here. As long as you've come to the right conclusion and have done some calculations to show that efficiency is larger for a bigger volume than a smaller volume, you'll get the marks.

Pages 202-203 — Energy Resources and Their Uses
Warm-up
Renewable — bio-fuel, solar, tidal, geothermal, wave power, hydroelectricity, wind
Non-renewable — oil, coal, gas, nuclear fuel
1 E.g. a non-renewable energy resource will one day run out *[1 mark]* but a renewable energy resource can be replenished as it is used *[1 mark]*.
2.1 coal, oil, (natural) gas *[1 mark]*
2.2 E.g. generating electricity / burning coal on fires / using gas central heating / using a gas fire / coal in steam trains *[2 marks — 1 for each correct answer]*
2.3 Bio-fuels are solids, liquids or gases that are produced from plant products or from animal waste *[1 mark]*.
2.4 E.g. because fossil fuels will eventually run out / because fossil fuels harm the environment *[1 mark for any correct answer]*.

E.g. during winter, there are fewer hours of daylight, but the weather is usually more windy *[1 mark]*, so wind turbines will be able to generate more electricity during winter *[1 mark]*. However, during the summer, there will be more daylight hours and the weather will be less windy *[1 mark]*, so solar panels will be more favourable *[1 mark]*. By installing both, the university will have a more reliable electricity supply throughout the year *[1 mark]*.

.1 How to grade your answer:
Level 0: There is no relevant information. *[No marks]*
Level 1: There is a brief description of the reliability or environmental impact of one of the energy resources. *[1 to 2 marks]*
Level 2: There is a clear and detailed description of the reliability and environmental impacts of both energy resources, as well as some similarities between them. *[3 to 4 marks]*
Here are some points your answer may include:
Both energy resources are reliable.
Tides come in and out at known times.
Except in times of drought, there is always water available for a hydroelectric power plant to work.
Hydroelectric power plants require the flooding of valleys, which causes a loss of habitat for any animals living there.
The plants in the valley die during the flood and rot, which releases gases that contribute to global warming.
Using tides to generate electricity creates no pollution, but tidal barrages do alter the habitat of nearby animals.

.2 How to grade your answer:
Level 0: There is no relevant information. *[No marks]*
Level 1: There is a brief explanation of an advantage or a disadvantage of fossil fuels. *[1 to 2 marks]*
Level 2: There is some explanation of both advantages and disadvantages of fossil fuels. *[3 to 4 marks]*
Level 3: There is a clear and detailed explanation of the advantages and disadvantages of using fossil fuels. *[5 to 6 marks]*
Here are some points your answer may include:
Advantages:
Fossil fuels are reliable.
They are extracted at a fast enough rate that there are always some in stock.
Power plants can respond quickly to peaks in demand.
Running costs of fossil fuel power plants aren't that expensive compared to other energy resources.
Fuel extraction costs are also low.
Disadvantages:
Fossil fuels are slowly running out / they are a non-renewable energy resource.
Burning fossil fuels releases carbon dioxide into the atmosphere.
Carbon dioxide in the atmosphere contributes to global warming.
Burning coal and oil also releases sulfur dioxide, which causes acid rain.
Acid rain can damage soil and trees. This can damage or destroy the habitats of animals.
Coal mining can spoil the view by damaging the landscape.
Oil spillages kill sea life and birds and mammals that live near to the sea.

Page 204 — Trends in Energy Resource Use

.1 35 + 23 + 5 = 63 %
[2 marks for correct answer, otherwise 1 mark for reading all three values correctly from the graph]

.2 E.g. the country is using a larger percentage renewable energy resources to generate electricity in 2015 than they were the previous year / overall, they are using a smaller percentage of fossil fuels to generate their electricity in 2015 than they were in 2014 *[1 mark]*.

2 How to grade your answer:
Level 0: There is no relevant information. *[No marks]*
Level 1: There is a brief explanation why the UK is using more renewable energy resources. *[1 to 2 marks]*
Level 2: There is some explanation of why the UK is using more renewable energy resources and the factors that restrict the increase in their use. *[3 to 4 marks]*
Level 3: There is a clear and detailed explanation of why the UK is using more renewable energy resources and the factors that restrict the increase in their use. *[5 to 6 marks]*
Here are some points your answer may include:
Reasons the UK is using more renewable energy resources:
We understand more about the negative effects that fossil fuels have on the environment, so more people want to use renewable energy resources that have less of an impact on the environment.
Fossil fuel reserves will run out, so we have to find an alternative for them.
Pressure from the public and other countries has lead to government targets for the use of renewable energy resources. This can lead to increased government funding for renewable energy resources.
Pressure from the public and the global community/other countries has also lead to private companies creating more environmentally-friendly products that use renewable energy resources.
Factors that limit the use of renewable energy resources:
Building new power plants to replace existing fossil fuel powered ones costs money.
Some renewable energy resources are less reliable than fossil fuels.
Research into improving renewable energy resources costs money and will take time.
Personal products that use renewable energy resources, like hybrid cars, are generally more expensive than similar ones that use fossil fuels.

Topic P2 — Electricity

Page 205 — Current and Circuit Symbols
Warm-up
A — cell, B — switch, C — filament lamp, D — fuse.
1.1 There is no source of potential difference *[1 mark]*
1.2 Current is the rate of flow of **charge** *[1 mark]*.
2.1 0.5 A *[1 mark]*
Remember that the current is the same at any point in a single closed circuit loop.
2.2 $Q = I \times t$ *[1 mark]*
2.3 $t = 2 \times 60 = 120$ s
Charge = 0.5×120 *[1 mark]*
= **60** *[1 mark]* **C** *[1 mark]*

Page 206 — Resistance and V = IR
1 $V = I \times R$
$V = 3 \times 6$ *[1 mark]* = **18 V** *[1 mark]*
2.1 She could have varied the length of the wire between the crocodile clips *[1 mark]* and divided the reading on the voltmeter by the reading on the ammeter to find the resistance for each length *[1 mark]*.

Answers

2.2

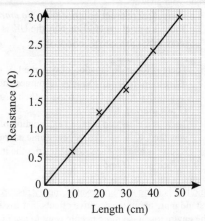

[1 mark for resistance on vertical axis and length on horizontal axis, 1 mark for appropriate values labelled on both axes, 1 mark for correctly plotted points, 1 mark for suitable line of best fit.]

2.3 The resistance is proportional to the length *[1 mark]*. This is shown by the graph being a straight line through the origin *[1 mark]*.

Pages 207-209 — Resistance and I-V Characteristics

1.1 C *[1 mark]*

At a constant temperature, the relationship between pd and current is linear — when this is true, the resistor is said to be ohmic.

1.2 I-V characteristic *[1 mark]*

1.3 A resistor at a constant temperature is an example of an **ohmic** conductor. It is also an example of a **linear** component.
[1 mark for each correct answer]

2.1

[1 mark]

2.2 A diode only lets current flow through it in one direction *[1 mark]*.

2.3 The student put the diode/power supply in the circuit the other way around *[1 mark]*. The resistance of a diode is very large when current goes through it one way and very small when current goes through in the opposite direction *[1 mark]*.

3.1 It is used to alter the current *[1 mark]* so the potential difference can be measured for each current *[1 mark]*.

3.2 At 3 A the pd is 12 V *[1 mark]*
$V = I \times R$
$R = V \div I$ *[1 mark]* $= 12 \div 3$ *[1 mark]* $= $ **4 Ω** *[1 mark]*

3.3 The resistance increases as the current increases *[1 mark]*. This is because the increase in current causes the temperature to rise *[1 mark]*.

3.4 A resistor is ohmic when the relationship between current and potential difference is linear *[1 mark]*. The graph is linear until approximately 3.5 V, so the resistor is ohmic in this range *[1 mark]*.

4.1 E.g. adjust the variable resistor to change the current through the circuit. Record the current through the diode using the ammeter, and the potential difference across it using the voltmeter *[1 mark]*. Use the equation $V = IR$ (in the form $R = V \div I$) to calculate the resistance of the diode at this current using the current and potential difference measurements *[1 mark]*. Repeat this for a number of different values of current (e.g. at least 6), changing the current by a fixed amount each time (e.g. 1 mA) *[1 mark]*.

4.2 E.g.

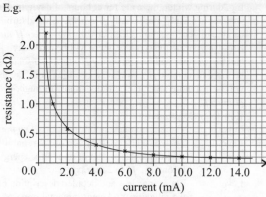

[1 mark for smooth line passing through or close to all points]

4.3 E.g. she has only carried out the experiment for positive values of current / current flowing in one direction *[1 mark]*. This means she cannot make a conclusion about the effect of the size of the current, because the device may behave differently for current that flows in the opposite direction / because diodes are known to have a very high resistance for one direction of current flow but not the opposite *[1 mark]*.

Page 210 — Circuit Devices

1.1

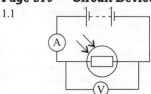

[1 mark for correct LDR symbol, 1 mark for LDR, ammeter and power supply in series, 1 mark for voltmeter in parallel across LDR.]

1.2 It decreases *[1 mark]*

1.3 E.g. automatic night lights / burglar detectors *[1 mark]*

2 As the temperature increases, the resistance of the thermistor decreases *[1 mark]*. This means the current in the circuit increases *[1 mark]*. As the current increases, the brightness of the light increases *[1 mark]*. When the cooker's surface is cold, the resistance is high and the current is too small to light the bulb *[1 mark]*.

Page 211 — Series Circuits

1 A *[1 mark]*.

In a series circuit, there should only be one closed loop of wire.

2.1 $10 + 30 = $ **40 Ω** *[1 mark]*

2.2 $V = I \times R$
$V = 75 \times 10^{-3} \times 30$ *[1 mark]* $= $ **2.25 V** *[1 mark]*

3 The potential difference across the 8 Ω resistor is:
$6 - 2 = 4$ V *[1 mark]*
$V = I \times R$, so the current through the 8 Ω resistor is:
$I = V \div R = 4 \div 8$ *[1 mark]* $= 0.5$ A *[1 mark]*
This is the same as the current through R, so the resistance of R is: $R = V \div I = 2 \div 0.5$ *[1 mark]* $= $ **4 Ω** *[1 mark]*

Page 212 — Parallel Circuits

1

[1 mark]

2.1 6 V *[1 mark]*

Potential difference is the same across all components in parallel.

2.2 $V = IR$ so $I = V \div R$ *[1 mark]*
A_1: $I = V \div R = 6 \div 4$ *[1 mark]* $= $ **1.5 A** *[1 mark]*
A_2: $I = V \div R = 6 \div 12$ *[1 mark]* $= $ **0.5 A** *[1 mark]*

2.3 The current from the supply splits into 1.5 A and 0.5 A. So A_3 reads $1.5 + 0.5 = $ **2 A** *[1 mark]*

3   How to grade your answer:
    Level 0:   There is no relevant information. *[No marks]*
    Level 1:   There is a brief explanation about the effect of
                adding resistors in series or parallel.
                [1 to 2 marks]
    Level 2:   There is a comparison between adding resistors
                in series and parallel and an explanation of their
                effects. *[3 to 4 marks]*
    Level 3:   A logical and detailed comparison is given,
                explaining why adding resistors in series increases
                the total resistance but adding them in parallel
                reduces it. *[5 to 6 marks]*
    Here are some points your answer may include:
    In series, resistors share the potential difference from the power
    source.
    The more resistors that are in series, the lower the potential
    difference for each one, and so the lower the current for each
    one.
    Current is the same all around a series circuit, so adding a
    resistor will decrease the current for the whole circuit.
    A decrease in total current means an increase in total resistance.
    In parallel, all resistors have the same potential difference as the
    source.
    Adding another resistor in parallel (forming another circuit loop)
    increases the current flowing in the circuit, as there are more
    paths for the current to flow through.
    An increase in total current means a decrease in total resistance
    (because $V = IR$).

Page 213 — Investigating Resistance

1.1
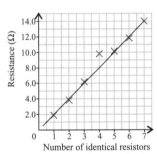

Resistance = **8.0 Ω**
*[1 mark for a straight line of best fit that excludes the point
plotted for 4 resistors, 1 mark for correct prediction of
resistance]*

1.2
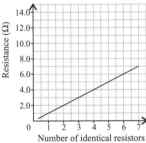

*[1 mark for a straight line of best fit with a positive gradient,
1 mark for the gradient of the line being half of the gradient of
the line drawn in 1.1]*

2   How to grade your answer:
    Level 0:   There is no relevant information. *[No marks]*
    Level 1:   There is a brief description of the techniques
                used to measure resistance of the circuit. The steps
                mentioned are not in a logical order.
                [1 to 2 marks]
    Level 2:   There is a good description of the techniques
                used to measure resistance of the circuit. Most
                steps are given in a logical order and they could be
                followed to produced valid results.
                A correct circuit diagram may be included.
                [3 to 4 marks]
    Level 3:   A logical and detailed description is given, fully
                describing the method for investigating the effect
                of adding resistors in parallel. The method could
                easily be followed to produce valid results.
                A correct circuit diagram may be included.
                [5 to 6 marks]
    Here are some points your answer may include:
    Connect a battery or cell in series with an ammeter and a fixed
    resistor.
    Measure the source potential difference using the voltmeter.
    Measure the current through the circuit using the ammeter.
    Calculate the resistance of the circuit using $R = V \div I$.
    Connect a second identical resistor in parallel with the first
    resistor.
    Do not connect the second resistor across the ammeter.
    Measure the current and use this to calculate the resistance of the
    circuit.
    Repeat this for several identical resistors.
    Plot a graph of number of identical resistors against overall
    resistance of the circuit.
    A correct circuit diagram, similar to:

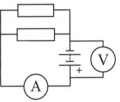

*So long as you draw a correct diagram with at least two resistors in
parallel, you would get the marks. You could also draw your circuit with
several resistors in parallel, all separated with switches.*

Page 214 — Electricity in the Home

Warm-up
            The live wire is **brown** and is at a potential difference of **230** V.
            The earth wire is **green and yellow** and is at a potential
            difference of **0** V.
1.1   230 V *[1 mark]*
        50 Hz *[1 mark]*
1.2   How to grade your answer:
        Level 0:   There is no relevant information. *[No marks]*
        Level 1:   There is a brief explanation of the function of
                    the live and neutral wires and some attempt at
                    explaining why the toaster would not work.
                    [1 to 2 marks]
        Level 2:   There is a good explanation of the function of the
                    live and neutral wires and why the fault would not
                    allow a current to flow through the toaster.
                    [3 to 4 marks]
        Here are some points your answer may include:
        The purpose of the neutral wire is to complete the circuit.
        Current flows into the toaster via the live wire, through the
        toaster, and out of the device by the neutral wire.
        The fault means that a closed loop/low-resistance path has been
        formed between the live and neutral wire before the current in
        the live wire has reached the toaster.
        So no (or very little) current will flow through the toaster.
        This means that the toaster will not work.
2.1   To stop an electric current from flowing out of the live wire and
        potentially causing an electric shock (i.e. for safety)
        [1 mark]. To make it easy to identify the live wire *[1 mark]*.

Answers

2.2   The man has an electric potential of 0 V *[1 mark]* and the wire has an electric potential (of 230 V) so a potential difference exists between them *[1 mark]*. This causes a current to flow through the man *[1 mark]*.

2.3   Yes *[1 mark]*. Although there is no current flowing when it is switched off, there is still a potential difference *[1 mark]*, so touching the live wire in the socket could cause a current to flow through you to the Earth *[1 mark]*.

Pages 215-216 — Power of Electrical Appliances

1   The **power** of an appliance is the energy transferred **per second**. Energy is transferred because the **current** does work against the appliance's resistance. *[1 mark for each correct]*

2.1 $E = P \times t$ *[1 mark]*

2.2 $E = 50 \times 20$ *[1 mark]* = **1000 J** *[1 mark]*

2.3   The power of the car is higher *[1 mark]*. So more energy is transferred away from the chemical energy store of the battery per second *[1 mark]*.

3.1   Energy is transferred electrically from the power source *[1 mark]* to the thermal energy store of the water *[1 mark]* and the kinetic energy store of the motor *[1 mark]*.

3.2   Work done = power × time $(E = P \times t)$
Work done = 400×60 *[1 mark]* = **24 000 J** *[1 mark]*

3.3   Time of economy mode = $160 \times 60 = 9600$ s
Energy transferred in economy mode
= power × time = $400 \times 9600 = 3\ 840\ 000$ J *[1 mark]*
Time of standard mode = $125 \times 60 = 7500$ s
Energy transferred in standard mode = 600×7500
= 4 500 000 J *[1 mark]*
Energy saved = 4 500 000 − 3 840 000 *[1 mark]*
= **660 000 J** *[1 mark]*

4.1   How to grade your answer:
Level 0:   There is no relevant information. *[No marks]*
Level 1:   There are some relevant points, but the answer is unclear. There is some description of the experimental set-up, but the details are unclear. There are explanations of the measurements and calculations that should be made, but they may be incomplete. *[1 to 2 marks]*
Level 2:   There is a clear description of how the equipment listed should be set up and used to carry out an experiment safely. There are full explanations of the measurements and calculations that should be made to determine the useful output power of the motor.
[3 to 4 marks]
Here are some points your answer may include:
Securely attach the clamp stand to the edge of a bench/worktop.
Set up the motor so that it is connected to the circuit, and clamped to the clamp stand. Make sure there is at least a metre of clear space between the motor and the ground.
Attach one end of the string to the axle of the motor (so that it will wind around the axle when the motor spins).
Attach the other end of the string to the 1 kg mass securely, so it hangs from the string.
Set up the ruler to stand vertically, parallel to the string.
Attach a marker to the bottom of the mass so that the distance moved by the mass can be accurately measured.
Turn on the motor, and, using the stopwatch, record the time taken for the motor to lift the mass through a fixed vertical height, e.g. 60 cm, measured by the metre ruler.
Repeat this at least two more times, and calculate an average value of the time taken from the three results.
Use the height to calculate the change in gravitational potential energy of the mass, and so the useful energy transferred by the motor.
Calculate the useful power by dividing this value of energy by the average value of time taken.

4.2   0.01 s *[1 mark]*.

4.3   The errors in the student's time measurements will mostly be caused by human error and her reaction time *[1 mark]*. Human reaction times are typically much larger than the smallest time measured by the stopwatch (0.2-0.9 s compared to 0.01 s) *[1 mark]*.

Page 217 — More on Power

Warm-up
A power source supplies **energy** to a charge. When a charge passes through a component with **resistance**, it does **work**, so the charge's energy **decreases**.

1.1 $E = V \times Q$ *[1 mark]*

1.2 $E = 6 \times 2$ *[1 mark]* = **12 J** *[1 mark]*

1.3   Multiplying the potential difference by the current gives the power *[1 mark]*. In 1.2 the energy was transferred by the two coulombs of charge in one second *[1 mark]*. This is the same as the power *[1 mark]*.

2.1 $P = I \times V$
so $I = P \div V = 75 \div 230$ *[1 mark]* = 0.3260...
= **0.33 A (to 2 s.f.)** *[1 mark]*

2.2 $P = I^2 \times R$
so $R = P \div I^2 = 2.5 \div 0.50^2$ *[1 mark]* = **10 Ω** *[1 mark]*

Page 218 — The National Grid

1.1   Potential Difference *[1 mark]*, Current *[1 mark]*

1.2   A step-up transformer increases the potential difference, a step-down transformer decreases it *[1 mark]*.

2.1   Transformer A = step-up transformer *[1 mark]*
Transformer B = step-down transformer *[1 mark]*

2.2   How to grade your answer:
Level 0:   There is no relevant information. *[No marks]*
Level 1:   There is a brief explanation of the function of the step-up transformer and how this results in smaller energy losses. *[1 to 2 marks]*
Level 2:   There is a good explanation of the function of the step-up transformer and how reducing the energy lost increases the efficiency of the national grid.
[3 to 4 marks]
Here are some points your answer may include:
Transformer A increases the potential difference.
This decreases the current at a given power.
This decrease in current decreases energy lost to the thermal energy stores of the cables and surroundings.
Efficiency is useful output energy transfer ÷ total input energy transfer, so reducing the energy lost to thermal stores makes the transmission of electricity more efficient.

2.3   The potential difference across the power cables is very high and too large for domestic devices *[1 mark]*. Transformer B reduces the potential difference to lower, usable levels *[1 mark]*.

Topic P3 — Particle Model of Matter

Pages 219-220 — The Particle Model and Motion in Gases

Warm-up
From left to right: liquid, solid, gas

1   When the temperature of a gas increases, the average energy in the **kinetic** energy stores of the gas molecules increases. This **increases** the **average** speed of the gas molecules. If the gas is kept at a constant volume, increasing the temperature **increases** the pressure.
[3 marks for all correct, otherwise 1 mark for two correct or 2 marks for three correct]

2.1   There would be more air particles in the same volume *[1 mark]*, so the particles would collide with the tyre walls (and each other) more often *[1 mark]*. This would mean the pressure would increase *[1 mark]*.

2.2 On a hot day, the air particles in the tyre would have more energy in their kinetic energy stores *[1 mark]*, so they would move faster and hit the tyre walls more often *[1 mark]*. As the particles are moving faster, they also have a larger momentum, so the force each particle exerts on the tyre walls is larger *[1 mark]*. Hitting the tyre walls with a greater force and more often creates a higher pressure *[1 mark]*.

A *[1 mark]*

The volume of each container is the same (0.04 m³ = 40 000 cm³). A fixed mass and volume of a gas has a lower pressure at a lower temperature.

The large lid will pop off first *[1 mark]*. As the temperature of the gas increases, the particles have more energy in their kinetic energy stores. The momentum of the particles increases, so the force they exert on a unit area of the container walls increases *[1 mark]*. The particles also hit the walls more often, which also increases the force acting on a unit area *[1 mark]*. As the large lid as a larger area, the total force acting on it at any temperature will be higher than the total force acting on the smaller lid *[1 mark]*. So the force required to remove one of the lids will be reached by the larger lid first *[1 mark]*.

Pages 221-222 — Density of Materials

.1 $\rho = m \div v$ *[1 mark]*

.2 $\rho = 10\,000 \div 0.5$ *[1 mark]* = **20 000 kg/m³** *[1 mark]*

.3 The density is the same for the whole block,
so $\rho = 20\,000$ kg/m³
$\rho = m \div v$
so $m = \rho \times v = 20\,000 \times 0.02$ *[1 mark]* = **400 kg** *[1 mark]*

2 Level 0: There is no relevant information. *[No marks]*
Level 1: There is a brief description of the set-up of apparatus. There is no mention of how to measure volume or how to calculate density. *[1 to 2 marks]*
Level 2: There is a detailed explanation of the set-up of apparatus, with a description of the measurements needed to be taken and how these are used to find the density. *[3 to 4 marks]*

Here are some points your answer may include:
Place the empty beaker on the mass balance.
Zero the mass balance before putting acetic acid in the beaker.
Pour some acetic acid into the beaker.
Write down the mass of the acid shown on the mass balance.
Read the volume of the acid from the scale on the beaker.
Use the equation density = mass ÷ volume to calculate the density of the acetic acid.

3.1 First measure the mass of the object using a mass balance *[1 mark]*. Then submerge the object in the water and measure the volume of water displaced *[1 mark]*.
The volume of the displaced water in the measuring cylinder is equal to the volume of the object *[1 mark]*.
Use density = mass ÷ volume to calculate the density of the object *[1 mark]*.

3.2 $\rho = m \div v$
1 ml of water = 1 cm³ *[1 mark]*
A: $\rho = 5.7 \div 0.30 = 19$ g/cm³. So A is gold. *[1 mark]*
B: $\rho = 2.7 \div 0.60 = 4.5$ g/cm³. So B is titanium. *[1 mark]*
C: $\rho = 3.0 \div 0.30 = 10$ g/cm³. So C is silver. *[1 mark]*

4 Volume of empty aluminium can
= volume displaced by full can − volume of cola
= 337 − 332 = 5 ml *[1 mark]*
5 ml = 5 cm³ *[1 mark]*
$\rho = m \div v = 13.5 \div 5$ *[1 mark]* = **2.7 g/cm³** *[1 mark]*

Page 223 — Internal Energy and Changes of State

1 When a system is heated, the internal energy of the system **increases**. This either increases the **temperature** of the system or causes a change of state. During a change of state the temperature and **mass** of the substance remain constant.
[2 marks for all correct, otherwise 1 mark for two correct]

2.1 Gas to liquid: condensing
Liquid to gas: evaporating/boiling
[1 mark for both correct]

2.2 E.g. a change where you don't end up with a new substance / you end up with the same substance in a different form *[1 mark]*.

3.1 E.g. the energy stored in a system by its particles. / The sum of the energy in the particles' kinetic and potential energy stores *[1 mark]*

3.2 Any two from: mass, specific heat capacity, total energy transferred to the system *[2 marks]*

4 10 g *[1 mark]* E.g. because when a substance changes state, its mass doesn't change. So the mass of the water vapour equals the mass of the water originally in the test tube minus the mass of water left at the end *[1 mark]*.

Pages 224-225 — Specific Latent Heat

1.1 The amount of energy required to change the state of one kilogram of a substance with no change in temperature *[1 mark]*.

1.2 $E = mL$ so $L = E \div m$ *[1 mark]*
$L = 1.13 \div 0.5$ *[1 mark]* = **2.26 MJ/kg** *[1 mark]*

2.1 The substance is melting *[1 mark]*.

2.2 As the substance is heated, its internal energy increases *[1 mark]*. As the substance melts (during 3-8 minutes), all of this energy is used to break apart intermolecular bonds *[1 mark]* so there is no increase in the substance's temperature as it changes state *[1 mark]*.

2.3 Melting point = −7 °C *[1 mark]*
Boiling point = 58 °C *[1 mark]*

3.1 Any two from: e.g. take temperature measurements at smaller time intervals / continue measuring after the first non-zero temperature measurement to be sure the ice has finished melting / find the mass of any remaining solid ice at the end of the experiment to determine the exact mass of ice that melted / use a temperature probe to automatically record temperature values at accurate times *[2 marks]*.

3.2 Total energy required to melt the ice is given by $E = mL$
$E = 0.05 \times 334\,000 = 16\,700$ J *[1 mark]*
The time in which energy was transferred to the ice and only caused the ice to melt is given by the flat part of the graph, since this is where the temperature didn't change. The flat part of the graph starts at 3 minutes, and finishes at 142 minutes. So the total time for the flat section
= 142 − 3 = 139 minutes = 139 × 60 = 8340 s *[1 mark]*
So, average rate of energy transfer
= total energy transferred ÷ time taken for energy transfer
= 16 700 ÷ 8340 *[1 mark]*
= 2.002...
= **2 J/s (to 1 s.f.)** *[1 mark]*

3.3 The student is incorrect. For the second experiment to be a valid test of the experiment's repeatability, it has to be identical to the first experiment *[1 mark]*. Since the student has used ice in a different form for the second experiment, the method and conditions are not the same, so the student cannot make conclusions about the first experiment's repeatability from the results *[1 mark]*.

Topic P4 — Atomic Structure

Pages 226-227 — Developing the Model of the Atom

Warm-up
1×10^{-10} m
10 000

1.1 Our current model shows that the atom can be broken up (into protons, neutrons and electrons) *[1 mark]*.

1.2 The plum pudding model *[1 mark]*. This was where an atom was thought to be a sphere of positive charge, with electrons spread throughout it *[1 mark]*.

1.3 The neutron *[1 mark]*.

2.1 An electron can move into a higher energy level / further from the nucleus, by absorbing EM radiation *[1 mark]*, and move into a lower energy level / closer to the nucleus, by emitting EM radiation *[1 mark]*.

2.2 ion *[1 mark]*

2.3 Positive (or +1) *[1 mark]*
An atom is neutral. Losing an electron takes away negative charge, so the remaining ion is positive.

3 Level 0: There is no relevant information. *[No marks]*
Level 1: There is only one correct discovery mentioned with a brief description of the observation that led to it. *[1 to 2 marks]*
Level 2: Two correct discoveries are given with a detailed description of how observations led to them. *[3 to 4 marks]*
Here are some points your answer may include:
Discovery: The atom is mostly made up of empty space / most of the atom's mass is concentrated at the centre in a tiny nucleus.
Observation: Most of the alpha particles fired at the thin gold foil passed straight through.
Discovery: The atom has a positively charged central nucleus.
Observation: Some of the positive alpha particles were deflected back towards the emitter, so they were repelled by the nucleus.

4.1 Proton: (+)1 *[1 mark]*
Neutron: 0 *[1 mark]*

4.2 The protons and neutrons are in the central nucleus *[1 mark]* and the electrons surround the nucleus (arranged in shells) *[1 mark]*.

4.3 26 electrons *[1 mark]*. Atoms are neutral *[1 mark]*. Protons and electrons have equal but opposite charges. For these charges to cancel, there must be the same number of each *[1 mark]*.

Pages 228-230 — Isotopes and Nuclear Radiation

Warm-up
Gamma — weakly ionising, alpha — strongly ionising, beta — moderately ionising.

1.1 radioactive decay *[1 mark]*

1.2 Atoms with the same number of protons *[1 mark]* but different numbers of neutrons (in their nucleus) *[1 mark]*.

1.3 An atom losing (or gaining) at least one electron *[1 mark]*.

1.4 Alpha decay *[1 mark]*

2 E.g. Alpha particles have a small range in air and will be stopped by a thin sheet of material *[1 mark]*. So the alpha radiation inside the detector cannot escape the detector *[1 mark]*.

3.1 23 *[1 mark]*
Remember that the mass number is the little number in the top-left. It's the total number of protons and neutrons in the nucleus.

3.2 $23 - 11 = 12$ neutrons *[1 mark]*
The number of neutrons is the difference between the mass number and the atomic number.

3.3 $^{24}_{11}$Na *[1 mark]*
An isotope has the same number of protons (so the same atomic number), but a different number of neutrons (so a different mass number).

3.4 The atomic number of the neon isotope is lower, so there are fewer protons in the neon isotope *[1 mark]*. So the charge on the neon isotope's nucleus is lower than the charge on the sodium isotope's nucleus *[1 mark]*.

4 How to grade your answer:
Level 0: There is no relevant information. *[No marks]*
Level 1: There is a brief explanation of the method of locating the leak and of the radiation used. *[1 to 2 marks]*
Level 2: There is some explanation of the method of locating the leak and of the radiation used. *[3 to 4 marks]*
Level 3: There is a clear and detailed explanation of the method of locating the leak and of the radiation used. *[5 to 6 marks]*
Here are some points your answer may include:
The isotope travels along the pipe.
If there is no leak, the radiation doesn't escape the pipe/not much radiation can escape the pipe/some of the radiation is blocked by the pipe.
If there is a leak, the isotope escapes the pipe and some/more radiation can reach the detector.
This causes the count-rate to increase.
An increase in count-rate indicates a leak.
The isotope could be beta-emitting because beta radiation would be blocked by the pipe but would not be blocked by the small amount of ground above the pipe.

OR The isotope could be gamma-emitting because it can escape the pipe and reach the detector, and more gamma radiation would get to the detector if there was a leak.

5.1 For 0.5 mm thickness:
uncertainty = range ÷ 2 = $(122 - 99) \div 2 = \mathbf{11.5}$ *[1 mark]*
For 0.6 mm thickness:
mean = $(93 + 95 + 98) \div 3$
$= 95.33... = \mathbf{95}$ (to nearest whole number) *[1 mark]*

5.2 The results for a thickness of 0.6 mm are the most precise, as they have the smallest range / they have the smallest uncertainty / the individual results are closest to the mean value for count-rate *[1 mark]*. It's not possible to know whether they are the most accurate, as you can't tell from the data how close to the true value the measurements are *[1 mark]*.

5.3 E.g. the thicker the paper, the less beta radiation reaches the detector / the more beta radiation is absorbed by the paper *[1 mark]*.

5.4 If the half-life was shorter than or close to the duration of the experiment, the count-rate would reduce significantly during the experiment *[1 mark]*, and it would not be possible to conclude if a decrease in count-rate was due to the paper or the decay of the substance *[1 mark]*.

Page 231 — Nuclear Equations

1.1 It increases the positive charge on the nucleus / makes the nucleus 'more positive' *[1 mark]*.

1.2 The atomic number increases *[1 mark]* but the mass number stays the same *[1 mark]*. This is because emitting an electron (beta decay) involves a neutron turning into a proton *[1 mark]*.
Remember that a neutron turns into a proton in order to increase the positive charge on the nucleus. (Because emitting the electron has taken away some negative charge.)

1.3 No effect *[1 mark]*
When an electron moves to a lower energy level, it loses energy in the form of an EM wave, which doesn't change the charge or mass of the nucleus.

2.1 The atomic numbers on each side are not equal *[1 mark]*.

2.2 $^{0}_{-1}$e *[1 mark]*
The other particle must be an electron (a beta particle), as this will balance the equation.

2.3 $^{226}_{88}$Ra $\longrightarrow$ $^{222}_{86}$Rn + $^{4}_{2}$He
[3 marks in total — 1 mark for each correct symbol]
You know that the mass number of the radium is 226 (that's what 'radium-226' means). You also know that an alpha particle is $^{4}_{2}$He, so you can find the mass and atomic numbers of radon by balancing the equation.

2.4 Rn-222 has $222 - 86 = 136$ neutrons *[1 mark]*
2 alpha decays = $2 \times 2 = 4$ neutrons released *[1 mark]*
$136 - 4 = \mathbf{132}$ *[1 mark]*

Pages 232-233 — Half-life

1.1 E.g. the time taken for the count-rate of a sample to halve *[1 mark]*.

1.2 75 seconds *[1 mark]*
The initial count-rate is 60 cps. Half of this is 30 cps, which corresponds to 75 seconds on the time axis.

1.3 After 1 half-life, there will be $800 \div 2 = 400$ undecayed nuclei remaining. After 2 half-lives, there will be $400 \div 2 = 200$ undecayed nuclei remaining.
So $800 - 200 = \mathbf{600}$ nuclei will have decayed.
[2 marks for correct answer, otherwise 1 mark for calculating the number of decayed/undecayed nuclei after one half-life]

1.4 After 2 half-lives, there are 200 undecayed nuclei.
The ratio is 200:800,
which simplifies to **1:4** *[1 mark]*
You don't even need the numbers to work out this ratio. For any radioactive isotope, after two half lives, the initial number of undecayed nuclei will have halved and then halved again. It will be one quarter of the original number, so the ratio is always 1:4.

2 Isotope 1, because more nuclei will decay per second *[1 mark]*.

3.1 It takes a total of 2 hours and 30 minutes for the activity to halve from 8800 Bq to 4400 Bq,
so its half-life = $(2 \times 60) + 30 = \mathbf{150}$ minutes *[1 mark]*

3.2 Check how many half-lives pass during 6 hours and 15 minutes:
6 hours and 15 minutes = $(6 \times 60) + 15 = 375$ minutes
$375 \div 150 = 2.5$ half-lives
The activity can only be worked out if a whole number of half-lives have passed, so calculate how many half-lives have passed from the time when activity = 6222 Bq:
1 hour 15 minutes = $60 + 15 = 75$ minutes
$375 - 75 = 300$ minutes
$300 \div 150 = 2$ half-lives.
So now you can calculate the activity after 2 half-lives, with an initial activity of 6222 Bq:
After 1 half-life, the activity will be $6222 \div 2 = 3111$ Bq
After 2 half-lives, the activity will be $3111 \div 2 = 1555.5$ Bq
$1555.5 = \textbf{1600 Bq (to 2 s.f.)}$
[2 marks for correct answer, otherwise 1 mark for finding how many half-lives will have passed between 1 hour and 15 minutes and 6 hours and 15 minutes]

4.1

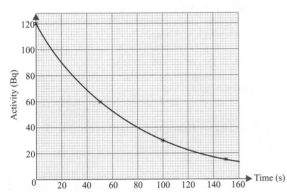

[3 marks in total — 2 marks for all points plotted correctly, otherwise 1 mark for three points plotted correctly, 1 mark for smooth curve.]

Start the graph at 120 Bq. After 50 s, this will have halved to 60 Bq. After another 50 s (i.e. 100 s altogether), it will have halved again, to 30 Bq. Plot these points, then join them up with a nice smooth curve.

4.2 70 Bq (accept between 68 Bq and 72 Bq)
[1 mark for correct value from your graph]

4.3 After 200 s, $15 \div 2 = 7.5$ Bq
After 250 s, $7.5 \div 2 = \textbf{3.75 Bq}$ *[1 mark]*
E.g. radioactive decay is random *[1 mark]* and the effect of randomness on the activity will be greater for lower activities *[1 mark]*.

Page 234 — Irradiation and Contamination

1 Any two from: e.g. using shielding / working in a different room to the radioactive source / using remote-controlled arms to handle sources / wearing protective suits *[2 marks]*

2.1 Contamination is when unwanted radioactive particles get onto an object *[1 mark]*. Irradiation is when an object is exposed to radiation *[1 mark]*.

2.2 Any two from: e.g. wearing protective gloves / using tongs / wearing a protective suit or mask *[2 marks]*.

3 How to grade your answer:
Level 0:   There is no relevant information. *[No marks]*
Level 1:   There is a brief explanation of the dangers of contamination or radiation. *[1 to 2 marks]*
Level 2:   There is some explanation of the dangers and risks of contamination and radiation.
[3 to 4 marks]
Level 3:   There is a clear and detailed explanation of the dangers and risks of contamination and radiation, used to justify the conclusion that the clockmaker should be more concerned about contamination. *[5 to 6 marks]*

Here are some points your answer may include:
Alpha particles are strongly ionising.
Alpha particles are stopped by skin or thin paper.
Being irradiated won't make the clockmaker radioactive.
But irradiation may do some damage to his skin.
However, the radiation cannot penetrate his body and cause damage to his tissue or organs.
If the clockmaker's hands get contaminated with radium-226, he

will be exposed to more alpha particles, close to his skin.
Or he may accidentally ingest (eat) some.
Or if particles of the radium get into the air, he could breathe them in.
The radium will then decay whilst inside his body.
This means that the alpha particles can do lots of damage to nearby tissue or organs.
So he should be more concerned about contamination.

Topic P5 — Forces

Page 235 — Contact and Non-Contact Forces

Warm-up
Scalar — mass, time, temperature
Vector — acceleration, weight, force

1 Vector quantities have both magnitude and direction. *[1 mark]*

2 Contact force: e.g. friction / tension / normal contact force / air resistance *[1 mark]*
Non-contact force: e.g. weight / gravitational force *[1 mark]*

3.1

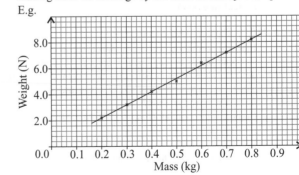

[1 mark for correct arrow length, 1 mark for correct direction]

3.2 Both arrows need to be longer (to indicate the stronger interaction) *[1 mark]*.
The arrows need to be the same size as each other *[1 mark]*.

Pages 236-237 — Weight, Mass and Gravity

1 **Mass** is the amount of matter in an object. **Weight** is a force due to gravity. Mass is measured **kilograms** whilst weight is measured in **newtons**. The weight of an object is **directly** proportional to its mass. *[3 marks for all correct, 2 marks for 3-4 correct, 1 mark for 1-2 correct]*

2 A point at which you can assume the whole mass of an object is concentrated. / The point from which the weight of an object can be assumed to act. *[1 mark]*

3.1 $W = mg$ *[1 mark]*

3.2 $W = 350 \times 9.8$ *[1 mark]* = **3430 N** *[1 mark]*

3.3 New mass = $350 - 209 = 141$ kg *[1 mark]*
$W = mg = 141 \times 3.8$ *[1 mark]* = 535.8
$= \textbf{536 N (to 3 s.f.)}$ *[1 mark]*

4.1 E.g. the standard mass may no longer have the same mass as it is labelled with *[1 mark]*.

This is because some of the rusted standard mass is made of a different substance (the rust) instead of pure iron as when it was originally measured and labelled. Also, the rust could flake off the standard mass, leaving it with a lower mass than before.

4.2 Systematic error *[1 mark]*, because the weight of the plastic tray will be included in each of the weight measurements, making them all too large by the same amount *[1 mark]*.

4.3 E.g.

[1 mark for all points plotted correctly and 1 mark for a straight line of best fit drawn through or close to all points]

4.4   Since $W = mg$, by comparing this to the equation for a straight-line graph, $y = mx + c$, you can see that the gravitational field strength, g, is equal to the gradient of the graph, m *[1 mark]*.

E.g. $g = \dfrac{\text{change in } y}{\text{change in } x} = \dfrac{8.4 - 2.0}{0.82 - 0.18}$ *[1 mark]*

$= \mathbf{10\ N/kg}$ *[1 mark]*

You'll get the calculation marks here as long as your calculation of the gradient is correct for your line of best fit.

Page 238 — Resultant Forces and Work Done

1   C *[1 mark]*

The resultant force is the sum of the two forces acting on each runner, taking into account the direction. For runner C, the resultant force is 130 N − 100 N = 30 N.

2.1 $W = Fs = 50 \times 15$ *[1 mark]* $= \mathbf{750}$ *[1 mark]*
       Unit: **J** or **Nm** *[1 mark]*

2.2   The temperature of the suitcase increases *[1 mark]* because doing work causes some energy to be transferred to the thermal energy store of the suitcase *[1 mark]*.

3.1   100 N *[1 mark]*

As the ladder isn't moving, the resultant force is zero, and so the weight of the ladder is equal to the normal contact force acting on the ladder.

3.2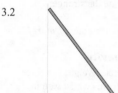

[1 mark for correct arrow length (same as 30 N arrow length), 1 mark for correct direction]

Page 239 — Calculating Forces

Warm-up
       Horizontal component = 4 N
       Vertical component = 3 N

1.1   1 cm = 100 N *[1 mark]*
1.2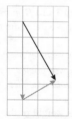

       Magnitude = **430 N**
       [1 mark for correct construction of resultant force, 1 mark for correct magnitude]

Page 240 — Forces and Elasticity

1.1   Elastic deformation is when an object returns to its original size after the deforming force is removed *[1 mark]*. Inelastic deformation is when an object has been deformed such that it cannot return to its original size or shape after the deforming force is removed *[1 mark]*.

1.2   Compressing, bending *[1 mark for both correct]*

2.1 $F = ke$ so $k = F \div e$
       $e = 20$ cm $= 0.2$ m
       so $k = 250 \div 0.2$ *[1 mark]* $= \mathbf{1250}$ *[1 mark]*
       Unit = **N/m** *[1 mark]*

2.2   E.g. Agree — the extension will be 40 cm, because force is proportional to extension, so doubling the force doubles the extension *[1 mark]*, assuming that the spring hasn't gone past its limit of proportionality *[1 mark]*.

Page 241 — Investigating Springs

1.1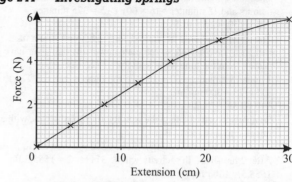

[1 mark for points plotted correctly, 1 mark for line of best fit showing linear relationship at the start, 1 mark for curved line of best fit towards the end of the graph]

1.2   Spring constant = Force ÷ Extension
                           = gradient of the linear section of the graph
       $k = 3 \div 0.12 = \mathbf{25\ N/m}$
       [2 marks for correct answer between 24 and 26 N/m, otherwise 1 mark for correct calculation]

2   Work done on spring = energy stored in the spring's elastic potential energy store
       $E = \tfrac{1}{2}ke^2 = \tfrac{1}{2} \times 25 \times 0.08^2$ *[1 mark]* $= \mathbf{0.08\ J}$ *[1 mark]*

Pages 242-243 — Distance, Displacement, Speed and Velocity

Warm-up
       Displacement and **velocity** are both **vector** quantities. This means they have both a size and a direction. Speed and **distance** are both **scalar** quantities. They do not depend on direction.

1.1   7 m *[1 mark]*
1.2   12 m *[1 mark]*
1.3

A •————————→ C————————————————————• B

       [1 mark for arrow of correct length in the correct direction]

1.4   2 m *[1 mark]*
2   330 m/s *[1 mark]*
3   Any three from: fitness / age / distance travelled / terrain *[3 marks — 1 mark for each correct answer]*
4   No — velocity is speed in a given direction *[1 mark]*. The satellite travels at a constant speed, but is always changing direction so its velocity is always changing *[1 mark]*.
5.1 $s = vt$ *[1 mark]*
5.2   Typical walking speed = 1.5 m/s (accept 1-2 m/s) *[1 mark]*
       $t = s \div v = 6000 \div 1.5$ *[1 mark]*
       $= \mathbf{4000\ s}$ (accept 3000-6000 s) *[1 mark]*
5.3   Typical cycling speed = 6 m/s (accept 5-7 m/s) *[1 mark]*
       $s = vt$ so $t = s \div v = 6000 \div 6$ *[1 mark]* $= 1000$ s *[1 mark]*
       $4000 - 1000 = \mathbf{3000\ s}$ (accept 1800-5200) *[1 mark]*
5.4 $t = 20 \times 60 = 1200$ s *[1 mark]*
       $s = vt$ so $v = s \div t = 9600 \div 1200$ *[1 mark]* $= \mathbf{8\ m/s}$ *[1 mark]*
6   Speed of sound = $331 + (0.6 \times -60) = 295$ m/s *[1 mark]*
       Jet speed = $0.80 \times 295 = 236$ m/s *[1 mark]*
       $s = vt$
       $= 236 \times 5.0 \times 10^4$ *[1 mark]*
       $= 11\ 800\ 000$ m $= \mathbf{11\ 800\ km}$ *[1 mark]*

Page 244 — Acceleration

Warm-up
       A sprinter starting a race — 1.5 m/s^2
       A falling object — 10 m/s^2
       A bullet shot from a gun — 2×10^5 m/s^2

1   The object is slowing down *[1 mark]*.
2.1 $a = \Delta v \div t$ *[1 mark]*
2.2 $a = \Delta v \div t = 4 \div 1$ *[1 mark]* $= \mathbf{4\ m/s^2}$ *[1 mark]*
3     $a = \Delta v \div t$
       $t = \Delta v \div a$ *[1 mark]* $= 20 \div 2.5$ *[1 mark]* $= \mathbf{8\ s}$ *[1 mark]*
4     $v^2 - u^2 = 2as$ so
       $a = (v^2 - u^2) \div 2s = (18^2 - 32^2) \div (2 \times 365)$ *[1 mark]*
       $= -0.9589...$
       So deceleration = **0.96 m/s^2** (to 2 s.f.) *[1 mark]*

Pages 245-248 — Distance-Time and Velocity-Time Graphs

1.1

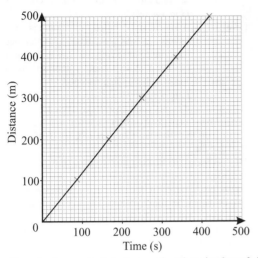

[3 marks for graph plotted correctly, otherwise 1 mark for three points correct, 1 mark for any suitable straight line]

1.2 360 m (accept between 350 m and 370 m) *[1 mark]*

1.3 210 s (accept between 200 s and 220 s) *[1 mark]*

1.4 E.g. refer to the same point on the boat / make sure that the timings are measured from exactly level with the posts / make sure timings are made close to the posts to avoid parallax / use a stopwatch instead of a watch *[1 mark for any correct answer]*

2.1 12 minutes *[1 mark]*

2.2 Accelerating *[1 mark]*

3.1 $v = \Delta s \div t$ = gradient of line
Speed = $(92 - 20) \div (6 - 3) = 72 \div 3 = $ **24 m/s**
(accept between 23 m/s and 25 m/s)
[3 marks for correct answer, otherwise 1 mark for realising speed is the gradient of the line, 1 mark for correct calculation]

3.2 Speed = gradient of a tangent to the line
$v = \Delta s \div \Delta t = (16 - 0) \div (3 - 1) = 16 \div 2 = $ **8 m/s**
(accept between 6 m/s and 10 m/s)
[3 marks for correct answer, otherwise 1 mark for a correct tangent to the line, 1 mark for correct calculation]

4.1

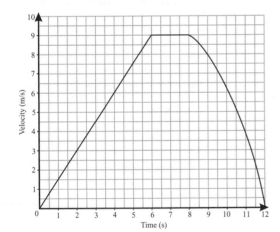

[1 mark for correct shape of graph, 1 mark for graph ending at 0 m/s]

4.2 $a = \Delta v \div t$ = gradient of the line
Acceleration = $(9 - 0) \div (6 - 0) = $ **1.5 m/s²**
[2 marks for correct answer, otherwise 1 mark for correct calculation]

4.3 $s = vt$ = area under the line *[1 mark]*
0-6 s: area = $\frac{1}{2}bh = \frac{1}{2} \times 6 \times 9 = 27$ m *[1 mark]*
6-8 s: area = $bh = 2 \times 9 = 18$ m *[1 mark]*
Total distance in 8 s = $27 + 18 = $ **45 m** *[1 mark]*

4.4 1 square is worth 0.5 s on the x-axis (time)
1 square is worth 0.5 m/s on the y-axis (velocity)
[1 mark for both correct]
$s = vt = 0.5 \times 0.5 = 0.25$ m *[1 mark]*
Squares under the line between 8 s and 12 s = 91 *[1 mark]*
$91 \times 0.25 = 22.75$ m *[1 mark]*
Total distance = $45 + 22.75 = 67.75 = $ **68 m** *[1 mark]*
(accept between 63 and 72 m)

5.1 The instantaneous acceleration can be found by finding the gradient of a tangent drawn at that point. So, draw a tangent at $t = 26$ s
E.g.

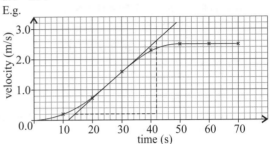

[1 mark]
gradient = $\dfrac{\text{change in } y}{\text{change in } x} = \dfrac{2.6 - 0.2}{42 - 14}$ *[1 mark]*
   = 0.0857...
   = **0.086 m/s² (to 2 s.f.)** *[1 mark]*
You'll get the marks here as long as you've drawn a sensible tangent at $t = 26$ s, and your calculation of the gradient is correct for the tangent you've drawn.

5.2 Advantage of light gates: e.g. the light gates will be able to measure both the speed of the car and the time very accurately / the light gates will be able to measure both the speed of the car and the time to a high resolution *[1 mark]*.
Disadvantage of light gates: e.g. the measurement points have to be marked out every 50 cm, so some changes in acceleration may be missed between measurements / the car has to be kept travelling in a straight line to easily pass through the gate and provide an accurate measurement *[1 mark]*.
Advantage of the ticker tape method: e.g. it will provide many potential data points, taken at regular time intervals / the results are less affected by deviations in the straight line path of the car *[1 mark]*.
Disadvantage of the ticker tape method: e.g. speeds have to be calculated manually from the distance measured between marks, which may introduce errors into the values / the tape may provide a resistive force against the motion of the car, causing the car to have a lower acceleration than it would without the tape *[1 mark]*

Page 249 — Terminal Velocity

1 The resultant vertical force on an object falling at its terminal velocity is zero.
Terminal velocity is the maximum velocity an object can fall at. *[1 mark for both correct]*

2 The drag from the water acting on the fish is increasing. *[1 mark]*

3.1 As both objects fall, they accelerate due to gravity *[1 mark]*. As their velocities increase, so does the air resistance acting on them *[1 mark]*. The air resistance acts in the opposite direction to the acceleration, reducing the resultant forces acting on each object. Eventually the resultant forces on the objects are zero and they fall at constant velocities *[1 mark]*.

3.2 The book has a larger surface area than the ball, so experiences more air resistance *[1 mark]*. This means that the resultant force on the book reaches zero sooner, and so it has a lower terminal velocity *[1 mark]*.

Pages 250-251 — Newton's First and Second Laws

1   If the resultant force on a stationary object is zero, the object will remain stationary *[1 mark]*.

2   Newton's Second Law states that the acceleration of an object is **directly** proportional to the **resultant** force acing on the object and **inversely** proportional to the **mass** of the object. *[3 marks for all correct, 2 marks for 2-3 correct, 1 mark for one correct]*

3.1   E.g. friction *[1 mark]*, air resistance / drag *[1 mark for either]*

3.2   Resultant force on an object at a constant velocity is zero.
so 5000 = 3850 + second force
Second force = 5000 – 3850 = **1150 N**
[1 mark for correct answer]

4.1 $F = ma$ *[1 mark]*

4.2 $F = 5.0 \times 9.8$ *[1 mark]* = **49 N** *[1 mark]*

5    $a = \Delta v \div t$
$a = 24 \div 9.2$ *[1 mark]* = $2.6...$ m/s² *[1 mark]*
$F = ma$
$F = 1450 \times 2.6...$ *[1 mark]* = $3782.6...$
    = **3800 N (to 2 s.f.)** *[1 mark]*

6   Typical speed of a lorry is 25 m/s (accept 20-30 m/s) *[1 mark]*
$v^2 - u^2 = 2as$
$a = (v^2 - u^2) \div 2s = (0^2 - 25^2) \div (2 \times 50)$ *[1 mark]*
$= -625 \div 100 = -6.25$ m/s² (accept 4-9 m/s²) *[1 mark]*
$F = ma = 7520 \times -6.25$ *[1 mark]*
    = **(–) 47 000 N** (accept 30 100-67 700 N) *[1 mark]*

Page 252 — Inertia and Newton's Third Law

Warm-up
When two objects interact, they exert equal and opposite forces on each other.

1.1   320 N *[1 mark]*

1.2   Normal contact force *[1 mark]*

1.3   640 N *[1 mark]*

Weight is the force exerted by the Earth on the gymnast (because of the gymnast and the Earth interacting). An equal but opposite force acts on the Earth because of the gymnast.

2.1   The tendency to continue in the same state of motion *[1 mark]*

2.2   E.g. how difficult it is to change the velocity of an object / ratio of force over acceleration / $m = F \div a$
[1 mark for any correct definition]

Page 253 — Investigating Motion

1.1   E.g. as force increases, so does acceleration / acceleration is proportional to force
[1 mark for any correct conclusion]

1.2 $F = ma$ *[1 mark]*

1.3   At a force of 4.0 N, the acceleration is 2.25 m/s²
So $m = F \div a$ *[1 mark]* = $4.0 \div 2.25$ *[1 mark]*
    = $1.77... =$ **1.8 kg** *[1 mark]*

You'll still get the marks if you took readings from a different part of the graph, so long as you get the correct final answer.

2   To test the effect of varying the mass of the trolley, the force on the trolley has to remain constant *[1 mark]*. Adding masses to the trolley increases both the force on and mass of the trolley, so the effect of varying the mass cannot be found *[1 mark]*.

Page 254 — Stopping Distances

1.1   The distance travelled during the driver's reaction time *[1 mark]*

1.2   The distance travelled under the braking force of the vehicle *[1 mark]*

2   Stopping distance = thinking distance + braking distance
12 + 24 = **36 m** *[1 mark]*

3   Work is done by friction between the brakes and the wheels *[1 mark]*. This causes energy to be transferred to the thermal energy stores of the brakes, so they increase in temperature *[1 mark]*.

4   Level 0:   There is no relevant information. *[No marks]*
    Level 1:   There is a brief explanation of why good brakes and tyres are important. *[1 to 2 marks]*

Level 2:   There is an explanation of why good brakes and tyres are important with some explanation as to the safety implications of poor brakes or tyres. *[3 to 4 marks]*

Level 3:   A logical and detailed explanation is given which includes at least 2 examples of explaining the importance of having the tyres and brakes in good condition, at least 2 safety implications and at least 1 effect on stopping distance. *[5 to 6 marks]*

Here are some points your answer may include:
A good tread depth on tyres removes water.
This means there is a large amount of grip (friction) between the road and the tyres.
This decreases the braking (and so stopping) distance in wet conditions.
It also means the car will be less likely to skid in wet conditions.
Brakes that are in good condition allow a larger braking force to be applied.
This means that the braking distance of the car is shorter.
Brakes that are in good condition are also less likely to overheat under a large braking force.
So the car is less likely to go out of control or cause a crash.

Pages 255-256 — Reaction Times

1   0.2 - 0.9 s *[1 mark]*

2   Any three from: tiredness / alcohol / drugs / distractions *[3 marks — 1 mark for each correct answer]*

3.1   E.g. clicking a mouse when a computer screen changes colour *[1 mark]*

3.2   Student A: $(7.0 + 7.1 + 6.9) \div 3 = $ **7.0 cm** *[1 mark]*
Student B: $(8.4 + 8.2 + 8.3) \div 3 = $ **8.3 cm** *[1 mark]*

3.3   Student A, because the average distance fallen by the ruler was less for Student A than Student B *[1 mark]*.

3.4   E.g. use the same ruler, always have the same person dropping the ruler. *[2 marks — 1 mark for each correct answer]*

3.5   Their reaction times will get longer *[1 mark]*.

4   Hold a ruler between the open forefinger and thumb of the person being tested *[1 mark]*. Align their finger to the zero line of the ruler, then drop the ruler without warning *[1 mark]* and have the test subject close their thumb and finger to catch the ruler *[1 mark]*. The distance the ruler falls can be read from the ruler *[1 mark]*. The time taken for it to fall can be calculated, as the acceleration (due to gravity) is constant. This is the reaction time of the test subject *[1 mark]*.

5   Level 0:   There is no relevant information. *[No marks]*
    Level 1:   There is a brief explanation of how the man's reaction time may be affected and at least one mention of an implication this has for safety. *[1 to 2 marks]*
    Level 2:   There is an explanation of how the man's reaction time may be affected and the implications this has for safety. *[3 to 4 marks]*

Here are some points your answer may include:
Listening to loud music may mean that the driver is distracted.
This may increase his reaction time.
An increased reaction time means an increased thinking distance.
Driving quicker also increases the distance the car travels during the man's reaction time.
All of these things increase stopping distance, which means the man may not be able to stop in time to avoid hitting a hazard.
He may be unable to see an upcoming hazard because it is dark.
Driving late at night might mean that the man is tired.
He may not be able to hear an upcoming hazard because of the loud music.
This reduces the stopping distance required to avoid hitting a hazard and may lead to the driver having a collision.

6    $v^2 - u^2 = 2as$
$v^2 = 0 + (2 \times 9.8 \times 0.45)$ *[1 mark]* = 8.82
$v = 2.969...$ m/s *[1 mark]*
$a = \Delta v \div t$
$t = \Delta v \div a = 2.969... \div 9.8$ *[1 mark]*
    = $0.303... = $ **0.30 s (to 2 s.f.)** *[1 mark]*

Answers

Page 257 — Momentum

Warm-up

1: Momentum is a property of...
2: ...moving objects.
3: It is a...
4: ...vector quantity and is equal to...
5: ...mass × velocity.

1.1 $p = mv$ *[1 mark]*
1.2 $m = p \div v$ *[1 mark]* = 5500 ÷ 25 *[1 mark]* = **220 kg** *[1 mark]*
2 In Figure 1, the total momentum of the system is equal to the mass of the moving ball multiplied by its velocity *[1 mark]*. As it hits the line of balls, it transfers this momentum to them and comes to a stop. All of this momentum is transferred along the line of balls to the ball at the end of the line, which is why the middle balls don't move *[1 mark]*. This final ball has the same momentum as the first ball, causing it to move with the same velocity (because all of the balls have the same mass) that the moving ball in Figure 1 had *[1 mark]*. In Figure 2, the total momentum of the system is equal to the total momentum in Figure 1 *[1 mark]*.

Topic P6 — Waves

Page 258 — Transverse and Longitudinal Waves

1.1 Wave A is a **transverse** wave and wave B is a **longitudinal** wave. *[1 mark]*
1.2 E.g.

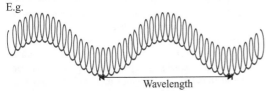

Wavelength

[1 mark for correctly labelled wavelength]
1.3 Amplitude is the maximum displacement of a point on a wave from its undisturbed position *[1 mark]*.
1.4 E.g. ripples on the surface of water / light / any other electromagnetic wave *[1 mark]*
2.1 Horizontal arrow drawn pointing away from the loudspeaker *[1 mark]*
2.2 $T = 1 \div f = 1 \div 200$ *[1 mark]* = **0.005 s** *[1 mark]*
2.3 In longitudinal waves, the oscillations/vibrations are parallel to the wave's direction of energy transfer *[1 mark]*, but in transverse waves, the oscillations/vibrations are perpendicular/at right angles to the wave's direction of energy transfer *[1 mark]*.

Page 259 — Experiments with Waves

1.1 E.g. the student could use a strobe light *[1 mark]*. When the frequency of the strobe light matches that of the wave, the wave fronts will appear stationary (and the student can then measure the stationary wave) *[1 mark]*.
1.2 There are 9 wavelengths in the distance of 18 cm.
Therefore, wavelength = 18 cm ÷ 9 = 2 cm *[1 mark]*
$v = f\lambda = 12 \times 0.02$ *[1 mark]*
= **0.24 m/s** *[1 mark]*
2 How to grade your answer:
Level 0: There is no relevant information. *[No marks]*
Level 1: A simple method to find the speed of waves on a string is partly outlined. *[1 to 2 marks]*
Level 2: A method to find the speed of waves on a string is outlined in some detail. *[3 to 4 marks]*
Level 3: A method to find the speed of waves on a string using suitable apparatus is fully explained in detail. *[5 to 6 marks]*
Here are some points your answer may include:
Connect a string over a pulley to a vibration transducer. Connect a signal generator to the vibration transducer and switch it on. Adjust the frequency of the signal generator to produce clear waves on the string.
For as many half-wavelengths on the string as you can, measure the distance they cover.
Divide this by the number of half-wavelengths to find the average half-wavelength of the waves on the string.
Double this value to find the wavelength, λ, and note down the frequency of the frequency generator, f.
Use the formula $v = f\lambda$ to calculate the speed of the waves on the string, v.
To get more accurate results the experiment can be repeated for different frequencies and a mean value calculated.

Page 260 — Wave Behaviour and Electromagnetic Waves

Warm-up

wave is reflected — it bounces back off the material
wave is absorbed — it transfers all energy to the material
wave is transmitted — it passes through the material unaffected

1.1 All waves in the electromagnetic spectrum are **transverse**. *[1 mark]*. All electromagnetic waves travel at the same speed in **a vacuum**. *[1 mark]*
1.2 microwaves *[1 mark]*
1.3 E.g. energy is transferred from the thermal energy store of a toaster's heating element *[1 mark]* by (infrared) radiation to the thermal energy store of bread inside the toaster *[1 mark]*.
2 Some of the light is reflected back *[1 mark]* and some of the light is transmitted through the lens *[1 mark]*.

Page 261 — Refraction

1.1

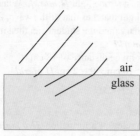

air
glass

[1 mark for wave fronts bending in the correct direction, 1 mark for wave fronts inside the glass being joined up with those in the air.]

1.2

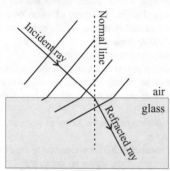

Normal line

Incident ray

air
glass

Refracted ray

[1 mark for incident ray drawn and labelled correctly, 1 mark for normal line drawn and labelled correctly, 1 mark for refracted ray drawn and labelled correctly.]

2.1 The ray bends towards the normal as it crosses the boundary *[1 mark]*.

2.2 The light ray would bend away from the normal *[1 mark]* because it would speed up / because light travels slower in glass than in a vacuum *[1 mark]*.

Page 262 — Radio Waves

Warm-up

True, True, False, True.

1 How to grade your answer:
Level 0:   There is no relevant information. *[No marks]*
Level 1:   A simple method of generating radio waves is described. *[1 to 2 marks]*
Level 2:   A method of generating radio waves and how these waves generate an electrical signal in a distant TV aerial is described. *[3 to 4 marks]*
Here are some points your answer may include:
An alternating current flows in the circuit the transmitter is connected to.
Alternating currents are made up of oscillating charges/electrons.
As the electrons oscillate in the transmitter, they produce oscillating electric and magnetic fields/radio waves.
Radio waves are transmitted to and then absorbed by the distant TV aerial.
The energy carried by the waves is transferred to the electrons in the material of the receiver.
This causes electrons in the receiver aerial to oscillate.
This generates an alternating current/an electrical signal.
This alternating current has the same frequency as the original current used to generate the radio wave.

2 How to grade your answer:
Level 0:   There is no relevant information. *[No marks]*
Level 1:   There is a brief explanation of the differences between radio wave types used for broadcasting *[1 to 2 marks]*
Level 2:   There is some explanation of the differences between radio wave types used for broadcasting, including their different ranges and how this affects which broadcast can be heard. *[3 to 4 marks]*
Level 3:   There is a clear and detailed explanation of the differences between radio wave types used for broadcasting, including their different ranges and how this affects which broadcast can be heard. *[5 to 6 marks]*

Here are some points your answer may include:
FM radio is transmitted using very short wavelength radio waves
These radio waves can only be received while the receiver is in direct sight of the transmitter.
This is because these wavelengths are easily absorbed by obstacles, e.g. buildings, and cannot diffract.
Therefore, the signal cannot be received in France.
Long-wave radio waves can be transmitted over long distances.
This is because long-wave radio waves diffract around the curved surface of the Earth.
Long-wave radio waves can also diffract around obstacles such as mountains.
Hence the signal can be received in France.

Page 263 — EM Waves and Their Uses

1.1 The microwaves are absorbed by water molecules in the potato *[1 mark]*. This transfers energy to the water molecules, causing the water in the potato to heat up *[1 mark]*. The water molecules transfer the energy they have absorbed to the rest of the molecules in the potato, cooking it *[1 mark]*.

1.2 The glass plate does not absorb any microwaves *[1 mark]* as it does not contain any water molecules, and so it does not heat up *[1 mark]*.

1.3 infrared *[1 mark]*

1.4 Satellites are located above the atmosphere *[1 mark]*. The atmosphere contains water molecules *[1 mark]*. The microwaves used in microwave ovens could not reach satellites as they would be absorbed by water molecules in the atmosphere *[1 mark]*. Different wavelengths which are not absorbed by the atmosphere must be used to communicate with satellites *[1 mark]*.

2 It is dark so there is very little visible light for a normal camera to pick up *[1 mark]*. The person trying to hide is warmer than the surroundings and so emits more infrared radiation *[1 mark]*. This makes the person stand out from the surroundings if observed through infrared radiation *[1 mark]*.

Page 264 — More Uses of EM Waves

Warm-up

UV Rays: A, C, D
Visible Light: B
X-rays: E, F
Gamma Rays: F

1.1 E.g. the patient is injected with a gamma-emitting source *[1 mark]*. Gamma radiation is detected outside of the body, which is used to follow the source's progress around the patient's body *[1 mark]*.

1.2 E.g. they can pass out of the patient's body / they can be detected outside of the patient's body *[1 mark]*.

1.3 X-rays are directed at the patient. The X-rays are absorbed by bones *[1 mark]*, but transmitted by less dense body material, such as flesh *[1 mark]*. A screen behind the patient detects the X-rays and a negative image is formed with brighter areas where fewer X-rays are detected *[1 mark]*.

1.4 E.g. wear lead aprons / stand behind lead screens / leave the room whilst treatment is taking place *[1 mark]*.

Pages 265-266 — Investigating Infrared Radiation

1.1 Matte black *[1 mark]*

1.2 Shiny white *[1 mark]*

1.3 E.g. use a radiation detector to measure the emitted radiation / use a ruler to make sure he measures the radiation emitted from each side from the same distance *[1 mark for any sensible suggestion]*

2 How to grade your answer:

Level 0: There is no relevant information. *[No marks]*

Level 1: There is a brief description of the apparatus used to investigate the absorption of different surfaces. *[1 to 2 marks]*

Level 2: There is some description of a method and apparatus to investigate the absorption of different surfaces. At least one method to ensure the experiment is a fair test is mentioned. *[3 to 4 marks]*

Level 3: There is a clear and detailed description of a method and apparatus to investigate the absorption of different surfaces. At least two methods to ensure the experiment is a fair test are mentioned. *[5 to 6 marks]*

Here are some points your answer may include:

Use two metal plates of the same material, but with different surfaces on one side (the front of the plate) — e.g. one shiny, one matte or one black, one white.

The plates should be the same size and thickness / identical in all other ways to make it a fair test.

On the back of each plate, a ball bearing is attached with candle wax.

The ball bearings should be identical to make the experiment a fair test.

The amount of wax used to attach each ball bearing should be the same, to ensure the test is fair.

The front of the plates are then faced towards a lit bunsen burner. The distance between each plate and the bunsen burner should be the same to ensure the experiment is a fair test.

The time taken for the wax to melt and the ball bearing to fall is measured for both plates using a stopwatch.

The stopwatch should be stopped at the same point for each plate (e.g. the ball bearing starting to fall, or hitting the table/floor) for it to be a fair test.

The times taken for each ball bearing can then be compared to see which surface is better at absorbing radiation.

The faster the time, the better the surface is at absorbing radiation.

3.1 Any three from: e.g using the same mass of water in each can / using the same equipment for each can / starting measurements at the same temperature for each can / using cans that are the same size and shape / using cans that are made from the same material *[3 marks]*.

Each of these make sure that the rate of change of temperature is only affected by the paint on the can, not any other properties of the cans, the water, or the experimental set-up. This ensures that it is a fair test, and so the experiment will produce valid results.

3.2 E.g. the water in can A / the can painted with matt navy blue paint will cool fastest *[1 mark]*. This is because dark and matt surfaces are better emitters of infrared radiation than light and shiny/glossy surfaces *[1 mark]*.

3.3 E.g.

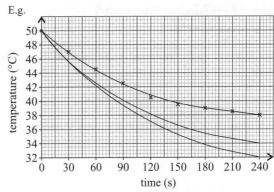

[1 mark for all points drawn correctly, and 1 mark for a smooth curve of best fit which passes through or close to all the points]

Page 267 — Dangers of Electromagnetic Waves

1.1 X-rays and gamma rays transfer so much energy to living cells that they can knock off electrons (ionise atoms) *[1 mark]*. This can cause mutation of genes, leading to cancer *[1 mark]*.

1.2 Any two from: sunburn / premature aging / blindness / (increased risk of) skin cancer *[2 marks]*

2.1 Compare risk of chest scan to risk of head scan,

$10\,000 \div 2500 = 4$

Risk is 4 times greater, so dose is 4 times greater *[1 mark]*.

Dose = $2 \times 4 = $ **8 mSv** *[1 mark]*

2.2 How to grade your answer:

Level 0: There is no relevant information. *[No marks]*

Level 1: The risks and benefits are identified but no comparison is made about whether one outweighs the other. *[1 to 2 marks]*

Level 2: There is some discussion about balancing the benefits with the risks. *[3 to 4 marks]*

Level 3: There is a detailed explanation of the benefits and risks, and an informed explanation of why the procedure may go ahead. *[5 to 6 marks]*

Here are some points your answer may include:

The radiation dose is large, so the risk of developing cancer from the procedure is higher than in some other procedures.

However, the procedure might better inform a decision on future treatment.

So future treatment may be more effective.

The benefit of treating the condition needs to be compared with the risk of the procedure (and any subsequent treatment).

An assessment needs to be made about the risk of dying (or poor quality of life) from the underlying condition and the potential benefits for treatment.

Other less risky procedures might lead to similar benefits and these need to be considered.

If the benefits outweigh the risks considerably, then it is worth carrying on with the procedure.

334

Topic P7 — Magnetism and Electromagnetism

Pages 268-269 — Permanent and Induced Magnets

Warm-up
        non-contact

1.1   A region in which a magnet or magnetic material will experience a force *[1 mark]*.

1.2   Any two of e.g. iron/steel/nickel/cobalt *[2 marks]*

1.3

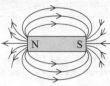

*[2 marks in total — 1 mark for correct shape,
1 mark for arrows pointing from north to south]*

1.4   The correct statements are:
The closer together the magnetic field lines, the stronger the magnetic field *[1 mark]*.
Magnetic field lines point from the north pole to the south pole of a magnet *[1 mark]*.

2.1   The block of cobalt becomes an induced magnet when it is placed in the magnetic field of the bar magnet *[1 mark]*, which causes a force of attraction between the paperclip and the cobalt *[1 mark]*

2.2   When the bar magnet is removed, the cobalt will quickly demagnetise *[1 mark]*, so the paperclip will become unstuck *[1 mark]*

3.1   How to grade your answer:
Level 0:   There is no relevant information. *[No marks]*
Level 1:   There is a brief description of how the compass should be used. *[1 to 2 marks]*
Level 2:   There is a good description of the method used to determine the magnetic field, including the effect on a compass when placed in a magnetic field. *[3 to 4 marks]*
Here are some points your answer may include:
The needle of a compass points in the direction of the magnetic field it is in.
Put the magnet on a sheet of paper.
Move the compass along the field lines of the horseshoe magnet.
Mark the direction of the compass needle at each point.
Join up the marks to create a diagram of the magnetic field lines.

3.2   E.g. it would point (to geographic) north *[1 mark]* because it is aligning itself with the magnetic field of the Earth *[1 mark]*.

Page 270 — Electromagnetism

1.1

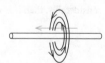

*[2 marks in total — 1 mark for correct shape,
1 mark for correct direction]*
You can work this out using the right-hand thumb rule — point your right thumb in the direction of the current and your curled fingers will show the direction of the field lines. Bingo.

1.2   The direction of the field will also be reversed *[1 mark]*.

1.3   Increase the current *[1 mark]*.

2.1   E.g. put a block of iron in the middle of the solenoid *[1 mark]*.

2.2   Repelled *[1 mark]*, because the direction of the current means that the left-hand end of the solenoid acts as a north pole *[1 mark]*, and like poles repel *[1 mark]*.

Page 271 — The Motor Effect

1    $F = BIl$, so $B = F \div Il$
$B = 1.2 \div (0.4 \times 0.75)$ *[1 mark]*
$= 1.2 \div 0.3 = \mathbf{4\ T}$
[1 mark for correct value, 1 mark for correct unit]

2   A *[1 mark]*
The force acting on the wire is at a maximum when the wire is perpendicular to the magnetic field between the magnets (0°) and is zero when the wire is parallel to the magnetic field (90°).

Page 272 — Electric Motors

1   It will move towards you, out of the paper *[1 mark]*.
Use Fleming's left-hand rule here. Point your first finger in the direction of the field (i.e. from the north pole to the south pole of the magnets). Point your second finger in the direction of the current (shown in the diagram). Your thumb will then show the direction of motion of the wire.

2.1   clockwise *[1 mark]*

2.2   E.g. the interacting magnetic fields (of the coil and the magnets) causes a force on each arm of the coil *[1 mark]* in the opposite direction (which causes the coil to rotate) *[1 mark]*.

2.3   E.g. swap the contacts every half turn (e.g. using a split-ring commutator) to reverse the direction of the current *[1 mark]*. This swaps the direction of the forces for each arm and keeps the direction of rotation constant *[1 mark]*.

Mixed Questions

Pages 273-278 — Biology Mixed Questions

1.1   E.g. producing bile / converting lactic acid to glucose / storing glucose as glycogen / breaking down amino acids *[1 mark]*

1.2   Enzymes speed up chemical reactions in living organisms. *[1 mark]*

1.3   pH 9 *[1 mark]*

1.4   The enzyme will not work *[1 mark]* because the acid will change the shape of its active site/denature the enzyme *[1 mark]* and the substrate will no longer fit *[1 mark]*.

1.5   Alcohol is a risk factor for lung cancer. *[1 mark]*

2.1   To stop the loss of water by evaporation *[1 mark]*.

2.2

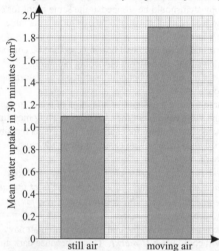

[1 mark for correctly drawn bars, one mark for correctly labelled axes.]

2.3   The greater the air flow around the plant, the greater the transpiration rate *[1 mark]*.

2.4   E.g. increasing air flow carries more water vapour away from the plant / reduces the concentration of water vapour outside the leaves *[1 mark]*. This increases the rate of diffusion of water from the leaf cells from an area of higher water concentration to an area of lower water concentration *[1 mark]*.

2.5 $1.2 - 0.8 = \mathbf{0.4\ cm^3}$ *[1 mark]*
The range is the difference between the highest and lowest values.

2.6 | 30 minutes ÷ 60 = 0.5 hours
1.9 ÷ 0.5 = **3.8 cm³/hour** *[2 marks for correct answer, otherwise 1 mark for correct working.]*

3.1 | mitochondria *[1 mark]*

3.2 | glucose + oxygen → carbon dioxide + water *[1 mark for both reactants correct, 1 mark for both products correct.]*

3.3 | Glucose is combined with nitrate ions *[1 mark]* to make amino acids *[1 mark]*, which are then joined together to make proteins *[1 mark]*.

4.1 | The hormone is secreted directly into the blood *[1 mark]*. It is then carried in the blood to the target organ *[1 mark]*.

4.2 | C *[1 mark]*

4.3 | B *[1 mark]*

4.4 | It stimulates ovulation / the release of an egg from an ovary *[1 mark]*.

4.5 | ovaries *[1 mark]*

4.6 | A constantly high level of oestrogen inhibits the production of FSH *[1 mark]*, so there are no mature eggs for fertilisation to take place *[1 mark]*.

5.1 | oxygen *[1 mark]*

5.2 | light intensity *[1 mark]*

5.3 | Tube 1 *[1 mark]*

5.4 | Tube 1 shows that in the dark, the algae are producing more carbon dioxide than they take in *[1 mark]*. The concentration of carbon dioxide is high because the cells are respiring, but not photosynthesising (as there's no light for photosynthesis to take place) *[1 mark]*. Tube 2 shows that in the light, the algae are taking up more carbon dioxide than they produce *[1 mark]*. The concentration of carbon dioxide has reduced because the cells are photosynthesising faster than they are respiring *[1 mark]*.

5.5 | Any two from: e.g. the temperature of the boiling tubes / the volume of hydrogencarbonate indicator / the concentration of hydrogencarbonate indicator / the number of beads in each tube / the concentration of algal cells in each bead *[2 marks]*.

5.6 | Light intensity *[1 mark]* because the rate of photosynthesis is increasing as the light intensity increases *[1 mark]*.

5.7 | carbon dioxide concentration *[1 mark]*

6.1 | RR *[1 mark]*

6.2 | round seed shape *[1 mark]*

6.3 |

	R	R
r	Rr	Rr
r	Rr	Rr

[1 mark]
The parents' genotypes were **RR** *[1 mark]* and **rr** *[1 mark]*.

Pages 279-285 — Chemistry Mixed Questions

1.1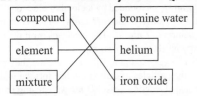

[2 marks if all three correct, otherwise 1 mark if 1 correct]

1.2 | Mixtures with a precise purpose *[1 mark]* that are made by following a formula / a recipe *[1 mark]*.

2.1 | Dissolve the rock salt in water and filter *[1 mark]*.

2.2 | It contains two elements/more than one element in fixed proportions *[1 mark]* held together by chemical bonds *[1 mark]*.

2.3 | ionic *[1 mark]*

3.1 | Group: 6 *[1 mark]*
Explanation: There are 6 electrons in the outer shell *[1 mark]*.

3.2 | 2– ions *[1 mark]*, as oxygen atoms need to gain two electrons to get a full outer shell *[1 mark]*.

3.3 | Oxidation *[1 mark]*

4.1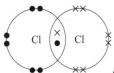

[1 mark for shared pair of electrons, 1 mark for six further electrons in the outer shell of each chlorine atom]

4.2 | E.g. atoms with the same number of protons / of the same element / with the same atomic number *[1 mark]* with different numbers of neutrons / different mass numbers *[1 mark]*.

4.3 | Hold a piece of damp litmus paper in the unknown gas *[1 mark]*. It will be bleached white in the presence of chlorine *[1 mark]*.

4.4 | Chlorine is more reactive than iodine *[1 mark]*, so would displace iodine from sodium iodide solution / the solution would go from colourless to brown *[1 mark]*.

5.1 | endothermic *[1 mark]*

5.2 | higher *[1 mark]*

5.3 | It takes more energy to break the bonds in the reactants than is released when the bonds in the products form *[1 mark]*, so overall energy is taken in from the surroundings *[1 mark]*.

5.4 | E.g. in a sports injury pack *[1 mark]*.

6.1 | alkanes *[1 mark]*

6.2 | (fractional) distillation *[1 mark]*

6.3 | cracking *[1 mark]*

6.4 | Decane *[1 mark]*, because the molecules are bigger *[1 mark]*, so will have stronger intermolecular forces / more energy is needed to break the forces between the molecules *[1 mark]*.

6.5 | $C_5H_{12} + 8O_2 → 5CO_2 + 6H_2O$ *[1 mark for correct reactants and products, 1 mark for balancing]*

7.1 | The electrons in the outer shell *[1 mark]* of the metal atoms are delocalised *[1 mark]*. There is strong electrostatic attraction between the positive metal ions and the shared negative electrons *[1 mark]*.

7.2 | Iron: solid *[1 mark]*. Silver: liquid *[1 mark]*

7.3 | Iron *[1 mark]*, because it has a higher melting/boiling point *[1 mark]*, so more energy is needed to break the bonds *[1 mark]*.

8.1 | Copper is lower in the reactivity series/less reactive than carbon *[1 mark]*, so can be extracted by reduction using carbon *[1 mark]*.

8.2 | Bacteria are used to convert copper compounds in the ore into soluble copper compounds *[1 mark]*. This produces a leachate that contains copper ions *[1 mark]* which can be extracted by electrolysis/displacement with iron *[1 mark]*.

8.3 | The atoms in copper form layers which slide over each other, so it can be drawn out into wires *[1 mark]*. Copper contains delocalised electrons which are free to move and carry an electric charge *[1 mark]*.

8.4 | The tin atoms in bronze distort the structure of the copper *[1 mark]*. This means the layers can no longer slide over each other *[1 mark]*, so bronze is harder than copper *[1 mark]*.

Answers

9.1 It described atoms as having a tiny, positively charged nucleus at the centre *[1 mark]*, surrounded by a cloud of electrons *[1 mark]*.

9.2 Atoms consist of a small nucleus *[1 mark]* which contains the protons and neutrons *[1 mark]*. The electrons orbit the nucleus in fixed energy levels/shells *[1 mark]*.

10.1 The particles in a gas expand to fill any container they're in *[1 mark]*. So the particles of carbon dioxide formed will expand out of the unsealed reaction vessel *[1 mark]*, causing the mass of substance inside the reaction vessel to decrease *[1 mark]*.

10.2 E.g. add a set volume and concentration of hydrochloric acid to the reaction vessel *[1 mark]*. Add a set volume and concentration of sodium carbonate solution *[1 mark]*, connect the reaction flask to a gas syringe *[1 mark]* and start the stop-watch *[1 mark]*. Record the volume of gas collected at regular intervals until the reaction is finished *[1 mark]*. Repeat the experiment, keeping everything the same except for the concentration of acid *[1 mark]*.

10.3 Change in volume = 12.0 cm^3

Mean rate of reaction = $\dfrac{\text{amount of product formed}}{\text{time}}$

$= \dfrac{12.0}{30} = $ **0.40 cm^3/s** *[2 marks for correct answer, otherwise 1 mark for using the correct equation to calculate rate]*

11.1 Any two from: e.g. it dissolved in oceans / photosynthesis / trapped in rocks and fossil fuels *[2 marks — 1 mark for each correct answer]*

11.2 E.g. methane *[1 mark]*. It is increasing due to more agriculture / waste production *[1 mark]*.

11.3 How to grade your answer:

Level 0: There is no relevant information. *[No marks]*

Level 1: There are a few examples of other pollutant gases, but little discussion of how they are made or what their impacts could be. *[1 to 2 marks]*

Level 2: There are a number of examples of other pollutant gases, with some discussion of how they are made and what their impacts could be. *[3 to 4 marks]*

Level 3: There are a number of examples of other pollutant gases, with a detailed discussion of how they are made and what their impacts could be. *[5 to 6 marks]*

Here are some points your answer may include:

Other pollutant gases include carbon monoxide, sulfur dioxide and nitrogen oxides.

Carbon monoxide is produced when fuels undergo incomplete combustion.

Carbon monoxide can cause fainting, coma or even death.

Sulfur dioxide is produced when fuels that contain sulfur impurities are burned.

Sulfur dioxide can mix with water in clouds to produce sulfuric acid, so cause acid rain.

Sulfur dioxide can cause respiratory problems.

Nitrogen oxides are produced when nitrogen and oxygen from the air react/combine due to the heat of burning.

Nitrogen oxides can mix with water in clouds to produce nitric acid, so cause acid rain.

Nitrogen oxides can cause respiratory problems.

12.1 M_r(LiOH) = A_r(Li) + A_r(O) + A_r(H) = 7 + 16 + 1 = **24** *[1 mark]*

12.2 Number of moles = mass ÷ molar mass = 1.75 ÷ 7 = **0.25 mol** *[2 marks for correct answer, otherwise 1 mark for using the correct equation to calculate moles]*

12.3 From the reaction equation, 0.50 mol Li forms 0.50 mol LiOH. Mass of LiOH = number of moles × molar mass = 0.50 × 24 = **12 g** *[3 marks for correct answer, otherwise 1 mark for number of moles of LiOH produced, 1 mark for using the correct equation to calculate mass]*

13.1 Zinc is more reactive than hydrogen *[1 mark]*. This means zinc forms positive ions more easily than hydrogen *[1 mark]*.

13.2 Reduction *[1 mark]*, because the hydrogen ions gain electrons *[1 mark]*.

13.3 $4OH^- \rightarrow O_2 + 2H_2O + 4e^-$ *[1 mark for correct reactants and products, 1 mark for balancing]*

If you had '$-4e^-$' on the left hand side of the equation instead of '$+4e^-$' on the right, you still get the marks.

14.1 How to grade your answer:

Level 0: There is no relevant information. *[No marks]*

Level 1: There is a brief description of the similarities and differences between lithium and sodium, but no explanation of these observations. *[1 to 2 marks]*

Level 2: There is a detailed comparison of the similarities and differences between lithium and sodium, and some explanation of the observations. *[3 to 4 marks]*

Level 3: There is a detailed comparison of the similarities and differences between lithium and sodium, and a good explanation of the observations. *[5 to 6 marks]*

Here are some points your answer may include:

Both react to form positive, 1+ ions.

Both elements are in Group 1, so have one electron in their outer shell.

Not much energy is needed to remove this one outer electron and give the elements a full outer shell of electrons.

Both react with acid.

Sodium reacts more vigorously with acid than lithium.

Sodium is lower down in the group, so the outer electron in sodium is further away from the nucleus than the outer electron in lithium.

The attraction between the outer electron and the nucleus of sodium is less than the attraction between the outer electron and the nucleus in lithium.

Less energy is needed to remove the outer electron of sodium, making it more reactive than lithium.

14.2 Any answer in the range 80–160 °C *[1 mark]*

Pages 286-292 — Physics Mixed Questions

1.1 E.g. a permanent magnet produces its own magnetic field *[1 mark]*. An induced magnet is a material that on becomes magnetic when it is put in a magnetic field *[1 mark]*.

1.2

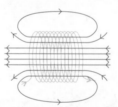

[1 mark for field lines pointing in the correct direction, 1 mark for drawing straight, parallel field lines inside the coil, 1 mark for drawing the field outside the coil]

2.1 Radioactive decay is where a nucleus releases radiation to become more **stable**. It is a **random** process, which means you **cannot** predict which individual nucleus in a sample will decay next. *[2 marks for all correct, otherwise 1 mark for two correct]*

2.2 E.g. The rate of decay of a source of unstable nuclei/a radioactive source *[1 mark]*.

It is measured in becquerels/Bq *[1 mark]*.

2.3 E.g. the time taken for the activity of a sample to halve *[1 mark]*.

3.1 three-core cable *[1 mark]*

3.2 Live — **brown** — **230** *[1 mark]*

Neutral — blue — **0** *[1 mark]*

Earth — green and yellow — 0 *[1 mark]*

3.3 Energy is transferred **electrically** from the mains supply to the **kinetic** energy store of the fan's blades. *[1 mark for each correct answer]*

3.4 Energy transferred = Power × Time = 30 × (30 × 60) *[1 mark]*

= **54 000 J** *[1 mark]*

4.1 C *[1 mark]*

4.2 $V = IR$ *[1 mark]*

4.3 $R = V \div I = 240 \div 1.2$ *[1 mark]* = **200 Ω** *[1 mark]*

5.1   water ripples, gamma rays *[1 mark for both correct]*

5.2 $T = 1 \div f = 1 \div 40$ *[1 mark]* $= 0.025$ s
    0.025×1000 *[1 mark]* $= \mathbf{25}$ **ms** *[1 mark]*

5.3 $v = f\lambda$ *[1 mark]*

5.4 $v = 40 \times 0.6$ *[1 mark]* $= \mathbf{24}$ **m/s** *[1 mark]*

6.1

[1 mark for an arrow in the right direction, 1 mark for it being the same length as the driving force arrow]

6.2 $s = vt$ *[1 mark]*

6.3 $s = 5.0 \times 30$ *[1 mark]* $= \mathbf{150}$ **m** *[1 mark]*

6.4 $E_k = \frac{1}{2}mv^2$
    $E_k = \frac{1}{2} \times 0.50 \times 5.0^2$ *[1 mark]* $= \mathbf{6.25}$ **J** *[1 mark]*

6.5   Efficiency = Useful output energy transfer
               ÷ Total input energy transfer *[1 mark]*

6.6 $0.65 =$ Useful output energy transfer ÷ 1200
    Useful output energy transfer $= 0.65 \times 1200$ *[1 mark]*
                      $= \mathbf{780}$ **J** *[1 mark]*

7.1   increasing acceleration *[1 mark]*
    steady speed *[1 mark]*
    constant acceleration *[1 mark]*

7.2   Acceleration = gradient of the graph *[1 mark]*
    Acceleration $= \Delta v \div \Delta t = (7 - 4) \div (7 - 5)$ *[1 mark]*
                $= 3 \div 2 = \mathbf{1.5}$ **m/s²** *[1 mark]*

7.3 $F = ma$
    So $a = F \div m$ *[1 mark]* $= (-)440 \div 83$ *[1 mark]*
        $= (-)5.30...$ m/s²
    So deceleration $= \mathbf{5.3}$ **m/s²** *[1 mark]*

Remember, force is a vector quantity. It's negative here because it's acting in the opposite direction to the motion of the cyclist. That's what gives you a negative acceleration (deceleration).

7.4   Distance travelled whilst reacting (thinking distance):
    Assume a 0.5 s reaction time (accept 0.2-0.9 s) *[1 mark]*
    From the graph, the cyclist's speed is 7 m/s, so:
    $s = vt = 7 \times 0.5 = 3.5$ m (accept 1.4-6.3 m) *[1 mark]*
    Distance travelled whilst braking (braking distance):
    $v^2 - u^2 = 2as$
    $u = 7$ m/s, $v = 0$, $a = -5.3$ m/s
    $s = (v^2 - u^2) \div 2a = (0^2 - 7^2) \div (2 \times -5.3)$ *[1 mark]*
      $= -49 \div -10.6 = 4.62...$ m *[1 mark]*
    Stopping distance = thinking distance + braking distance
                    $= 3.5 + 4.62... = 8.12...$ m $= 8.1$ m
                    (accept 6.0-11.0 m)
    Stopping distance is less than 12 m, so the cyclist won't hit the car *[1 mark]*.

8.1   E.g.

[1 mark for wave fronts correctly changing direction, 1 mark for wave fronts being spaced further apart]

8.2   How to grade your answer:
    Level 0:   There is no relevant information. *[No marks]*
    Level 1:   There is a brief description of how the speed of different parts of the wave front change between air and diamond. *[1 to 2 marks]*
    Level 2:   There is a good description of how different parts of a wave front travel at different speeds when crossing a boundary. There is some description of how this results in refraction.
                  [3 to 4 marks]
    Level 3:   There is a detailed explanation of how the difference in speed for different parts of a wave front results in a difference in distance travelled. There is a clear description of how this results in refraction when crossing a boundary at an angle.
                  [5 to 6 marks]
    Here are some points your answer may include:
    Light travels faster in air than it does in diamond.
    When the light ray crosses the boundary between diamond and air at an angle, it means different parts of the wave front cross the boundary at different times.
    The parts of the wave front that have crossed the boundary travel faster than the rest of the wave front that is still travelling through the diamond.
    Distance = speed ÷ time.
    So in the time it takes the entire wave front to cross over the boundary, the parts of the wave front that have spent more of that time travelling through air have travelled further.
    This difference in distance travelled between points along the wave front causes the ray to bend (refract) away from the normal.

9.1   E.g.

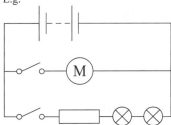

[2 marks for all circuit symbols correctly drawn, otherwise 1 mark for 4 symbols correctly drawn. 1 mark for filament lamps and resistor in series with each other, 1 mark for motor in parallel with other components, 1 mark for correct placement of switches]

9.2 $E = QV$ and $Q = It$ so $E = VIt$ *[1 mark]*
    $E = 6.0 \times 70.0 \times 10^{-3} \times (15 \times 60)$ *[1 mark]* $= 378$ J
    $\Delta E = mc\Delta\theta = 0.0250 \times 120 \times 6$ *[1 mark]* $= 18$ J
    $378 - 18$ *[1 mark]* $= \mathbf{360}$ **J** *[1 mark]*

9.3   E.g. he could lubricate the parts within the motor *[1 mark]*. This would reduce friction and the amount of energy being wasted/ dissipated to the thermal energy store of the motor *[1 mark]*.

The Periodic Table

Group 0

Periods

1

$$\begin{array}{c} 1 \\ \text{H} \\ \text{Hydrogen} \\ 1 \end{array}$$

Group 1 **Group 2**

Relative atomic mass

Group 3 Group 4 Group 5 Group 6 Group 7

$$\begin{array}{c} 4 \\ \text{He} \\ \text{Helium} \\ 2 \end{array}$$

Atomic (proton) number

2

| 7 Li Lithium 3 | 9 Be Beryllium 4 | | | | | | | | | | | 11 B Boron 5 | 12 C Carbon 6 | 14 N Nitrogen 7 | 16 O Oxygen 8 | 19 F Fluorine 9 | 20 Ne Neon 10 |

3

| 23 Na Sodium 11 | 24 Mg Magnesium 12 | | | | | | | | | | | 27 Al Aluminium 13 | 28 Si Silicon 14 | 31 P Phosphorus 15 | 32 S Sulfur 16 | 35.5 Cl Chlorine 17 | 40 Ar Argon 18 |

4

| 39 K Potassium 19 | 40 Ca Calcium 20 | 45 Sc Scandium 21 | 48 Ti Titanium 22 | 51 V Vanadium 23 | 52 Cr Chromium 24 | 55 Mn Manganese 25 | 56 Fe Iron 26 | 59 Co Cobalt 27 | 59 Ni Nickel 28 | 63.5 Cu Copper 29 | 65 Zn Zinc 30 | 70 Ga Gallium 31 | 73 Ge Germanium 32 | 75 As Arsenic 33 | 79 Se Selenium 34 | 80 Br Bromine 35 | 84 Kr Krypton 36 |

5

| 85 Rb Rubidium 37 | 88 Sr Strontium 38 | 89 Y Yttrium 39 | 91 Zr Zirconium 40 | 93 Nb Niobium 41 | 96 Mo Molybdenum 42 | [98] Tc Technetium 43 | 101 Ru Ruthenium 44 | 103 Rh Rhodium 45 | 106 Pd Palladium 46 | 108 Ag Silver 47 | 112 Cd Cadmium 48 | 115 In Indium 49 | 119 Sn Tin 50 | 122 Sb Antimony 51 | 128 Te Tellurium 52 | 127 I Iodine 53 | 131 Xe Xenon 54 |

6

| 133 Cs Caesium 55 | 137 Ba Barium 56 | 139 La Lanthanum 57 | 178 Hf Hafnium 72 | 181 Ta Tantalum 73 | 184 W Tungsten 74 | 186 Re Rhenium 75 | 190 Os Osmium 76 | 192 Ir Iridium 77 | 195 Pt Platinum 78 | 197 Au Gold 79 | 201 Hg Mercury 80 | 204 Tl Thallium 81 | 207 Pb Lead 82 | 209 Bi Bismuth 83 | [209] Po Polonium 84 | [210] At Astatine 85 | [222] Rn Radon 86 |

7

| [223] Fr Francium 87 | [226] Ra Radium 88 | [227] Ac Actinium 89 | [261] Rf Rutherfordium 104 | [262] Db Dubnium 105 | [266] Sg Seaborgium 106 | [264] Bh Bohrium 107 | [277] Hs Hassium 108 | [268] Mt Meitnerium 109 | [271] Ds Darmstadtium 110 | [272] Rg Roentgenium 111 | [285] Cn Copernicium 112 | [286] Nh Nihonium 113 | [289] Fl Flerovium 114 | [289] Mc Moscovium 115 | [293] Lv Livermorium 116 | [294] Ts Tennessine 117 | [294] Og Oganesson 118 |

The Lanthanides (atomic numbers 58-71) and the Actinides (atomic numbers 90-103) are not shown in this table.

Physics Equations List

You'll probably be given a list of equations like this in your exams.

The exact equations you'll be given will depend on which exam board your GCSE is set by.

Here are some common equations you might find useful for the Physics part of this book:

Topic P1 — Energy

$E_e = \frac{1}{2}ke^2$	elastic potential energy = 0.5 × spring constant × (extension)^2
$\Delta E = mc\Delta\theta$	change in thermal energy = mass × specific heat capacity × temperature change

Topic P2 — Electricity

$V_p I_p = V_s I_s$	potential difference across primary coil × current in primary coil = potential difference across secondary coil × current in secondary coil

Topic P3 — Particle Model of Matter

$E = mL$	thermal energy for a change of state = mass × specific latent heat

Topic P5 — Forces

$v^2 - u^2 = 2as$	(final velocity)^2 − (initial velocity)^2 = 2 × acceleration × distance

Topic P6 — Waves

$\text{period} = \dfrac{1}{\text{frequency}}$	

Topic P7 — Magnetism and Electromagnetism

$F = BIl$	force on a current-carrying conductor (at right-angles to a magnetic field) = $\dfrac{\text{magnetic flux}}{\text{density}}$ × current × length